A(

AQUARIUM FISH

Donald Wilkie

PELHAM BOOKS

The sections on Invertebrates and Plants are edited by Donald
Wilkie in conjunction with H. Douglas Kemper Jr.

First published in Great Britain by
Pelham Books Ltd
27 Wrights Lane
London W8

British Library Cataloguing in Publication Data

Wilkie, Donald
  Aquarium fish.
  1. Aquarium fishes
  I. Title   II. Pesci d'acquario. *English*
  639.3′4   SF457

  ISBN 0-7207-1702-7

Produced by ERVIN s.r.l., Rome
Illustrations by Amedeo Gigli and Egidio Imperi

Printed and bound in Italy
by Arnoldo Mondadori Editore, Verona

CONTENTS

MARINE FISHES

INVERTEBRATES

Foreword

My early memories of Don Wilkie are aboard a small boat in Tomales Bay pulling in stingrays and leopard sharks on a set line, keeping them alive in wash tubs, and then driving them north through California in our tank truck toward Vancouver. He has spent most of his professional life devoted to this kind of field activity; gathering information and specimens to develop exhibits and programs in, aquaria, first in Vancouver, then Philadelphia, and finally at the T. Wayland Vaughan Aquarium-Museum in La Jolla, where he has been Director for twenty years.

While at the Philadelphia Aquarium he organized the capture of several pilot whales in Newfoundland and pioneered in their care and maintenance. He is a superb field biologist and strong scuba diver with years of experience collecting live fish and invertebrates along the North American Pacific coast from Mexico to British Columbia. While he is best known for his work in Southern California and the Sea of Cortez, he has also collected specimens in Micronesia and Hawaii. As Director of the T. Wayland Vaughan Aquarium-Museum, he is well known for his research into fish coloration, and for his publications on fish diseases and animal husbandry.

As a professional involved in collecting and maintaining aquarium fishes, Mr. Wilkie is suggesting that, while collecting brings a whole new dimension to the·aquarist, it should be done with conservation in mind.

Murray A. Newman, Ph.D.
Director
Vancouver Public Aquarium

Preface

This book is written as a guide and reference for the hobbyist. Emphasis is on fishes, but some invertebrates and plants have also been included. The fishes chosen are a sampling of those commonly kept and known to do well in captivity. In addition, some species have been selected for aquarists who have special interests, such as keeping large, rare or unusual fishes, or simply wishing to try something new. A few species from western North America have not appeared previously in the popular aquarium literature.

Definitive descriptions of fishes are not given here, since the aquarist deals almost exclusively with living specimens on which he cannot perform the counts, measurements and internal anatomical comparisons necessary for accurate identifications. The system of classification used in this book is based upon Nelson (1984), *Fishes of the World*, 2nd edition, which includes many references on the classification and biology of fishes and their scientific descriptions.

The theory and practice of aquarium management discussed in this book is based upon that employed in the aquarium at Scripps Institution of Oceanography in La Jolla, California, U.S.A., where it is the philosophy that aquaria are more meaningful and successful if fishes are kept together in natural groupings in naturalistic habitats. It is recognized that an aquarium does not duplicate the natural environment; however, the closer it comes to doing so the healthier and less stressed will be its inhabitants. The hobbyist will find a tremendous variation in the adaptability of fishes to the aquarium. Fishes that do well under a wide variety of aquarium conditions are described as hardy. Many species, however, are difficult to maintain in captivity for a variety of reasons; and a number of the large open-ocean and deep-water species have not yet been maintained even in the most sophisticated systems developed to date. Much of the art and science of aquarium management is involved in maintaining suitable water quality, and a wide variety of systems have been developed toward this end. Many freshwater fishes – goldfish, for example – are "hardy" because they have adapted in nature to a wide range of water conditions and can survive in the simplest of aquaria. Coral-reef fishes, on the other hand, live in an environment where the temperature and water chemistry vary little, so these fishes are usually very sensitive to water quality.

In general it is best if the hobbyist masters a fresh-water aquarium before attempting to keep marine fishes, although the principles of water management are similar. The basic management system described in this book is relatively unsophisticated and is only one way to maintain fishes successfully in captivity. It is, however, a proven system and has been used by many aquarists for many years. Some hobbyists may view this system only as a starting point, while others will find it meets their needs. The successful hobbyist will probably find that it is not the system which dictates his success so much as his confidence and experience with it, and his knowledge of the fishes he wants to keep.

A section has been included on collecting not only because of the fun of catching your own fishes but because it gives the aquarist the opportunity of observing a fish in its own environment, especially if scuba or snorkeling is used. The knowledge gained leads to a better understanding of ecology and better fish-keeping. One of the benefits of keeping native fishes which you catch yourself is the greater appreciation of nature that you gain from it.

Donald Wilkie

Acknowledgments

I would like to thank the teachers, ichthyologists and aquarists who have contributed to my knowledge and encouraged my interest in aquatic life, especially Dr Casimir C. Lindsey and Dr Tom Northcote of the University of British Columbia, Dr Richard Rosenblatt of the University of California, San Diego, and Dr Murray Newman of the Vancouver Public Aquarium. Special thanks are due to Stephen Spotte, author and director of the Mystic Marine Life Aquarium, who reviewed the entire manuscript, and Betty Shor of Scripps Aquarium who painstakingly edited the penultimate draft. Invaluable assistance was received from several specialists who contributed significantly to the accuracy of major sections: Dr George Barlow, University of California, Berkeley, and Dr Paul Loiselle, behavior and taxonomy of cichlids; Dr Stanley Weitzman of the Smithsonian Institution, characins; Mr Michael Kent, University of California, Davis, diseases of fishes; Bob Snodgrass, aquarium management. Susanne Wilkie, Glenda Neeley and Ed Spicer assisted with library research, while Jean Muller did a masterful job of translating my scrawl into manuscript copy and Vivian McKenna generously assisted with typing.

Finally, I would like to thank my wife Pat for her patience; in some ways my writing of this book was as difficult for her as it was for me.

D. W.

AQUARIUM MANAGEMENT

There is no magic involved in becoming a successful aquarist. The mythical "wet thumb" is merely a matter of understanding a few basic principles and having enough interest to give an aquarium attention each day. An essential part of this attention is learning to observe changes in the appearance of the fishes that may indicate a problem. Daily care need not be time-consuming. A few minutes' observation and maintenance is all that is necessary in addition to the normal feeding. The aquarist who is just beginning may be overwhelmed by the diversity of approaches and array of equipment involved in maintaining aquaria. There is no cause for concern as there is more than one successful way to maintain an aquarium. We will concentrate on a simple but well-established system. As the aquarist gains experience, he may wish to implement more complex and sophisticated systems.

An aquarium may be a miniature representation of a natural habitat, or it may simply be a box of unrelated fishes. Fishes not only do better in a habitat which represents their natural environment, but they also usually behave in a more interesting and natural manner. We believe for both aesthetic and educational reasons that a naturalistic approach is most desirable. Although our remarks will center on fishes, the same general principles apply to aquatic invertebrates.

In addition to maintaining aquatic specimens, the aquarist may wish to do some of his own collecting.

History. We do not know who the first successful fish-keepers were. Early records indicate that the Sumerians (Sumeria is now part of Iraq) kept fish in ponds more than 4,500 years ago. As early as 1000 B.C. the Chinese are known to have raised carp for food. Perhaps the first marine fish-keepers were the Romans, who kept fish in ponds connected to the oceans as a source of fresh food. However, until the relationship between oxygen, aquatic animals and plants was understood, few fishes were successfully maintained in small aquaria. It was not until 1850 that aquarium-keeping became well established. The first public display aquarium was opened at Regent's Park in England in 1853, while the first commercial exploitation of aquatic displays took place in 1856 when P. T. Barnum opened an exhibit at his American Museum in New York. Development of aquaria began to accelerate, and by 1928 there were 45 display aquaria open to the public. By 1980, this had grown to over 500 worldwide.

Today, modern materials, equipment and air transportation make it possible for hobbyists as well as display aquaria to obtain a wide variety of fishes from all parts of the world and to maintain them with a high degree of success.

Selecting the aquarium. The home aquarist has a wide range of choices of both off-the-shelf and custom-made aquaria. For most hobbyists, an aquarium of 60–120 liters (15–

The practice of keeping fishes in an aquarium is relatively new and very few public aquaria existed before the 20th century. The New York Aquarium at Battery Park, one of America's first, was opened in 1898.

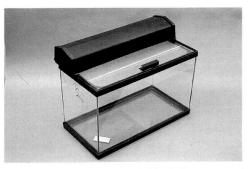

All-glass aquaria are recommended for both seawater and fresh water: They usually have a decorative plastic frame which supports the cover and light. Photo by Bill Call.

Plastic aquaria are attractive but easily scratched. Photo by Bill Call.

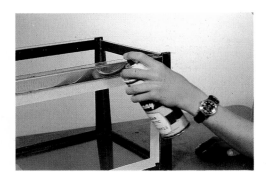

Metal-framed aquaria are subject to corrosion. The frame should be sprayed with a protective finish when used with seawater.

30 gal.) is a convenient size with which to begin. This is small enough to be cared for easily but large enough to be attractive, provide stability in water quality and hold a reasonable number of fishes. A low-profile shape should be chosen rather than a tall one, since this provides greater surface area for gas exchange. The aquarist has the choice of three main types of construction:

1) metal-framed glass tanks with glass set in some kind of sealant;
2) all-glass tanks held together with silicone rubber adhesive;
3) plastic tanks.

Metal-framed tanks are adequate for fresh water, but will corrode when used with seawater and should be avoided even if the metal is covered with a corrosion-resistant coating. Plastic tanks tend to become scratched and some, especially older ones, tend to yellow with age. All-glass tanks are inert to both fresh water and seawater, are resistant to scratching and are the best overall choice. Some have an external plastic frame for aesthetic purposes as well as to support the top. Large aquaria can be constructed in a variety of ways. A common approach is to construct a tank of 2 cm (0.75 in) plywood coated with polyester resin. Either glass or acrylic can be used for a window and held in place with silicone rubber adhesive.

Tank sizes and weights. The aquarium should be placed in a quiet part of a room, away from direct sunlight which can both overheat the aquarium and cause unwanted algae growth. Large aquaria are heavy and require a sturdy stand, placed in an area where the floor will support it safely. A 60-liter (15-gal.) aquarium will weigh about 65 kg (145 lb) when filled with water and furnished with sand and decorations. A 400-liter (100-gal.) aquarium is deceptively heavy and weighs over 400 kg (900 lb).

The aquarium should have a glass cover to prevent escape of fish, to lessen evaporation, and to protect the light fixture from spray. The cover must, however, be designed to permit free exchange of the air above the water with the surrounding atmosphere. The back of the tank should be painted or covered for aesthetic reasons, and it may be desirable to cover the ends as well to minimize disturbance of the fishes. Naturalistic plastic backgrounds can be purchased and placed inside the aquarium.

Water treatment. Maintaining good water quality is the first requirement for a successful aquarium and the end toward which water treatment efforts are directed. The metabolic processes of fishes and other aquatic organisms lead to changes in the composition of seawater, which necessitate treatment if the life-supporting properties of the aquarium water are to be sustained.

Aeration. Aeration facilitates gas exchange between the aquarium water and the atmosphere. Oxygen, depleted during respiration, is replaced and excess carbon dioxide driven off. Aeration can be accomplished with mechanical air pumps and air stones, or with the water motion provided by the filters. Gas exchange occurs at the surface of the aquarium, as well as between the water and the air bubbles. Power filters produce rapid water movement and surface aeration which greatly facilitates gas exchange, but they do pose one potential danger. An air leak on the intake side of the pump can draw in air and produce supersaturation of the water and fish's blood with nitrogen. As the nitrogen comes out of solution in the blood of the fish, it can cause damaging or fatal embolisms. As little as a 10% increase in nitrogen can be dangerous, and a 25% increase is often rapidly fatal. Low levels of supersaturation which may be otherwise undetected can cause a later outbreak of exophthalmia or "popeye."

Filtration. Filtration not only provides clear water, it also provides the essential water treatment that enhances the life-supporting capabilities of the aquarium water. For convenience and discussion, we will consider three types of filtration.

Mechanical filtration – Mechanical filtration is the removal of particulate matter which produces turbidity. Not only does it improve clarity, it removes particulate matter before it can decompose and produce toxic substances. Simple mechanical filters use compressed air to draw water through filter media such as sand, pebbles, filter wool and rubber, or plastic foam. Glass wool should not be used in filters, since it can fragment and cause gill damage. Filters may be simple plastic boxes containing media and placed inside or outside the aquarium. In most cases outside filters are preferred, since they are easier to service without disturbing the aquarium's occupants.

A reliable air pump is one of the most important pieces of aquarium equipment. A spare is advisable. Photo by Bill Call.

One-piece foam filters consisting of an airlift which draws the water through a foam block are extremely simple and easy to use, and even when placed inside the aquarium are easy to maintain. They are particularly useful in hospital and holding tanks where aesthetics are not of prime importance.

Power filters – Several types of power filter are available. These use an electric pump to force the water through the media and have the advantage of a higher flow rate than is normally available with air-operated filters. Power filters frequently use diatomaceous earth as the filter medium. Diatomaceous earth or diatomite is the fossilized remains of marine diatoms. It is a very fine, but highly porous, material that comes in different size grains and can produce extremely clean water. Since it must be discarded after a single use, it has the disadvantage of being messy.

Biological filtration – Biological filtration is the conversion of harmful metabolic wastes from fishes and other aquatic organisms into less toxic substances. The removal of these substances by plants is sometimes included in the final step of the process. In the aquarium, the wastes of most concern are proteins which break down to produce ammonia, a highly soluble and toxic substance. Fortunately, naturally occurring bacteria can be utilized to convert ammonia to nitrite compounds, which are much less toxic and are ultimately converted to nitrates. Nitrates are relatively harmless. In planted fresh-water aquaria, ni-

13

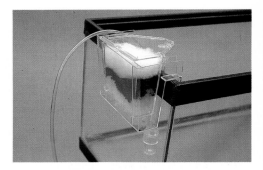

One of the simplest and most effective filter systems uses the subsand filter. In addition to clarifying the water and providing aeration, subsand filters provide a large surface area for biological filtration.

Outside filters may be used alone, or for supplemental filtration with activated carbon. They provide very limited biological filtration. Photo by Bill Call.

Inside filters provide mechanical filtration and aeration but very little biological filtration. Photo by Bill Call.

Sponge filters do provide good surface area for biological filtration and are easy to use. They are most useful in reserve or holding tanks. Photo by Bill Call.

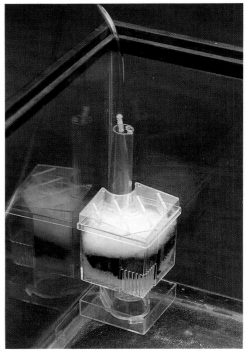

trates are taken up by plants as one of their major nutrients. In the marine aquarium where plant growth may be minimal, the nitrate level can be kept low by partial water changes. It is commonly recommended that 10% of the water be changed every two weeks but nitrate levels at least as high as 500 ppm are not normally cause for concern.

The cultivation of sufficient beneficial bacteria to convert ammonia to nitrate requires a filter bed with a large surface area for the bacteria. This is easily provided by using a subsand filter within the aquarium. Airlifts are used to draw the water through the sand, where the waste matter is taken up and used by beneficial bacteria. Although particulate matter is trapped in the sand, this is not normally a problem in a properly functioning system. Occasional cleaning of the bottom sand with a sand-washing device is helpful. Reverse-flow subsand filters are also available and, although somewhat more complicated than downflow subsand filters, are usually more efficient.

One problem sometimes experienced with subsand filters is that fishes tend to dig and expose the filter plate. This allows the water to circulate freely without being filtered through the sand, but it can be overcome by placing a plastic screen over the bottom two or three centimeters (one inch) of substrate.

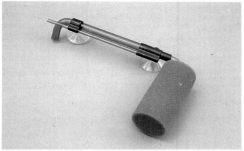

Power filters can provide a rapid turnover rate and ultra-clear water. They are often used in conjunction with sophisticated water-treatment systems which may include activated carbon, ion-exchange resins, etc. Photo by Bill Call.

Filter sand – In fresh-water aquaria, the filter sand should normally be an inert siliceous (silicon dioxide) sand. For marine aquaria, calcareous sand is preferred. Coral sand is probably best, but other calcareous materials can be used, including crushed dolomite or crushed limestone. The calcareous material provides a buffering action and helps to maintain the alkalinity of the seawater. From time to time a portion of the substrate should be replaced, since it tends to lose its buffering capacity as it becomes coated. The size of the substrate or filter media is important. The grain should be small enough to trap particulate matter and provide a large surface area for bacteria, but must be large enough to avoid becoming clogged. Grain sizes of 2–

4 mm (about 0.06–0.16 in) are recommended.

Although the subsand filter is a biological filter, it also provides mechanical filtration. Likewise mechanical filters, although primarily designed to improve water clarity, also provide a certain amount of biological filtration, depending on the amount of surface area available to the nitrifying bacteria.

Chemical filtration – Chemical filtration or chemical treatment refers to the use of chemical processes to maintain good water quality. Many of the treatments are more appropriate for use in public aquaria, hatcheries, or aquaculture facilities than for home aquaria. Some of the treatments already discussed include chemical treatment. Aeration, in a sense, is a chemical treatment since in driving off the excess carbon dioxide it helps to reduce acidity and raise the pH. The buffering of seawater by use of a calcareous substrate is also a chemical treatment. Likewise, in order to simulate the natural waters of tropical rain forests, aquarists may boil water and filter it through peat. This lowers the temporary hardness of the water and increases its acidity.

Other water treatments

Ozone and ultraviolet light – These treatments are used to sterilize aquarium water and must be done remotely from the aquarium, since their direct use on the aquarium is harmful. In addition to sterilizing the water, ozone can be

Biological filtration is the bacterial process which is responsible for the conversion of highly toxic ammonia (NH_3) to low-toxicity nitrates (NO_3). In a newly set up aquarium ammonia will increase until the bacterial populations become established

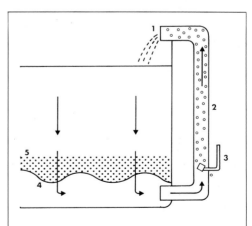

A subsand filter which covers the bottom of the tank provides a large surface area for the bacteria which are necessary for biological filtration.

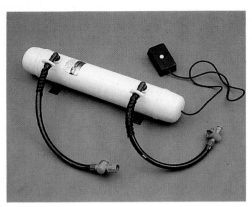

Ultraviolet light and ozone are used to sterilize aquarium water but are of questionable practical value for most home aquaria. Photo by Bill Call.

used for the direct oxidation of metabolic wastes. Although these treatments have been advocated for the cure and prevention of diseases, it is not clear that they play a significant role in the home aquarium, since returning sterilized water to the aquarium has no effect on pathogens already attached to the fishes or living in the substrate. There may be some value in flushing free-living stages of pathogens from the aquarium by using a high flow rate of sterilized water, but this has not been well established.

Exchange resins – Harmful substances can be selectively removed from the aquarium water with ion-exchange resins. This is still a largely experimental process and not of practical consideration for most aquarists. However, advanced aquarists may want to investigate its potential in specialized situations.

Activated carbon – Activated carbon is useful in removing dissolved organic and toxic substances from aquarium water. However, if not correctly used, it does little more than provide mechanical filtration and a certain amount of biological filtration. Activated carbon acts by attracting organic molecules to its adsorptive surfaces. For aquarium use, a fine granulated form is most convenient. It is most effective if it follows mechanical and biological filtration. This allows removal of organic particle matter that otherwise would soon saturate the carbon and reduce its usefulness. In the small home aquarium, charcoal can be effectively employed by placing it in a separate auxiliary filter which is operated for only one to two hours a day. Alternatively, it can be operated

continuously at a very slow rate such as one-tenth the principal filtration rate. The low daily turnover through the carbon helps to remove dissolved organic waste products as they are produced, with slow saturation of the carbon with other substances. To insure that the carbon remains adsorbent, half of it should be replaced each week. Changing half of the carbon also helps to insure against abrupt changes in water chemistry. Rejuvenation of carbon by heating is neither efficient nor cost-effective.

Activated carbon also has some specific uses. For example, it is very effective in removal of chlorine or chloramine from tap water before its use in the aquarium. It will also remove beneficial substances such as medication and should normally be turned off during prophylactic and therapeutic treatments. Caution: Sudden extensive use of charcoal can alter the water chemistry and cause stress to sensitive organisms.

The use of activated carbon in aquarium systems is complex and many aspects of its function are not yet fully understood.

Protein skimmers – Protein skimmers extract dissolved protein from the water by using air bubbles to produce a foam which can be removed and discarded. This procedure helps to keep down ammonia production and slows down the long-term build-up of dissolved nitrates.

pH – The acidity or alkalinity of water is usually expressed as its pH, a logarithmic scale which denotes concentration of hydrogen ions (H^+) in a solution. A pH of 7 is neutral, while pHs below 7 are acidic and those above all alkaline. The pH of fresh water can vary considerably. Water from tropical jungles tends to be low in dissolved solids because of high rainfall, and acidic because of soil acids that are continuously flushed into the watershed. On the other hand, streams which remain in contact with calcareous rocks for long periods become hard and alkaline.

In the well-maintained aquarium it is usually not necessary to adjust pH. Normal water management and regular partial water changes should keep the pH within an acceptable range. Aquarists who specialize in delicate species from soft acid waters will find it advantageous to simulate the natural conditions of their fishes. As previously mentioned, this may necessitate boiling water to reduce its temporary hardness and passing it through peat to increase its acidity.

In marine aquaria, a pH of 7.8–8.3 is

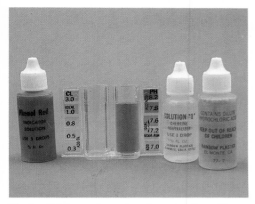

Simple pH kits can be used to determine the acidity or alkalinity of both fresh-water and seawater aquaria. Photo by Bill Call.

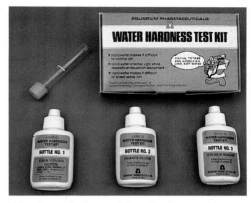

Although most fresh-water fishes will tolerate a wide range of water hardness, some have specific requirements, especially for reproduction. Inexpensive and easy-to-use measuring kits are available. Photo by Bill Call.

commonly recommended, although the harmful effects of a lower pH remain unclear and many marine fishes have been kept successfully at a lower pH. If the marine aquarist wishes to increase the pH in his tank, he may wish to use a buffer. Sodium bicarbonate can be added at a rate of 1 g per 15 liters. If after a day the pH still appears too low, the treatment can be repeated on a daily basis until the desired pH is obtained.

Hardness – Hardness refers to the quantity of dissolved cations, primarily those of calcium and magnesium, in fresh water. Several systems are used to describe hardness. Biologists usually express the total dissolved solids or T.D.S. in parts per million (ppm). German aquarists use °DH; each 1°DH is equivalent to 10 mg of calcium oxide (CaO) in 1 liter of water. Less frequently used by aquarists is the English (Clark) system; one English degree = 56/100°DH.

Most fresh-water aquarium fishes tolerate a wide range of water hardness and will survive in tap water. However, distilled water should be used to replace any water lost due to evaporation.

Salinity – Seawater is a complex mixture of dissolved solids derived from the earth's crust. Probably all of the elements known on earth are present in seawater, although some may be almost undetectable. The composition of seawater is remarkably constant the world over. Although the total amount of dissolved solids may vary in different parts of the ocean, the relative proportion of each element remains virtually constant. The salinity of seawater is usually expressed as the total weight of dissolved solids found in one kilogram of

SCALES OF HARDNESS

Water type	German scale	Dissolved solids
soft	0–5°DH	0–90 ppm
moderately hard	5–20°DH	90–360 ppm
hard	20–30°DH	360–540 ppm
very hard	>30°DH	>540 ppm
seawater		>30,000 ppm

water as parts per thousand (0/00). Oceanic seawater generally ranges from 32 to 38 0/00. In the Red Sea, due to evaporation, it reaches

40 0/00 and in more confined areas, such as the Dead Sea, it attains even higher levels. Coastal-water salinities may be lower. When

17

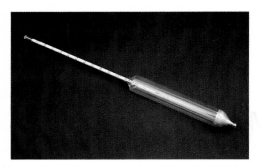

The salinity of a seawater aquarium should be maintained within the natural range of the aquarium inhabitants. Salinity can be estimated by using a simple hydrometer designed for aquarium use. Photo by Bill Call.

A thermostatically controlled heater should be used to maintain a uniform temperature in tropical tanks. A capacity of one watt per liter is usually sufficient. Photo by Bill Call.

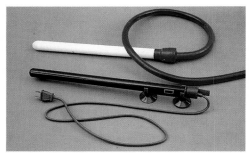

the total salinity is less than 30 0/00 it is usually defined as brackish.

Salinity can be estimated by chemical titration, by measuring the electrical conductivity of the water or by measuring its specific gravity. The latter method is adequate for aquarists who can obtain a suitable hydrometer at aquarium supply stores. Marine fishes vary greatly in their ability to tolerate low salinities. Some can move freely between seawater and fresh water. Most tropical-reef fishes probably do best at salinities between 30 and 36 0/00. Brackish-water fishes will often tolerate a wide range of salinities; but most flourish at salinities around 7 0/00 or a mixture of 20% seawater and 80% fresh water.

Heating. Fishes are very sensitive to temperature and have a preferred temperature range that they will seek if free to do so. Aquarium fishes should be kept at the temperatures that they normally experience in nature, preferably toward the lower end of the range since disease problems appear to be fewer, dissolved oxygen is higher, and metabolic activities slower. It is desirable to keep aquarium temperatures as constant as possible. In the aquarium, rapid temperature changes cause stress and often lead to outbreaks of disease. The temperature of the aquarium may be regulated by controlling the surrounding room temperature or, as is usually the case, by using an aquarium heater which has a thermostatic control. These can be of several types: immersible, totally submersible or under gravel. The amount of heat provided by an aquarium heater is expressed in watts. For average-sized home aquaria, the capacity of 1 watt per liter or 5 watts per gal. is usually recommended. Lower-capacity heaters are adequate in warm rooms. It is safer to use a heater of the smallest capacity that will provide uniform

temperature, since if the thermostat sticks in the on position, it is less likely to cause dangerous overheating.

Tropical marine and fresh-water fishes are normally maintained around 24°C (75°F), temperate-zone fishes at 15–20°C (59–68°F), while cold-water fishes are best maintained at temperatures below 10°C (50°F).

When installing heater and thermostats in an aquarium, it is best to pre-set the temperature. Mix warm and cool water in a bucket until the desired temperature is obtained. Place the thermostat and heater in the bucket and leave for several minutes to acclimate. Then rotate the thermostat dial until the heater just clicks on and off.

Cooling. Commercially constructed aquarium chiller units are available for the aquarist who wishes to keep cold-water organisms. Some aquarists have successfully made their own cooling units. One method is to obtain an old refrigerator cooling unit and modify it. A copper coil can be used to circulate the coolant within the aquarium, if it is suitably coated. This can be done with a good epoxy coating or by slipping a piece of flexible plastic tubing over the coil. Care must be taken to see that no copper is in contact with the seawater. Periodic testing should be done with a copper analysis kit, available from scientific supply firms and aquarium stores.

Lighting. As already stated, it is best to place the aquarium in a dimly lit part of the room. In order to see and properly enjoy the aquarium inhabitants and to simulate their natural environment, artificial lighting is desirable. This may be either incandescent or fluorescent. The former is inexpensive but produces heat, and the bulbs do not last very long. Fluorescent lights are usually preferred,

SELECTED SPECIFIC GRAVITY AND SALINITY VALUES

Salinity		1,020	1,021	1,022	1,023	1,024	1,025	1,026	1,027	1,028	1,029	1,030
Temperature		**Gravity**										
°C	°F											
10	50	26	27,5	29	30	31,5	33	34	35	36	38	39
15	59	27	28,5	30	31	32,5	34	35	36	37,5	39	40
20	68	28,5	30	31	32,5	34	35	36,5	38	39	40	42
25	77	30	31,5	33	34	35,5	37	38	40	41	42	44
30	86	32	33,5	35	36	37,5	39	40	41,5			

since they are available in a variety of spectra that can simulate natural light or provide special effects such as stimulating plant growth or enhancing the colors of organisms. Warm daylight fluorescent tubes are a good general choice for both marine and fresh-water aquaria. For optimum plant growth, the lights should remain on for at least 12 hours. Since at least some fish require rest, the lights should remain on no longer than 16 hours. For safety's sake, before handling lights or any other electrical equipment around the

Fluorescent bulbs are cool and available in a range of spectra which can be selected to enhance color or plant growth. Photo by Bill Call.

Solutions of copper salts are frequently used to control disease organisms. Levels should be monitored with a copper analysis kit to ensure a safe but adequate dosage. Photo by Bill Call.

aquarium, be sure to unplug it (with dry hands).

Stocking and care. In spite of constant warnings, aquarists can easily fall victim to the two most common fish-keeping pitfalls: overcrowding and overfeeding. Although the latter error usually becomes obvious, the former may remain a mystery. The overcrowded aquarium may start out well, perhaps even spectacularly, with an abundance of active fishes that fill the tank with color and motion. Unfortunately, this joy may be short-lived, with problems beginning to appear after one or two weeks. These may take the form of unexplained deaths or an outbreak of disease. Almost invariably the final result of an overcrowded tank is that the aquarist must start over again. Unfortunately, many become discouraged at this point and give up the hobby. Perhaps it cannot be stated enough to deter the overenthusiastic aquarists, but I will say it again: Do not overcrowd! Do not exceed the recommended stocking densities. Start conservatively and then, as your experience and confidence grow, you may wish to stock your aquaria more heavily. In theory a number of factors determine carrying capacity, including the size and shape of the tank, its surface area, the amount of biological filtration, the size of the fishes, the species of the fishes, and whether it is a fresh-water or marine aquarium. In practice the hobbyist normally uses a simplified formula based on the volume of water or the surface area of the aquarium and the length the fish will reach in captivity.

Don't overcrowd your aquarium. A 100-liter marine aquarium can safely support six 30 g fish or one 200 g fish.

A safe stocking level for commonly kept fresh-water fish is 75 square cm of surface area per cm of fish length (12 square in of surface area per in of fish length). This means that in a standard 60-liter (15-gal.) aquarium, you could hold 24 fish, each 2.5 cm (1 in) long. For marine fishes, you should allow four times as much surface area. Professional aquarists often think in terms of the number of gallons of seawater per pound of fish, and stock at a rate of 50 to 100 gallons of seawater per pound. At this rate, a 75-liter (20-gal.) aquarium would support four or five fish, 4 cm (1.5 in) long.

Selecting the population. Before deciding how to set up your aquarium, it is best to decide what fishes it will contain and how you will display them. You may wish to begin with one or two single-species tanks, but most aquarists choose a community tank.

Single-species tanks. These may contain a single fish of special significance, a breeding pair, or an aggregation of fishes. For rearing fishes, single-species tanks are usually the logical choice.

Although there is no interspecific aggression in this type of aquarium, intraspecific aggression can still be a problem. Fish of the same sex will often fight with each other and, even when the sexes are mixed, aggression may still occur as males attack unreceptive or spawned-out females. Within groups of fishes, pecking orders may develop and territorial disputes may occur. If aggression occurs in single-species tanks, the first step is to determine its cause. Once this has been established, the aquarist can often correct the problem with a little common sense. For example, territorial disputes in nest-guarding species may be corrected by making additional nesting sites available.

Community tanks. Although it is not essential to the well-being of the fishes, it is philosophically more satisfying if all of the fishes in a community tank come from the same geographical region. Ideally, a community tank depicts a natural assemblage of fishes in a setting representative of its own habitat. In practice, this may not be as easy as it sounds. The aquarium is usually too small and heavily populated for fishes to establish the same territories and relationships as they have in nature. In the aquarium, the combatants in a dispute usually do not have the same ability to escape as they do in the wild, and must remain together under conditions of constant stress. Sometimes these conflicts can be resolved only by removing the most aggressive member of the community. At other times, less dominant fishes must be removed to ensure their survival.

It is difficult to give all-encompassing rules for setting up a community tank. Compatibility has for the most part to be determined by considering the behavior and natural history of each species. Information on the suitability of various species for community tanks is given under the fish descriptions. Consult your dealer and other experienced aquarists for additional assistance. Some general suggestions are given below, but these are not absolute, nor do they cover all of the possibilities:

1. Don't keep small fishes with large-mouthed fishes that can consume them.
2. Don't mix fast-growing species with small species. Although they may be all the same size initially, those with the larger adult size can outgrow and consume the rest.
3. Bottom-living territorial fishes such as benthic damselfishes are often very aggressive.
4. Plankton-feeding fishes are usually not

aggressive, for example mid-water dam-selfishes such as *Chromis*.

5. Algae scrapers, although herbivorous, can be aggressive fin biters, for example the Panama fanged blenny *Ophioblennius*.
6. Don't keep sedentary fishes with nibblers; for example small benthic damselfishes can mortally injure much larger scorpionfishes.
7. Schooling fishes do best if several are kept together.
8. With some species, such as marine angelfishes, aggression may be much less if there is a noticeable size difference between the specimens. This can help the species establish a pecking order without actually fighting.
9. It is not advisable to add new fish to an established peaceful community tank.
10. Behavioral differences exist between fishes of the same species. A community group that is successful in one instance may fail in another because of individual differences within a species.
11. Constant alertness is necessary as aggressive tendencies of fishes can change with age and length of captivity.

Once you have determined what species you wish to display, it is time to go shopping. The first step is to choose a reputable dealer. Check to see what his customers say. Look carefully at his fish. Watch for the following points: Do his fish look healthy? Are the tanks kept clean? How long have the fish been quarantined? How were they captured? Aquarium fishes from the Philippines are often collected with the aid of cyanide, a dangerous poison. While the long-term effect on specimens that reach the hobbyist is difficult to assess, it is wise to avoid purchasing fishes taken in this manner. Do the fish have bitten or split fins? Are any obvious diseases present? Are scales missing? Is respiration rapid? Are the fish excessively active or lethargic? Are the eyes cloudy? Are the specimens thin? Are the fins clamped tightly against the body? A reputable dealer or an experienced aquarist is usually willing to help you with your initial purchases, but you can tell a lot through your own careful observations.

Setting up the aquarium. Choose materials that are suitable for simulating the fishes' natural habitat. Be sure they are not toxic. Some rocks contain heavy metals. Sand that you gather on your own may be contaminated. It could have been sprayed with insecti-

cide or other harmful chemicals. To be on the safe side, it is often wise to purchase your decorating materials at an aquarium store, at least initially. If necessary, questionable materials can be placed in the aquarium along with several test fishes. If the fish show no signs of distress after a few days, the materials are probably all right. Remember that fishes are more sensitive to the water they live in than we are to the water we drink.

Avoid using calcareous rocks in fresh-water aquaria if you wish to have soft acid water. Wash all materials thoroughly before placing them in the aquarium.

If you are going to use a subsand filter, place it in the aquarium and cover it with 5–8 cm (2–3 in) of suitable substrate, as previously described. Remember, if you keep fishes that dig, to cover the lower layer of sand with a piece of a plastic screen. For marine aquaria use a calcareous substrate, as previously described. Try to place the heater where it will be hidden behind decorations. As you decorate, keep in mind the habitat needs of the fishes and provide plenty of hiding places and retreats for those that require them. Leave plenty of swimming space for mid-water and pelagic species. In fresh-water aquaria, the plants may be placed directly in the filter sand, which should be deep enough to cover the roots. Some aquarists put a layer of peat or loam in the planting areas, often placing it inside a nylon bag to prevent it from being washed away. Plants, in pots, may be buried in the sand. To help prevent the plants from being uprooted, put pebbles or rocks around the base and over the roots. In most cases the fishes' feces will provide adequate nutrient for the plants, but liquid fertilizers can be added.

The type of substrate has an important effect on water quality. Calcareous sand such as coral sand is recommended for marine aquaria but should not be used in fresh-water aquaria if soft water is desired.

Marine plants used in marine aquaria are almost exclusively algae and acquire their nutrients directly from the water, not the substrate. Algae lack true roots and their holdfasts serve only to keep them in place, not to transport nutrients.

The novice aquarist may prefer to use artificial plants, rather than contend with yet another variable.

Adding the water. Tap water is suitable in most regions for the fresh-water aquarium, but it should be aerated vigorously for several hours or stand for at least two days to dissipate any chlorine. Alternatively, it can be filtered through activated carbon. The best source for information about your local water supply is an experienced aquarist or your dealer. Caution: Many communities now use chloramine to treat domestic water supplies. This substance is highly toxic and cannot be removed by aeration alone. It can be removed by filtration through activated granular carbon or by other methods.

Seawater may be taken directly from the ocean, but should be taken offshore if possible. It is best to filter it through diatomaceous earth or other fine material to remove microorganisms and suspended solids. For those without access to natural seawater, excellent artificial seawater formulas are available. Check with your local aquarium dealer.

When adding the water to the aquarium, pour it over a bowl or saucer placed on the bottom in order to minimize disturbing the substrate.

Conditioning the aquarium. A newly set up aquarium has few nitrifying bacteria to provide biological filtration. These can be intro-

duced by adding a small amount of garden soil or a bit of filter sand from an already established aquarium. Another method is to add one or two small test fish and let them introduce the needed bacteria. Whichever method you use, you should allow at least two weeks for the filter to become conditioned and the biological filtration to be in full operation although the addition of old filter sand may accelerate the process considerably. Alternatively, the display fish can be added immediately and the ammonia level controlled by making frequent partial water changes. However, the safest course is to allow the biological filtration to be established before adding the display fish.

Handling fish. Stress reduces a fish's ability to survive. It may be caused by a variety of factors, such as exhaustion from being pursued by hand net, struggling in a net, physical injury, competition with other fishes, fright, or simply by being placed in an unsuitable habitat. With careful planning, stress can be minimized. Simply chasing a fish in an aquarium to capture it can cause physiological changes from which it takes 24 hours or more to recover. This damaging effect can be minimized by using a large soft net with which the fish can be captured quickly and transferring it with as little struggle as possible. With delicate fishes, it is often desirable to use a plastic bag attached to a net frame and herd this into a container, so that the fish is never lifted from the water.

The ability of fishes to tolerate handling varies greatly. Some appear almost indestructible, while other species may appear to roll over and die at the clap of a hand. Some fish can be handled only a limited number of times. For these reasons, it is best to leave their habitat as undisturbed as possible once the aquarium has been set up.

Care must be used when introducing fish to the aquarium, as they can be subject to temperature and chemical stress as well as to handling stress. To reduce these effects, aquarists usually float the transportation bag in the aquarium to equalize the temperature and add aquarium water bit by bit over an hour or so. If the water in the bag is fouled, however, the transfer must be made more rapidly.

Daily care. Much of the daily care that the aquarium requires is obvious. Locate any missing fishes and remove them if dead or dying. Look for changes in the behavior or appearance of the fishes that foretell water problems or disease. Remove any uneaten

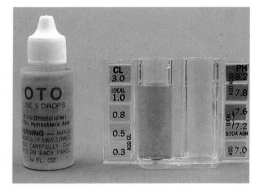

Chlorine and chloramine, especially the latter, are highly toxic. Their presence or absence can be determined with a simple test. Photo by Bill Call.

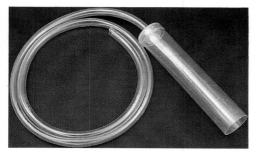

Change water and clean substrate regularly. Photo by Bill Call.

food. Check the temperature daily. This is most easily done by having a permanently installed thermometer, in or on each aquarium. Rectify any equipment problems. Keep cleaning to a minimum and carry it out as gently as possible.

About once a week the bottom sand should be vacuumed to remove detritus. A siphon with a large tube on the lower end can be used to clean the top layers of sand. Siphoning and vacuuming at the same time is usually the most practical way to accomplish the regular desired water changes. Any water lost through evaporation should be replaced with distilled water, not tap water or seawater, in order to prevent a gradual build-up of dissolved salts.

The inside of the front glass should be cleaned at least weekly. This can be done by using a pair of magnetic cleaners, available at your aquarium shop. These minimize fish disturbances but may not work well on stubborn spots.

Feeding. Fishes are poikilothermic, or cold-blooded; that is, their bodies are at the same temperature as the surrounding water. As a result, none of their food is used to produce heat, and they therefore require much less food than warm-blooded mammals. This fact is sometimes not well understood by everyone who cares for fish, especially the neighbor who looks after your aquarium while you are away on vacation. Although fish are in little danger of dying of obesity from overfeeding, they will succumb to uneaten food left on the tank bottom if it is allowed to decompose and foul the water. As a general rule, aquarium fishes should be fed small quantities once, twice, or three times a day. The smaller and younger they are, the more frequent the feedings. No food, other than live foods, should remain on the bottom after ten minutes.

It may require some ingenuity to ensure

that each fish gets a fair share of food. Aggressive fishes may have to be kept busy feeding at one end of the aquarium, while the more timid fish are surreptitiously fed at another location. Nocturnal fish may not feed except during the evening or night, and may require a separate feeding. Not infrequently, a pecking order develops, especially amongst fishes of the same species. This can lead to harassment of the less dominant fishes, which, unless removed, may become emaciated due to a combination of stress and starvation. With few exceptions, healthy fishes are convex in the "shoulder" area. Check this area frequently to detect early weight loss and correct it.

Food. With modern food technology, a wide variety of prepared aquarium foods is available ranging from liquid fry foods and flakes to large pellets. Don't overlook trout pellets and koi food as an economical source of food for larger aquarium fishes. A suitable prepared food is probably available for most commonly kept aquarium fishes. However, for a variety of reasons, it may be desirable to use natural foods either as a staple diet or as a supplement.

1. Prepared foods may not meet all of the nutritional requirements. For example, only a few of the many carotenoids (color pigments) present in fishes are normally available in prepared foods. This is why some fish become pale in captivity.
2. Some fishes have special requirements that cannot be met by any prepared foods available to date.
3. Natural foods may stimulate feeding by providing variety in the diet or by being

A wide variety of foods, both natural and prepared, is available.

23

A variety of excellent, prepared foods is available.

more palatable. Their use can also generate activity through longer feeding times and increased efforts to obtain and assimilate the food.

Natural foods include fresh and frozen seafoods; meats such as beef heart; vegetables such as peas, corn, spinach, broccoli, etc.; insects such as ants, maggots and grubs. A variety of suitable foods is usually obtainable from aquarium stores including frozen brine shrimp (*Artemia*) and frozen krill (plankton). Usually available also are live foods such as tubificid worms, mealworms, white worms, microworms and live adult brine shrimp.

Some live foods can be collected by the aquarist, while other organisms can be cultured. Both marine and fresh-water plankton can be gathered in a plankton tow net but take care not to admit unwanted predators or pests into the aquarium. This can largely be avoided by passing the plankton through a suitable-sized sieve, available from a biological supply house.

The most widely used cultured food is newly hatched brine shrimp or nauplii (*Artemia*). The dried eggs last almost indefinitely and can be easily hatched by placing them in salt water, either seawater or a 2–4% solution of sodium chloride and Epsom salts. Aerate well with an airstone. The eggs will hatch in about 24 hours at 24°C (75°F). After hatching, the brine shrimp nauplii should be separated from the eggshells and unhatched eggs. This can be done by wrapping brown paper around a glass container that holds the mixture. Remove the airstone and let the mixture settle. Then direct a light at a 1–2 cm (4–8 in) hole punched in the paper near the center of the container. The nauplii will aggregate in this region in the light path where they can be siphoned off, while the eggshells will float to the top and the unhatched eggs will sink to the bottom. Newly hatched brine shrimps are most nutritious if fed shortly after hatching, while they still carry egg yolk. They have been used extensively and successfully as a first food for many newly hatched fishes. They do, however, lack nutritional requirements for some species. Brine shrimp nauplii are also relatively large (250–350 milllimocrons) and many fish larvae require smaller food. Among the most useful is the rotifer (*Brachionus*), which is 60–180 millimicrons in diameter. However, *Brachionus* takes considerable effort to culture, as algae must also be maintained in order to feed it. An alternative to *Brachionus* is infusoria. This is a miscellaneous assortment of microorganisms, especially small ciliated protozoans that develop voluntarily in a solution of decomposing organic matter. It can be started from a package of organic material – available from your pet dealer or scientific supply house – or by allowing hay and grass to decompose in water.

Fishes vary greatly in their dietary requirements. Some are truly omnivorous, and thrive on a wide variety of foods. Others are highly specialized and do well only if they have access to their dietary staple food or to food closely approximating it. For example, many butterflyfishes feed extensively on coral polyps and most of these do poorly on any aquarium diet that we can conveniently provide at this time. As a general rule, the aquarist should find out all he can about his fish's natural diet, and then try to approximate it. Information is given under the species description in this book, but more can be found by a careful search of the literature, both popular aquarium literature and scientific publications. Once the natural diet is known, produce it as best you can using both prepared and natural foods. Provide variety, and let the fish help to tell you what it likes. But remember that fish, like people, may have preferences that do not necessarily meet all of their nutritional needs.

Collecting fishes

Collecting your own aquarium specimens can add a whole new dimension to your hobby. Not only do you have the thrill of providing your own specimens, you can learn much about their natural environment and habits that will help you to become a better aquarist. Remember, however, that the responsible aquarist should always have in mind the conservation of both the species he collects and the environment.

A vast array of methods can be used to collect fishes, many of them interchangeable between fresh-water and marine environments. The circumstances and practice will dictate your choice of methods.

HOOK AND LINE – Many a small boy fishing from a local pier has provided interesting fish for the aquarist. Usually the hook injury is of little consequence, especially if the barb is flattened or removed before use. Hook and line can also be used underwater by scuba divers. Jawfishes, for example, will often grasp a hook lowered into the hole in order to remove it from the burrow. Sedentary fish such as some rock fishes, snappers and groupers can often be captured by a diver dangling a line in front of their noses.

DIP NET – A long-handled dip net can be used to obtain specimens in small amounts of water, and by dip netting at night. Sometimes spreading chum or bait on the surface will facilitate capture. A light hung over the side of the vessel or pier will attract plankton, which in turn attracts fish that can then be dip netted.

SEINE – Seines vary from a short piece of netting attached between two poles to massive nets several hundred meters long. A simple pole seine about 3 meters (10 ft) by 1 meter (3 ft) high is very useful in capturing both marine and fresh-water fishes.

TRAPS – Like seines, traps come in a wide assortment of sizes and materials. Plastic minnow traps available from sporting goods stores can be used to capture both fresh-water and marine fishes. Larger traps baited with seafoods also work well. A simple but effective trap is a gallon jar. The diver places the jar in a strategic location, baits it, and moves back a short distance. After the fish have been allowed to enter, the lid is quickly placed over the opening. This method is particularly effective for capturing wrasses and damsels.

TIDEPOOLS – As the tide recedes, fishes are often trapped or choose to remain in tidepools. They can often be captured with a hand net. Bailing out the pool may facilitate capture.

SCUBA – Scuba has the advantage of allowing the collector to select the fishes he wishes to capture and to look for fishes in areas that are largely inaccessible from the surface, such as steep rocky faces. A wide variety of techniques is at the collector's disposal, but the

Many aquarists enjoy collecting their own specimens.

The intertidal zone contains a wealth of marine plants, invertebrates and fishes, many of them suitable for the home aquarium.

With the aid of scuba and hand net, the aquarist can catch many species of coral-reef fishes. Photo by Gini Kellogg.

25

Fishes captured in water deeper than about 5 meters should have the gas removed from their swim bladders in order to prevent decompression disease as they are brought to the surface.

After capture, specimens can be held in a simple holding net attached to an inner tube.

most commonly used device is a simple hand net. The fishes may be chased down and netted, or baited into the open and netted. A short piece of rod can be used to chase fish from holes and crevices. Some collectors use hand nets in pairs.

Another commonly used technique is to drive the fishes into a fine-meshed barrier or fence net. For many aquarium fishes, a net of 2 cm (0.75 in) mesh works well. This is small enough to avoid gilling the fish, but large enough to ensnare them briefly and allow them to be collected with a hand net. Suction devices such as slurp guns have been developed and are useful for capturing small sedentary fishes or hole-dwelling species such as gobies. As previously mentioned, wrasses can be trapped by divers using a baited 4-liter (1-gal.) jar.

DECOMPRESSION – Fishes with closed swim bladders experience embolisms and other injuries when brought to the surface from deep water. As a general rule, those deeper than about 10 m (33 ft) should be decompressed˙ or degassed before being brought to the surface. This can be done by placing them in a container which is brought to the surface in gradual stages. However, we prefer to evacuate the swim bladder at the depth of capture by inserting a small hypodermic needle between the scales and through the body wall into the bladder, then gently squeezing the gas out of the bladder.

A note on chemical methods. A variety of chemicals have been used to collect fishes. Cyanide, which is used widely in the Philippines, is dangerous to the collector and harmful to the environment and may decrease the longevity of fishes captured with it. Other chemicals can be used safely, but because of their potential harmful effects on the environment should not be used by the hobbyist. In most countries the use of these chemicals is regulated by law and requires a special permit. Violation of collecting regulations can result in severe penalties.

Holding and transporting specimens. After capture the fishes should be held in good-quality water that is near the temperature at which the fishes were caught. On the collecting boat or at shore the fish can be kept in a plastic garbage can and maintained in good condition with frequent water changes. During collecting a net suspended from an inner tube can be used as a holding pen. Similarly for longer terms, a holding pen can be placed in a sheltered area, but be wary of harbors, because of pollution and vandalism. Fishes in floating receivers can also fall victim to birds, sealions and predaceous fishes. Sometimes it may be desirable to set up a temporary aquarium. A plastic picnic cooler can be used for this purpose and can be aerated with a battery-powered air pump if no electricity is available. Even a subsand filter can be operated in this fashion.

To transport fishes from the collecting site to the home, conventional airline shipping boxes can be used. Pack the fishes in double plastic bags, one fish per bag if possible, leaving plenty of room (50% or more) above the water for oxygen. Twist the tops closed, double them over and secure with rubber bands. If high temperatures are anticipated during the trip, plastic bags of ice can be placed on top of the shipping bags so that they chill the oxygen above the water, which in turn will provide gradual sustained cooling.

Do not place the ice under the bags as overcooling can be detrimental.

Fishes properly packed in this fashion can survive in transit 24 hours or more, in good condition.

FRESH-WATER FISHES

Lungfishes

Although they are usually not considered for the home aquarium, lungfishes are of particular interest because they are among the most ancient of the living fishes, having arisen more than 300 million years ago. Their lungs developed probably as an adaptation to stagnant water and drought, possibly following Devonian times when subsidence of the earth's waters occurred. Six species are known today: one from Australia, four from Africa, and one from South America. They are indigenous to tropical regions that are subject to seasonal droughts. The Australian lungfish (*Lepidosiren*) is considered the most primitive and possesses only a single lung, does not aestivate, and can survive in well-oxygenated water without coming to the surface. The South African lungfishes (*Protopterus*) and the South American lungfish (*Lepidosiren*) possess paired lungs, aestivate in mud tunnels or mud balls during droughts, and when in water must come to the surface to breathe, or they will asphyxiate. When they are kept in an aquarium, an air space must be left at the surface. Lungfishes are close relatives of the *Crossopterygians*, which include the coelacanth (*Latimeria*), a group of fish thought to be extinct until 1938, when a specimen was captured off South Africa. All subsequent specimens have been caught at the Comoro Islands near Madagascar. Lungfishes are oviparous, and lay their eggs early in the wet season. The eggs, and usually the young, are guarded by the male.

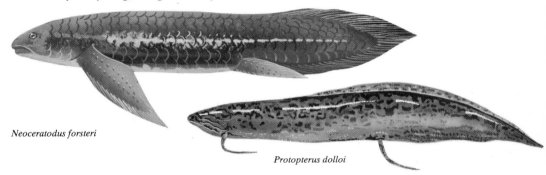

Neoceratodus forsteri

Protopterus dolloi

FAMILY CERATODONTIDAE
Order Ceratodontiformes
Neocerotodus forsteri – Australian lungfish

Size – To 180 cm (72 in)
Range – Queensland, Australia.
Feeding – In nature: fishes, amphibians, invertebrates, and some plant material, which is probably ingested because of the minute organisms that live upon it.

The Australian lungfish is considered the most primitive of the living lungfishes since it possesses only a single lung, cannot aestivate, and is able to survive without breathing at the surface. This is a robust species characterized by large paddle-like fins and large cycloid scales. Oviparous, it lays large eggs among aquatic plants. The adults guard both the eggs and the newly hatched young. The Australian lungfish is a protected species and is not available to the aquarist, but it can be seen at some public aquaria including the Vancouver Public Aquarium in Canada.

FAMILY PROTOPTERIDAE
Order Lepidosireniformes
Protopterus dolloi – African lungfish

Size – To 85 cm (36 in)
Range – Zaire river basin, Africa (Congo basin of Africa).
Feeding – In nature: slow-moving fishes and invertebrates. In aquarium: feed lean meat and fish. If necessary to initiate feeding, try guppies and small snails.
Aquarium care – Small specimens can be kept in the home aquarium and are occasionally found on the tropical fish market. This species can be very aggressive toward other species and is probably best kept alone. It does best at water temperatures of 20–30° C (68–84° F), but it will survive at higher temperatures. Be sure to leave an air space between the water surface and the aquarium cover. The aquarium may be planted with hardy plants such as *Cryptocoryne*.

Protopterus dolloi is one of four species of African lungfishes. The other three species are similar in appearance and range from 30 to 140 cm (12–55 in) at maturity.

FAMILY LEPIDOSIRENIDAE
Order Lepidosireniformes

Lepidosiren paradoxa – South American lungfish

Size – To 125 cm (48 in)
Range – Fresh waters of Central and South America.
Feeding – In nature: bottom fishes and invertebrates. In aquarium: will accept small pieces of meat, fish, crustaceans, and worms. It may be necessary to use live food, such as guppies, to initiate feeding.

Aquarium care – This species is rarely available to the aquarist, but it is a hardy fish and will survive under a wide range of conditions and temperatures down to 20°C (68°F). Be sure to leave an air space at the top of the aquarium so the fish may breathe at the surface.

ORDER POLYPTERIFORMES – FAMILY POLYPTERIDAE

Bichirs

The family Polypteridae includes 10 species of bichirs (*Polypterus*) and the reed fish (*Calamoichthys*). This family, which is primitive in origin, is confined to tropical Africa. Bichirs are elongate fishes covered with distinctive rhomboid-shaped ganoid scales, and possess a dorsal fin which is divided into a series of finlets. As in the lungfishes, the swim bladder is bilobed and serves as an accessory breathing organ. Bichirs will perish if prevented from breathing air for more than short periods. Being rather sluggish, their most common habitat is the margins of rivers, where they hide on the bottom during the day and emerge at night to prey on insect larvae, worms, other small invertebrates, and small fishes. They reproduce by spawning and the eggs hatch into distinctive larvae, with tree-like external gills. Several species have been kept successfully by both amateur and professional aquarists, and have proven to be both hardy and interesting aquarium fishes.

Polypterus bichir – Nile bichir

Size – To 70 cm (28 in)
Range – Nile River, and adjacent lakes and rivers.
Feeding – In nature: insect larvae, worms, small invertebrates and fishes. In aquarium: feed a varied diet including worms, mealworms, insect larvae, pieces of meat and fish.
Aquarium care – Bichirs are hardy and often become very tame. Although they are not always available at tropical

fish stores, they are worth looking out for. Provide an aquarium of suitable size with rocks and roots for cover. Water quality is not critical, and they do well at temperatures of 20–30°C (68–86°F). Bichirs may appeal to the aquarist who is interested in fishes with distinctive biological characteristics. Their ancient origin and unique swim bladders give them this quality.

Family Osteoglossidae

The Osteoglossids or "bony tongues" are a small family of fresh-water fishes that occur world-wide in the tropical realm. This family includes the arapima, which reaches a length of 4.5 m (15 ft) and is one of the largest fresh-water fishes in the world. The well-known and popular aquarium fish the arawana (*Osteoglossum bicirrhosum*) and its close relative *Osteoglossum ferreirai* also belong to the same family, as do two species of *Scleropages*, which occur in northern Australia and southeast Asia.

Osteoglossum bicirrhosum – arawana

Size – To 100 cm (36 in)
Range – Guyana and the Amazon Basin.
Feeding – In nature: the arawana cruises just beneath the surface of the water where it feeds on a wide variety of surface organisms, including insects such as beetles and spiders, crustaceans, snails, and to a lesser extent, fishes and surface debris. In aquarium: a wide variety of foods have been found suitable including small fishes, *Artemia*, *Daphnia*, insect larvae, mealworms, and prepared foods.
Aquarium care – Choose a tank suitable for the size of fish that is purchased, but preferably not smaller than 400 liters (100 gal.), and transfer to a larger aquarium as the fish grows. Arawana do best in soft water enriched with humus at temperatures of 23–27° C (73–81° F). Be sure the tank is well covered, as this species can be a spectacular leaper.

The arawana is an attractive and unusual aquarium specimen with its large eyes, large silver scales, and prominent barbels on the lower jaw. It is particularly attractive in an aquarium well stocked with plant life. It is easy to keep, and with reasonable care can be long-lived in captivity. The arawana is a mouth breeder. After spawning, one of the parents picks up the fertilized eggs and carries them in its mouth until they hatch. These fish are difficult to breed and rear in captivity.

Featherbacks

The featherbacks occur in the tropical fresh waters of Africa and southeast Asia. They are relatively large fishes, elongate and laterally compressed in shape. Because of their appearance, they are sometimes referred to as knifefish. The most unusual aspect of their appearance is the very long anal fin which stretches along the entire underside of the fish from just behind the head. The dorsal fin is small and feather-like, except that in one species of African featherback it is totally lacking. The belly, or ventral fins, are small or absent, but the pectoral fins are well developed. The anal fin is its principal means of propulsion. The featherback can swim forwards or backwards with equal ease. Only three genera, including four species, are known. All are relatively large fishes, ranging from 20 to 90 cm (8–36 in), and only juveniles are suitable for most home aquaria. Featherbacks are important food fish in regions of southeast Asia and India. In some regions, posts are driven in the bottom of rivers to provide spawning areas and thus enhance reproduction.

Notopterus chitala – East Indian featherback (East Indian knifefish)

Size – 290 cm (36 in)
Range – Tropical fresh waters of Burma, India and Thailand.
Feeding – In nature: this is a predatory species that feeds on small fishes and invertebrates. In aquarium: usually will accept pieces of fish and meat but small live fish may be required to initiate feeding.
Aquarium care – This is a large species and only small juveniles are suitable for even the largest home aquaria.

Water quality is not critical, but soft water enriched with humus is preferred, with temperatures maintained between 24 and 28°C (75–82°F).

Featherbacks are aggressive in aquaria and should be kept alone or possibly with other large fishes of a different species. The false featherfin (*Xenomystus nigri*) of Africa is smaller, and sometimes available on the aquarium market. It is less attractive, but more suitable for the home aquarist.

ORDER OSTEOGLOSSIFORMES – FAMILY PANTODONTIDAE

Fresh-water Butterflyfish

This family contains only a single species, the African butterflyfish *Pantodon buchholzi*, which is characterized by unusual pelvic fins with long feelers and large pectoral fins. The latter resemble butterfly wings, which the fish use to jump out of the water, but not for gliding. During the day, butterflyfish usually hide under leaves and floating debris and feed actively only in the evening and at night. They feed upon living animals that live at the water's surface, including terrestrial insects which accidentally land on the water.

Pantodon buccholzi – African butterflyfish

Pantodon has been successfully bred in captivity. Courtship is prolonged, and the male embraces the female during the spawning act.

Fertilization may be internal. The newly laid eggs float at the surface and hatch after approximately two days. The larvae are very small and will accept only the smallest foods.

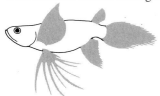

Size – To 10 cm (4 in)
Range – Still waters and pools associated with rivers in tropical West Africa.
Feeding – In nature: a wide variety of surface-dwelling organisms, including fishes, insects and invertebrates. In aquarium: a wide variety of food including mealworms, maggots and prepared food.
Aquarium care – Small specimens have been kept in aquaria as small as 75 liters (20 gal.), but the aquarium must be well covered as the fish is a notorious jumper. Larger aquaria of 300 liters (80 gal.) are preferred. This is a peaceful species. Since it lives at the surface, it makes a nice addition to many community tanks. Plants with floating leaves should be provided, and the water kept between 25 and 30°C (77–86°F).

31

Mormyrids

This family, found only in the tropical fresh waters of Africa, contains fish with the ability to generate radar, like electric fields, which they use to detect prey and objects in their immediate environment. Many of the fishes are unique in appearance. They have small eyes and often an unusual mouth with elongated jaws that form a proboscis. The dorsal and anal fins are usually situated posteriorly at a point where the body tapers abruptly toward the tail, which is deeply forked. Its teeth are small and few. Internally, mormyrids possess an unusually large cerebellum, a swim bladder, which extends into the skull, and a caudal musculature that has been modified into an electric organ. Mormyrids usually live in dimly lit marshes, along slow-moving stream margins and in other fresh-water areas with muddy bottoms. They are primarily active at night, but species which live in perpetually dimly lit environments are also active during the daytime. Their food consists primarily of worms and other sedentary invertebrates living near the surface of the mud. Little is known about their reproduction, but at least some species are believed to be bubblenest builders. Ten genera and approximately 100 species are known.

Gnathonemus petersi – Congo elephant fish

Size – To 23 cm (9 in)
Range – Tropical Africa, including the Congo, Cameroon, and Zaire.
Feeding – In nature: small mud-dwelling organisms. In aquarium: feed small worms, insect larvae, and plankton (*Daphnia*, *Cyclops*, etc.).
Aquarium care – Water quality is not critical. Keep between 20 and 28° C (68–82° F) in a dimly lit aquarium with surface plants, rooted plants, and hiding places amongst rocks and wood.

This is probably the best-known species of mormyrid to the hobbyist. It does well if kept in a dimly lit aquarium but care must be taken to see that it receives plenty of live food. The Congo elephant fish tolerates other species well and may be kept in community tanks. However, it may react adversely to other species of electric fishes.

Characins

Characins, one of the largest families of fishes with several hundred species, are a very important group for the aquarist, with many small, colorful, active species that are easy to obtain, inexpensive, and easy to maintain. With few exceptions other than the piranhas, characins are peaceful and do well in either community or single-species tanks. The classification of this group is complicated, and particularly confusing for the nonspecialist. A variety of schemes will be found in the literature. Some authorities recognize one family while others divide the group into as many as 16 families and group them in a suborder, the Characoidei (Greenwood *et al*. 1966, Nelson 1976, Géry 1977), or more recently a separate order, the Characiformes (Fink and Fink 1981). The characins, along with the minnows, order Cyprinodontoformes, and the catfish, order Siluriformes, are included in the superorder Ostariophysi. These fishes are characterized by possessing a sound-enhancing Weberian apparatus, a series of bones connecting the swim bladder with the inner ear; and an alarm substance (Shreckstoff) that is released when their skin is injured, which causes a fright response in other members of the same species. Characins vary from fusiform (neon tetras) to compressed (piranhas); also they nearly always have scales, either ctenoid or cycloid, and nearly always have well-developed teeth but lack barbels. They usually possess an adipose fin, ventral fins which are abdominally positioned, and a moderate to short anal fin.

DISTRIBUTION AND ECOLOGY. Characins live in the tropical fresh waters of Africa and South America with a few species extending into the temperate regions of North America. They inhabit all types of fresh water but are typically abundant in warm, clear, well-lit waters. Most are carnivorous. Reproduction is by spawning; the eggs may be laid in vegetation on the bottom, or in the water column. They usually hatch in one to six days with little or no parental care. The newly hatched fry may remain on the bottom for several days before feeding or swimming. Very small food, infusoria, or specially prepared food is required by them initially, followed by brine shrimp nauplii when the fishes' mouths are large enough to accept them.

Serrasalmus nattereri – red piranha (piranha caju)

Size – To 30 cm (12 in)
Range – Amazon and Orinoco river basins.
Feeding – In nature: carnivorous, with sharp cutting teeth that allow it to feed on large prey, primarily fishes but also other vertebrates including mammals, insects and invertebrates. In aquarium: pieces of fish supplemented with meat.

Aquarium care – Require a large tank; water quality is not critical; usually kept between 21 and 27° C (70–80° F). Highly aggressive; it is best to begin with a group of young specimens and rear them together in order to minimize fighting.

There are approximately 15 species of piranha in the genus *Serrasalmus*; many are similar in appearance and difficult to distinguish. *S. nattereri* is most commonly imported but can be confused with other species. The black piranha (*S. rhombeus*) is well known to aquarists and sometimes erroneously called *S. niger* (see Géry 1977).

33

TETRAS

Many of the characins known to aquarists are called "tetras," a common name derived from the subfamily name Tetragonopterinae, "the square fins," but which has become applied to a variety of small characins not necessarily closely related. Most tetras, common to the aquarium trade, are best kept in groups of six or more. Although aquaria as small as 20 liters (5 gal.) can be successfully employed, larger aquaria are preferred, especially if reproduction is desired. Many species have been raised successfully in captivity. Generally a well-planted aquarium with soft, slightly acid, water of good quality that is low in waste products, is required to promote spawning.

Paracheirodon innesi – neon tetra

Size – To 4 cm (1.5 in)
Range – Upper Amazon basin.
Feeding – In nature: favors insects and their larvae. In aquarium: freeze-dried and other prepared aquarium foods; if practical supplement with live insects.
Aquarium care – Can be kept in small aquaria. Keep in groups of six or more. Soft, slightly acid water, obtained by filtering through peat, is recommended. Include fine-leaved plants and provide at least moderate light. Keep between 21 and 23° C (70–73° F) to spawn.

The neon tetra is an inhabitant of jungle pools and small quiet streams. It is similar in appearance to the cardinal tetra, being smaller and less reddish toward the anterior.

Cheirodon axelrodi – cardinal tetra

Size – To 5 cm (2 in)
Range – Upper Rio Negro.
Feeding – As for the neon tetra.
Aquarium care – Keep groups of six or more in slightly acid soft water at 22–27° C (72–80° F) in an aquarium with fine-leaved plants. Difficult to breed.

The cardinal tetra is the most colorful of all characins and created a sensation in the aquarium world when it was discovered in the 1950s. Simultaneously described as *Hyphessobrycon cardinalis*; it was ruled that *C. axelrodi* had priority.

Hyphessobrycon serpae – serpa tetra

Size – To 5 cm (2 in)
Range – Amazon basin and Guyana.
Feeding – In nature: insects and other small organisms. In aquarium: does well on prepared aquarium foods.
Aquarium care – As for *H. ocellifer*.

Géry (1977) recognizes four closely related species that are difficult to tell apart. The serpa tetra is also a close relative of the jewel tetra *H. callistus*, for which it is sometimes mistaken.

Hyphessobrycon pulchripinnis – lemon tetra

Size – To 5 cm (2 in)
Range – Amazon basin.
Feeding – In nature: probably feeds on insects, small crustaceans and other small organisms. In aquarium: does well on most prepared aquarium foods.
Aquarium care – As for previous species but tends to be hardier and less demanding.

Lemon tetras belong to the widespread genus *Hyphessobrycon*, which currently includes over 60 species and which is likely to be split into several genera in the future.

Hemigrammus ocellifer – head-and-tail light fish (beacon fish)

Size – To 4 cm (1.5 in)
Range – Amazon basin, Guyana.
Feeding – In nature: insects and other small organisms. In aquarium: any good prepared food.
Aquarium care – A hardy species and easy to keep; often recommended for beginners. Water quality is not critical; but should be soft and slightly acid for breeding. Keep in at least a 30-liter (8-gal.) aquarium, planted with fine-leaved plants. Temperature 22–27° C (72–80° F).

This is one of several species with iridescent spots on the caudal peduncle and eye that may be found with the common name of "head-and-tail light fish."

Hyphessobrycon serpae

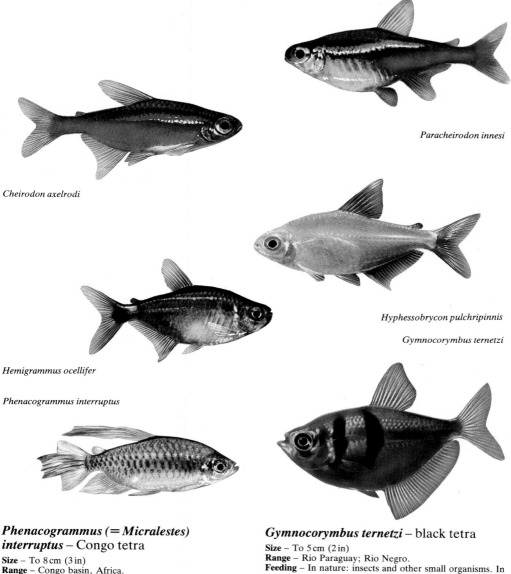

Paracheirodon innesi

Cheirodon axelrodi

Hyphessobrycon pulchripinnis

Gymnocorymbus ternetzi

Hemigrammus ocellifer

Phenacogrammus interruptus

Phenacogrammus (= Micralestes) interruptus – Congo tetra

Size – To 8 cm (3 in)
Range – Congo basin, Africa.
Feeding – In nature: insects and other small organisms. In aquarium: freeze-dried and other prepared aquarium foods, insects, *Artemia*.
Aquarium care – Easy to keep. Does best when not crowded; deserves a 75-liter (20-gal.) or larger aquarium. Water should be soft, slightly acid and kept at 25–27° C (77–81° F). Provide plants.

This is perhaps the most beautiful of all the African tetras, with its long dorsal fin, lobed caudal fin and delicate colors. It has been bred. The young hatch in about six days.

Gymnocorymbus ternetzi – black tetra

Size – To 5 cm (2 in)
Range – Rio Paraguay; Rio Negro.
Feeding – In nature: insects and other small organisms. In aquarium: prepared aquarium foods; insects.
Aquarium care – Can be kept in small aquaria. Water quality is not critical; keep at 24–28° C (75–82° F). Decorate with rocks and plants. Easily bred.

The black tetra is bred extensively by commercial breeders and supplied to pet stores. A good species for beginners.

Exodon paradoxus – exodon (paradox characin)

Size – To 15 cm (6 in)
Range – Northeastern South America; reported from the Rupununi River, Guyana, and the Branco River, Brazil.
Feeding – In nature: stomach analyses suggest that *Exodon* feeds primarily on scales of other fishes. In aquarium: live foods are readily accepted including small fishes.
Aquarium care – An aggressive species that is an active leaper, it should be kept in single-species or in community tanks with only robust species. Keep in a large tank and provide subdued sunlight at 24–28° C (75–82° F).

This is one of the most beautiful and active of the characins but is difficult to keep because of its aggressive nature. Hard to breed and rear. Mating is vigorous, and when successful the large eggs are spawned and deposited on plants. The young emerge in approximately a day. All in all, this species is an interesting challenge for the experienced aquarist.

Astyanax mexicanus

Astyanax mexicanus – Mexican characin (Mexican tetra)

Size – To at least 9 cm (3.5 in)
Range – Texas to Panama.
Feeding – In nature: small organisms. In aquarium: accepts a wide variety of foods, prepared and natural.
Aquarium care – A hardy species. Keep in a moderately planted aquarium and supply roots for cover and authenticity. Keep at normal room temperatures; 16–22° C (61–72° F) is often recommended, but optimal temperatures will be those that approximate the area of collection, which is usually unknown for purchased fish.

This was previously considered to be a sub-species of *A. fasciatus* but recent evidence suggests that only one species exists and it is therefore assigned the older specific name of *A. mexicanus*.

The blind cavefish is well known to aquarists and a favorite of many because of its uniqueness. It has been considered a separate species but genetic and reproductive studies suggest that it interbreeds freely with normal eyed fishes and is now classified as *A. mexicanus*. Young cavefishes have rudimentary eyes which disappear with age as the eye socket becomes overgrown with tissue. Those living in a dark environment are unpigmented and appear pink. When kept in an environment with light they become silvery. They are relatively easy to breed. After being spawned the fertilized eggs hatch in three to four days and the fry begin to swim and feed in about six days. The large-mouthed larvae will usually accept brine shrimp nauplii (*Artemia*) immediately.

Astyanax mexicanus (= *Anoptichthys jordani*) – blind Mexican cavefish

Size – To 9 cm (3.5 in)
Range – Caves of east-central Mexico.
Feeding – In nature: available animal matter. In aquarium: normal aquarium diets.
Aquarium care – A hardy species, but does best if kept in groups of its own kind in a spacious tank; water quality is not critical; does well over a wide temperature range; 18–24° C (64–75° F) is probably optimal. An illuminated tank with a cave-like decor provides realism.

Anoptichthys jordani

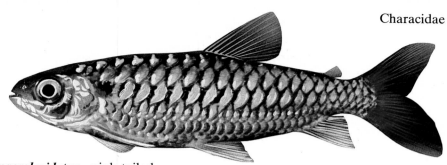

Chalceus macrolepidotus – pink-tailed characin (South American trout)

Size – To 25 cm (10 in)
Range – Guyana.
Feeding – In nature: carnivorous. In aquarium: chopped meat and fish, earthworms and many usual foods.
Aquarium care – A large hardy species but it requires a large aquarium of 400 liters (100 gal.) or more to thrive; this must be well covered to prevent the fish from jumping out. If possible keep six or more together in a well-planted aquarium at 24–26° C (75–79° F).

Large mirror-like scales and a red to pink tail make this a very attractive aquarium fish. It is a peaceful species with fish of its own size. In nature they form schools and are effectively caught by the natives with cast nets. The pink-tailed characin can be bred in captivity. Suspected mating pairs should be removed to an aquarium which includes bushy plants over which the pair will tend to spawn. As many as 3,000 eggs may be released which should be removed to a brood tank where they will hatch in about 48 hours at 27° C (81° F). The young should begin to swim and feed after about four days and should accept brine shrimp nauplii. As they grow, shift to larger foods including fish fry, worms and prepared foods. A similar species, *Chalceus erythrinus*, occurs in the Amazon River but has yellowish fins.

Brycinus (= Alestes) longipinnis – long-finned characin

Size – To 15 cm (6 in)
Range – Tropical West Africa.
Feeding – In nature: primarily flying insects. In aquarium: *Drosophila*, mealworms, prepared foods, other insects.
Aquarium care – A hardy compatible species but needs soft, slightly acid water to reproduce. The newly hatched fry approach 1 cm (0.4 in) in length and will accept brine shrimp nauplii readily. Removal of adults may be advisable to protect the eggs and young from being eaten. Provide a large 400-liter (100-gal.) aquarium and keep several fish together. Provide plants, stones and roots for cover but leave open spaces. Keep at 24–28° C (75–82° F).

Based on technical details including skull anatomy, Géry (1977) places the African characins in a separate family, Alestidae. Here for simplicity they are included in the Characidae. The long-finned characin frequently appears in aquarium literature as *Alestes longipinnis* and sometimes as *Bryconalestes*; but because it lacks an adipose eyelid it is now placed in the genus *Brycinus*. This species is almost indistinguishable from its close relative *B. chaperi*. (In the former the anterior margin of the dorsal fin is in front of mid-body while in the latter it is at or behind mid-body.) Both species are imported. Long-finned characins are reported to prefer clear running water in nature. They are best known from Sierra Leone and Zaire. Mature males can usually be distinguished by their elongate dorsal fin which is usually tinged with red. The females have "normal" dorsal fins, yellowish in color. The long-finned characin is known to spawn in open waters near plants. The fertilized eggs, approximately 2 mm (0.08 in) in diameter, sink to the bottom where they hatch in about six days.

Metynnis

Colossoma brachypomum

Colossoma brachypomum – pacu

Size – To 60 cm (24 in)
Range – Amazon basin.
Feeding – In nature: vegetarian; eats seeds, fruit and vegetable matter. In aquarium: pellet food supplemented with corn peas and other plant matter; will usually accept meat.
Aquarium care – This species gets very large and needs a tank of at least 750 liters (200 gal.). Keep at 20–25° C (68–77° F); use only plastic plants.

Pacu is the common name generally used for a variety of seed- and fruit-eating fishes belonging to the genera *Colossoma*, *Mylossoma*, and *Myleus*. They are deep-bodied, compressed fishes with two rows of teeth in the upper jaw. The outer row contains incisor-like teeth while the inner row is composed of molars capable of crushing nuts and other hard parts of plants. Many pacus are relatively large fishes and are of relatively little interest to the home aquarist unless he specializes in "giant" fishes. *Myleus pacu*, for example, reaches 60 cm (24 in). Approximately 20 species of "pacus" have been described, many of them difficult to tell apart and only tentatively identified. Pacus are important food fishes in Guyana and along the Amazon. They are taken by hook and line as well as by cast net and seine. Little is known of their reproductive behavior but some evidence indicates that they spawn in depressions scooped in the substrate. Some species make extensive migrations from the larger rivers to small tributaries where spawning takes place.

Metynnis spp. – silver dollar

Size – To 18 cm (7 in)
Range – Guyana; Amazon and Paraguay Rivers.
Feeding – In nature: plants. In aquarium: prepared pellet and flake food; supplement with lettuce and insects.
Aquarium care – Keep in schools in a large aquarium. Water quality is not critical, but they prefer soft, slightly acid water kept at between 24 and 31° C (75–88° F). Provide roots for cover. Use plastic plants if desired.

Silver dollars are deep-bodied, compressed characins, often disk-like and usually silver. They have a sharp-toothed ventral keel and are superficially similar to piranhas but differ from them in dentition, which is like that of the pacus. Over 20 species of *Metynnis* have been described by some authors while others recognize only five of them: *Metynnis argenteus*; *Metynnis hypsauchen*; *Metynnis lippincottianus*; *Metinnis mola*; *Metynnis luna*. The most commonly imported species are the silver dollar *Metynnis hypsauchen* which grows up to 15 cm (6 in) and the spotted silver dollar *M. lippincottianus* which reaches about 10 cm (4 in). Silver dollars have been raised in captivity. They spawn in a manner similar to that of other characins. After a driving courtship the two press against each other and release eggs and sperm with a quivering motion. The eggs, 2 mm (0.08 in) in diameter, are non-adhesive and hatch after two to three days at about 26° C (79° F). They begin to swim and eat after four to five days and will usually accept live brine shrimp nauplii.

Pencilfishes and their Relatives

The lebiasinids have sometimes been included in the family Characidae but now stand alone as a separate family. They are characterized by a small, terminal mouth, which in most species does not extend to the eye; a short dorsal fin; small pectoral fins; sometimes an adipose fin; and a lateral line which is incomplete, or in the case of the *Pyrrhulina* absent. The family currently includes the genera *Copeina*, *Copella*, *Pyrrhulina* and *Nannostomus*.

DISTRIBUTION AND ECOLOGY. Lebiasinids occur in northern South America including Guyana, Surinam and the Amazon drainage. Most species are adapted for life near the surface where they feed upon organisms above, on or just beneath the surface. Reproduction is typically by spawning in characid fashion with brief development times. Egg care is given in some cases.

Copella arnoldi (= Copeina arnoldi) – spraying characin

Size – To 8 cm (3 in)
Range – Lower Amazon basin.
Feeding – In nature: primarily surface-living insects such as ants, mosquito larvae, etc. In aquarium: insects, prepared foods.
Aquarium care – The spraying characin does best in an aquarium of 75 liters (20 gal.) or larger which should be well planted and have a tight-fitting cover. Overhanging leaves are desirable as spawning sites (see below). Keep at 24–26° C (75–79° F).

This species has usually been assigned to the genus *Copeina* but on the basis of the shape of the upper jaw (maxillary) is now placed in *Copella*. Its unusual reproductive behavior makes it of particular interest to aquarists. The male selects a spawning site on the underside of a leaf one to two inches above the water. One or more females join him and they begin to jump in pairs against the leaf, where both are held momentarily by the suction of their fins. One or more eggs are spawned and fertilized during each leap. This is repeated until perhaps 100 or more eggs adhere to the leaf in a cluster. After spawning the female loses interest in the eggs but the male lies beneath the eggs and splashes them with his caudal fin until they hatch, usually in 36–48 hours. The newly hatched fry fall into the water, where they remain just below the surface. They usually feed well on rotifers and infusoria but can often be started directly on brine shrimp nauplii. Several other species of *Copella* are popular aquarium fishes, including the "red-spotted copeina" *Copeina guttata*, which spawns in typical characin fashion in a shallow nest dug in the bottom of the aquarium.

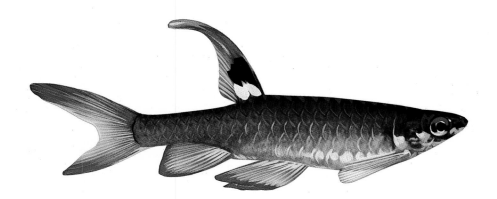

Nannostomus harrisoni (= Poecilobrycon harrisoni) – Harrison's pencilfish

Size – To 6 cm (2 in)
Range – Guyana, upper and middle Amazon.
Feeding – In nature: primarily small insects on the water surface but also feeds below the surface. In aquarium: small live insects such as fruit flies, ants, freeze-dried and other prepared aquarium foods.
Aquarium care – Does best in groups of six or more in peaty, soft, slightly acid water kept at 23–26° C (73–79° F). Can adapt to a small aquarium. Fine-leaved plants and a dark aquarium bottom should be provided.
Reproduction – Males of *N. harrisoni* usually have white-tipped pectoral fins. Females have rounder bellies. Set up a breeding tank with soft, slightly acid water and abundant fine-leaved plants. After spawning the male will fan the eggs, which hatch in about two days. The fry begin to swim in four days. Feed rotifers and infusoria followed by brine shrimp nauplii.

Pencilfishes are popular aquarium fishes. Most species are brightly colored, active and usually visible. They undergo a marked daily color change, having stripes during the day and dark blotches at night. They appear in the aquarium literature in several genera including *Nannostomus*, *Nannobrycon* and *Poecilobrycon*, but all have recently been assigned to *Nannostomus* (Weitzman and Cobb, 1975). In addition to Harrison's pencilfish other species likely to be encountered include:

Golden pencilfish, *Nannostomus beckfordi*. The basic coloration is pale golden yellow; a dark brown stripe runs from the snout over the eyes to the tail. This is a small species seldom over 5 cm (2 in). Not difficult to breed.

Dwarf pencilfish, *Nannostomus marginatus*. The basic coloration is silvery brown with dark dorsal, lateral and ventral stripes and a silver belly. The dorsal, anal and ventral fins are beautifully marked with red patches. Guyana. To 4 cm (1.5 in). Not difficult to breed but tends to eat its eggs.

Three-banded pencilfish, *Nannostomus trifasciatus*. This is a beautiful species. Brassy olive-green back, a silvery belly and three well-developed stripes along with red fin blotches distinguish this species. Best known from Brazil. To 5 cm (2 in).

Three-banded pencilfish, *Nannostomus unifasciatus*. Basic color is golden yellow-brown with a single broad stripe along each side and a light-colored belly; anal and caudal fins have a reddish base. Guyana, middle Amazon basin south to Bolivia. To 6.5 cm (2.5 in).

ORDER CHARACIFORMES – FAMILY ANOSTOMIDAE

Headstanders and Leporins

This family is similar in many respects to the Lebiasinidae. It contains two of the best and most popular aquarium fishes, the headstander, *Anostomus*, and the banded *Leporinus*. Anostomids are usually elongate, have a short anal fin, tubular nostrils, and a small nonprotractile mouth, a straight lateral line and usually have only three or four incisor-like teeth in each jaw. The genus *Abramites*, although somewhat deep-bodied, also belongs to this family.

DISTRIBUTION AND ECOLOGY. The family Anostomidae is wide-ranging and extends from Central America and the West Indies to Argentina. Anostomids are generally schooling fishes that prefer the slow-moving or still waters of forests. Many species shy away from bright light. Usually omnivorous, those that are headstanders adopt this posture in nature as they search the bottom for food, worms, larvae and algae, etc. When they are threatened their pike-like bodies are well adapted for rapid acceleration, allowing them to dart into cover. Many species are hardy, and adjust to a wide variation in water conditions, temperature, and tank-mates. Little information is available on the reproduction behavior of most species. The spotted *Leporinus*, however, is bred commercially.

Anostomus anostomus – striped headstander (striped anostomus)

Size – To 14 cm (5 in)
Range – Guyana and the adjoining watersheds, and the Amazon basin.
Feeding – In nature: omnivorous. In aquarium: will thrive on any of the usual aquarium foods but plant matter should be included; also worms.
Aquarium care – To allow optimal growth a large aquarium of 75 liters (20 gal.) or more should be provided. Prefers a well-planted aquarium and subdued light. Water quality is not critical; temperatures of 24–28° C (75–82° F) recommended.

Leporinus fasciatus – banded leporinus

Size – To 30 cm (12 in)
Range – Most of South America from Rio de la Plata north.
Feeding – In nature: omnivorous but include much plant material in their diet such as fruits, seeds and leaves. In aquarium: primarily plant matter; include fresh as well as prepared foods.
Aquarium care – Requires a large aquarium that should contain abundant hardy plants. Water quality is not critical; temperatures of 22–28° C (72–82° F) recommended.

Hatchetfishes

Fresh-water hatchetfishes (flying characins) are a small family of distinctively shaped fishes with a straight back, a highly compressed body, and large pectoral fins attached to a deep wedge-shaped muscular breast. They are considered to be the only fishes which truly fly (as opposed to glide), since they actually beat their pectoral fins. Their well-developed pectoral muscles allow them to propel themselves in a flight of 15 m (50 ft) or more near the surface of the water. The lower lobe of the caudal fin remains in contact with the surface of the water during most or all of the flight. Three genera are included in the family, *Carnegiella*, *Gasteropelecus* and *Thoracocharax*, with a total of nine species.

DISTRIBUTION AND ECOLOGY. Hatchetfishes are widespread in tropical America extending from Panama to Argentina including the Rio Payano in Panama, rivers of the Orinoco and Amazon basins, Rio Paraguay and Rio de la Plata. They are usually found in slow-moving streams, backwaters, marshes and protected regions of lakes. Hatchetfishes are a schooling species and appear to feed on insects at the water surface. It is unknown whether they use flight primarily to escape predators or to capture food.

REPRODUCTION. There are no known external sexual characteristics but in some species the developing eggs can be seen through the transparent body wall of the female. They are reported to spawn above vegetation and develop in typical characin fashion. Other hatchetfishes are imported for the aquarium trade including the black-winged hatchetfish *C. marthae*, the silver hatchetfish *Gasteropelecus levis*, the spotted hatchetfish *G. maculatus*, the common hatchetfish *G. sternicula*, and the starry hatchetfish *Thoracocharax stellatus*.

Carnegiella strigata – marbled hatchetfish

Size – To 4.5 cm (1.75 in)
Range – Guyana, Surinam, French Guiana, Amazon basin.
Feeding – In nature: small insects. In aquarium: should have insects to thrive; some prepared foods may be adequate.
Aquarium care – Keep at least six in as long an aquarium as feasible. Provide a good-fitting cover but leave an air space of 8 cm (3 in) or more. They will probably do best in soft peaty water kept at 23–30° C (73–86° F).

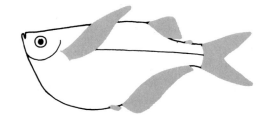

Minnows and Carps

This is the largest family of fishes, containing over 1,500 species that range in size from about 4 cm (1.5 in) to 250 cm (98 in). Cyprinids are typically moderately compressed fishes, with a protractile mouth; they have no teeth in the jaws or roof of the mouth, but one to three rows of teeth are present in the throat (pharyngeal teeth). The fins lack true unsegmented spines although one or two stiffened segmented rays may be present; the adipose fin is absent. The tail is usually forked. Scales are cycloid but absent from the head. The typical aquarium cyprinid has large shiny scales, a single soft dorsal fin at mid-body and a small terminal mouth. The family Cyprinidae is placed in the order Cypriniformes which no longer includes the characins, now elevated to an order, Characiformes. Both orders remain in the superorder Ostariophysi, characterized by the presence of the Weberian apparatus and the release of an alarm substance (Schreckstoff) when the skin is injured (Fink and Fink, 1981).

DISTRIBUTION AND ECOLOGY. Cyprinids are abundant in tropical and temperate waters over much of the world but do not occur naturally in South America, Australia or Madagascar. As would be expected of a family this large, members occur in all types of fresh-water environments which will support fish life ranging from torrential streams to rivers, lakes, and stagnant ponds, and in temperatures from near freezing to 38° C (100° F). Most cyprinids live and feed on or near the bottom. Cyprinids reproduce by spawning, usually among plants. When sexually mature, males of many species develop spawning tubercles, small raised pearly bumps on the head and body.

Cyprinus carpio

Cyprinus carpio – carp

Size – To 100 cm (40 in) but usually less than 50 cm (20 in)
Range – Carp were originally indigenous to temperate regions of Asia and Europe but have since been introduced to the fresh waters of much of the world.
Feeding – In nature: omnivorous; they eat a variety of plant and animal tissue. In aquarium: do well on pellet food.
Aquarium care – A very hardy species that can be kept in almost any container. Its ultimate size is regulated by the size of aquarium or pond. It may be kept indoors or out and will tolerate an extremely wide range of temperatures.

Carp are an important food fish in many regions and have been cultured intensively in ponds for centuries. For example, a half-hectare (one-acre) pond fertilized with farm manures typically yields more than 450 kg (1,000 lb) of fish per year. In nature carp can be found in ponds, lakes, slow-moving streams and rivers, and backwaters. Because they may displace native fishes, they should not be released into water systems that do not already contain them. In temperate regions, carp usually spawn in spring or early summer. During the early morning hours they court vigorously amongst shallow vegetation where they lay huge numbers of adhesive eggs. In artificial ponds mops may be used instead of vegetation. These may be removed to a brood tank for hatching and rearing. The eggs will hatch in three to seven days depending upon the water temperature. The larvae are 6–10 mm in length upon hatching and will accept brine shrimp nauplii or other similar-sized crustaceans. Suitable prepared foods for the fry are available.

43

Cyprinus carpio – koi

Size – To 100 cm (40 in)
Range – Do not occur naturally.
Feeding – In captivity they are usually fed pellet food which may contain carotenoid pigments to enhance the fish's colors.
Aquarium care – Koi are usually cultured in shallow ponds with concrete or rock bottoms. They can be kept with plants such as water lilies but the plants should be placed in containers with large rocks placed over the soil to prevent the koi from digging them up. Koi will tolerate temperatures from freezing to 38° C (100° F).

Many beautiful varieties of koi have been developed over the past 100 years by selective breeding. Choice specimens may bring tens of thousands of dollars at auctions while the more common varieties are very modestly priced. Unlike naturally occurring species, which are usually difficult to observe in ponds, koi are as attractive when viewed from above as they are through the glass of an aquarium.

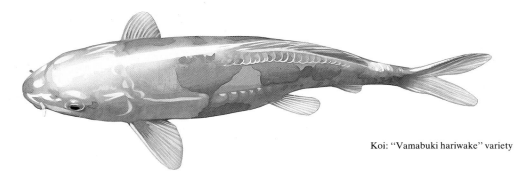

Koi: "Vamabuki hariwake" variety

GOLDFISH

Goldfish are the most familiar of all aquarium fishes and the easiest to keep. They have a long history as pets, apparently first being domesticated during the Sung Dynasty in China about 960 A.D. They were introduced into Europe by about 1700. Goldfish tolerate low levels of dissolved oxygen and high levels of dissolved wastes. Thus they can be kept in aquaria without artificial aeration and filtration and were kept successfully before the basic needs of the majority of fishes for oxygen were understood. A variety of color phases of goldfish occur in nature although natural selection forms the protectively colored drab greenish, and olive-bronze phases. Sometimes mistaken for carp, goldfish can be identified by their lack of barbels. Through selective breeding a number of standard varieties have been established. In addition to those illustrated, these include: the double-veiltail, telescope-veiltail, comet, celestial and the lionhead. Goldfish and carp can interbreed, producing a carp-like hybrid. Although goldfish do well in aquaria they are best adapted to pond life. In addition to being pets, many goldfish are used in research, environmental testing and teaching laboratories.

REPRODUCTION. Goldfish in ponds normally become sexually mature as the water warms in the spring. The males and rarely the females develop spawning tubercles on their gills while the females increase in girth. Sexual maturity in an indoor aquarium may be promoted by increasing the temperature from room temperature 20° C (68° F) to about 27° C (81° F). Courtship is often vigorous with much chasing by the male. Spawning takes place in fine-leaved vegetation or if desired on a spawning mop. Spawns of 2,000 to more than 10,000 eggs are usual. The eggs should be removed to a brood tank and will hatch in three or more days depending on temperature. The fry begin to feed about four days later. They are normally too small to accept brine shrimp nauplii during at least the first ten days and must be fed small zooplankton (rotifers, etc.), infusoria, finely strained boiled egg yolk or a suitable prepared fry food. For commercial production and selective breeding, goldfish are often spawned artificially by stripping the eggs and sperm of sexually mature fish, mixing them together in a dish and then introducing the fertilized eggs into a brood tank containing a spawning mat.

The selective breeding of koi has been largely developed by the Japanese, who have produced many varieties which have been named according to their color, place of origin, or a familiar object favored by the breeder. Those interested in learning more about koi will find *Koi of the World*, by Herbert Axelrod, a useful reference.

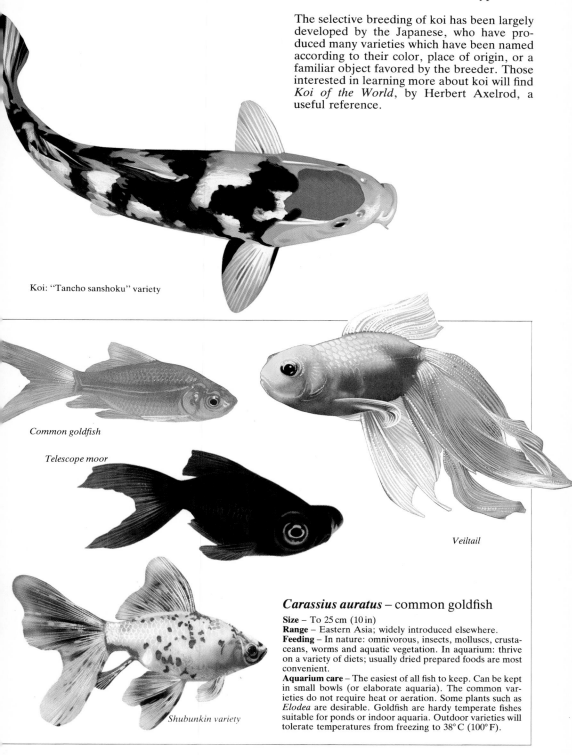

Koi: "Tancho sanshoku" variety

Common goldfish

Telescope moor

Veiltail

Shubunkin variety

Carassius auratus – common goldfish

Size – To 25 cm (10 in)
Range – Eastern Asia; widely introduced elsewhere.
Feeding – In nature: omnivorous, insects, molluscs, crustaceans, worms and aquatic vegetation. In aquarium: thrive on a variety of diets; usually dried prepared foods are most convenient.
Aquarium care – The easiest of all fish to keep. Can be kept in small bowls (or elaborate aquaria). The common varieties do not require heat or aeration. Some plants such as *Elodea* are desirable. Goldfish are hardy temperate fishes suitable for ponds or indoor aquaria. Outdoor varieties will tolerate temperatures from freezing to 38°C (100°F).

RASBORA

The generic name has been adopted as the common name for this group of fishes. Rasboras are small cyprinid fishes 3–13 cm (1–5 in) in length with elongate bodies that are moderately to strongly laterally compressed. The mouth is small, terminal and usually slopes upward. The fins are soft-rayed with one to three stiffened spines anteriorly; the tail is usually strongly forked, the pelvic fins are abdominal in position. The lateral line is usually present. Approximately 50 species have been described and about 36 species have been imported for the pet trade. Rasboras range from western India to the Philippines and south to Java. Species occur in all types of fresh-water habitats except torrential streams. Most are colorful, schooling species that are hardy and peaceful in the aquarium. They do well at temperatures from 21 to 27° C (70–81° F) and most will tolerate temperatures to 32° C (90° F).

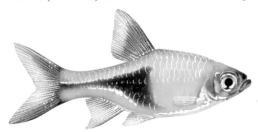

Rasbora heteromorpha – red rasbora (harlequin rasbora, T-bone)

Size – To 5 cm (2 in)
Range – Thailand, Malay Peninsula, Sumatra.
Feeding – In nature: a variety of small aquatic organisms near the surface or in the water column. In aquarium: will do well on prepared food but live food (insects, crustacea, worms, etc.) will encourage reproduction.
Aquarium care – Keep several together. Can be kept in small aquaria. Water should be soft and acidic. To promote reproduction temperatures of 23–27° C (73–81° F) are preferred. The aquarium should contain broad-leaved plants but leave room for schooling. Eggs are attached to the undersides of leaves and hatch in about 24 hours; the adults should be removed after spawning.

The red rasbora is an ideal aquarium fish. It is colorful, active and hardy, yet peaceful and gets along with others of its own kind as well as other peaceful species. Long-lived for a small species, it may live five or more years in captivity.

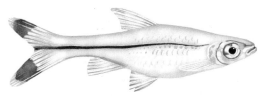

Rasbora maculata

Rasbora maculata – dwarf rasbora (spotted rasbora)

Size – To 2.5 cm (1 in)
Range – Malay Peninsula, Sumatra.
Feeding and aquarium care – As for the red rasbora.

Rasbora trilineata – scissortail rasbora

Size – To 6 cm (2.5 in)
Range – Malay Peninsula, Sumatra, Thailand.
Feeding and aquarium care – As for the red rasbora.

A hardy, peaceful species which has been commercially bred in the United States.

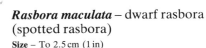

Rasbora trilineata

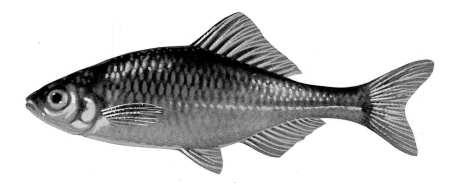

Rhodeus sericeus – bitterling

Size – To 9 cm (3.5 in)
Range – Europe except Scandinavia, and temperate western Asia.
Feeding – In nature: omnivorous. In aquarium: prepared aquarium foods: supplement with live foods if desired, worms, insect larvae, etc.
Aquarium care – Do well in unheated aquaria at temperatures up to 22°C (72°F). Can be kept in small aquaria which should be well planted.

Bitterlings prefer the sluggish waters of the lower reaches of rivers and pools with muddy bottoms. They are a peaceful and hardy aquarium species. Their reproductive behavior is highly specialized and interesting.

When mature the male develops a deep red throat and belly, while in the female a pink ovipositor becomes evident projecting from the anal fin. The female inserts her eggs into a fresh-water mussel. At the same time the male releases sperm nearby, which is ingested by the mussel. Fertilization takes place inside the mussel where the eggs remain until they hatch. The young stay in the mussel for an additional four to five weeks before emerging.

Chrosomus erythrogaster – southern red-belly dace

Size – To 5 cm (2.5 in)
Range – Mississippi River drainage.
Feeding – In nature: algae, zooplankton and aquatic insects. In aquarium: prepared foods that include plant material; *Daphnia*, worms, etc.
Aquarium care – A hardy species with a wide temperature and water-quality tolerance.

One of the many small temperate-zone North America cyprinids that can be kept easily in home aquaria.

47

BARBUS

Cyprinids of the genus *Barbus* (many have also been classified as *Puntius*) are abundant in tropical Asia and Africa, and are an important group of aquarium fishes referred to as "the barbs." Many are small and colorful. Most are active swimmers but have a peaceful disposition. A few are fussy eaters. Their general appearance is similar to that of rasboras – compressed fishes with shiny large scales and a single soft-rayed dorsal fin at mid-body. Water quality is normally not critical but it should be well oxygenated. Temperatures of 20–27° C (68–81° F) are suitable for most tropical species. Many species have been bred in captivity.

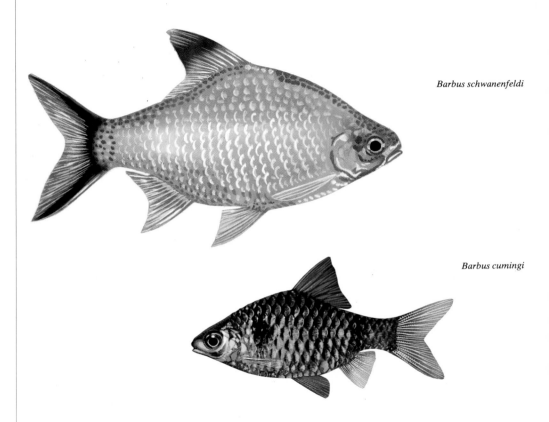

Barbus schwanenfeldi

Barbus cumingi

Barbus schwanenfeldi – Schwanenfeld's barb (tin-foil barb)

Size – To 35 cm (14 in).
Range – Sumatra, Borneo and Thailand.
Feeding – In nature: omnivorous, includes considerable plant material in its diet. In aquarium: prepared aquarium foods plus lettuce and other vegetation.
Aquarium care – An excellent aquarium species but requires a large tank. Does well in community tanks; but should not be kept with smaller fish. A dark peaty bottom is preferred. Use only sturdy plants. Water composition is not critical; temperatures from 21 to 26° C (70–79° F).

Barbus cumingi – Cuming's barb

Size – To 5 cm (2 in)
Range – Sri Lanka.
Feeding – In nature: omnivorous. In aquarium: prepared foods which include plant material; supplement with live food, *Daphnia*, worms, insects, etc.
Aquarium care – A hardy peaceful species that can get by in an aquarium as small as 40 liters (10 gal.). Water quality is not critical but soft, slightly acid water is preferable. Keep at 24–27° C (75–81° F). Keep several together.

An inhabitant of mountain and forest streams.

Barbus nigrofasciatus – black ruby barb

Size – To 5 cm (2 in)
Range – Sri Lanka.
Feeding – As for Cuming's barb.
Aquarium care – As for Cuming's barb but will do well at somewhat higher temperatures. Mature males become more colorful than females.

A good species for community tanks.

Barbus nigrofasciatus

Barbus pentazona – five-barred tiger barb (tiger barb, five-banded barb)

Size – To 5 cm (2 in)
Range – Malay Peninsula.
Feeding – In nature: omnivorous. In aquarium: dried foods that contain plant material; supplement with live foods.
Aquarium care – Hardy and relatively peaceful. Keep several together in aquaria of 40 liters (10 gal.) or more in soft water at temperatures of 20–27° C (68–81° F).

The classification of the "tiger barbs" is confusing with regard to both common and scientific names. They have been placed in the genera *Puntius* and *Capoeta* as well as *Barbus* and have been given a variety of subspecies names. A simplified naming scheme has been used here.

Barbus pentazona

Barbus (= Capoeta) tetrazona – four-barred tiger barb (Sumatra barb)

Size – To 7 cm (2.75 in)
Range – Sumatra and Borneo.
Feeding – In nature: omnivorous. In aquarium: does well on prepared aquarium foods which include plant material; supplement with live foods.
Aquarium care – An active species that has a tendency to nip tank-mates. Keep several together in a relatively large aquarium of 60 liters (15 gal.) or more provided with soft water and temperatures from 20 to 27° C (68–81° F).

Barbus tetrazona

Barbus conchonius

Barbus conchonius – rosy barb

Size – To 14 cm (5.5 in)
Range – India.
Feeding – In nature: omnivorous. In aquarium: prepared foods, plus some live food.
Aquarium care – Does well in both large and small aquaria kept at about 22° C (72° F). Water quality is not critical. Easy to breed.

This is a well-known fish to the hobbyist and looks particularly attractive in a well-planted single-species tank with dark reddish material on the bottom.

49

DANIOS

The "danios" include fishes from the genera *Danio* and *Brachydanio*. Several species are easy to maintain. They are slender, moderately compressed fishes with the dorsal and anal fins placed behind the mid-point of the body. The tail is moderately forked. The scales are smaller and less apparent than in the barbs and the colors more subdued than in the barbs and rasboras. The mouth is oblique, moderate in size and terminal to superior in position. They are lively schooling species and several individuals should be kept together. Danios are generally easy to raise. The sexes are similar but the male is smaller and more slender.

Brachydanio rerio – zebra danio

Size – To 5 cm (2 in)
Range – India.
Feeding – In aquarium: does well on any regular aquarium diet.
Aquarium care – Extremely easy to keep. A planted aquarium with swimming space is recommended: the beginner may wish to start with plastic plants. Can tolerate temperatures from 16 to 38° C (60–100° F). Males are

Labeo erythrurus – redfin shark (rainbow shark)

Size – To 12 cm (5 in)
Range – Thailand region.
Feeding – In nature: omnivorous grazers. In aquarium: standard aquarium diets including prepared aquarium foods that contain plant material.
Aquarium care – Should have an aquarium of at least 125 liters (30 gal.) with soft, slightly acid water that is well planted. Will tolerate a temperature range of 20–30° C (68–86° F). "Sharks" tend to be aggressive with their own kind and must have plenty of hiding places if more than one is to be kept. Suitable for community tanks.

The common name "shark" used for this species and its relatives is unfortunate, in the sense that it gives no indication of the classification of these fishes. With their cylindrical bodies, pointed heads and large "triangular" dorsal fins they are shark-like in appearance but the resemblance is only superficial. Anatomically their structure – skeleton,

Weberian apparatus, scales, skin, etc. – indicates their affinity with the cyprinids. Several species of "sharks" have become popular with aquarists. The red-tailed black shark, often called simply the red-tailed shark (*Labeo bicolor*), is considered by many to be the most desirable of the group. A stream-dwelling native of Thailand, it has similar aquarium requirements to the redfin shark. It has been bred in captivity. Unlike most cyprinids this species lays only 30–90 eggs, which are cared for by the male who fans them for the two to three days they take to hatch. The fry begin to swim freely and feed two to three days after hatching and usually require infusoria or rotifers for the first few days until they can manage brine shrimp nauplii. Commercial liquid fry food may also prove acceptable as a first food.

smaller and more slender than females and become more colorful. To breed, select a ripe female and place her in a breeding tank of 20–40 liters (5–10 gal., kept at 22–24° C (72–75° F) and planted with fine-leaved sturdy plants. Choose two active brightly colored males and place them with the female. Be sure the fish are fed frequently and provided with a nutritious diet. Supplements of live food are usually advised. The fish will spawn amongst the vegetation. Both parents should be removed immediately to prevent them from eating the eggs. The fry will hatch in one to two days. Start the young on rotifers, infusoria or other small food including prepared food for fry. After a few days they should accept brine shrimp nauplii.

This is an ideal choice for the beginning aquarist; but should not be overlooked by the experienced aquarist, especially when he is considering community tank species.

Brachydanio albolineatus – pearl danio

Size – To 5 cm (2 in)
Range – Southeast Asia.
Aquarium care and feeding – As for the zebra danio but keep at temperatures of 20–24° C (68–75° F).

ORDER CYPRINIFORMES – FAMILY COBITIDIDAE

Loaches

In spite of the worm-like bodies of many loaches these fishes are close relatives of the minnows, with which they share such characteristics as the Weberian apparatus, alarm substance (Schreckstoff) and abdominally positioned pelvic fins. Loaches characteristically have small eyes; small scales that may not be apparent to the naked eye; a small toothless mouth subterminal in position; three, four or more pairs of barbels with at least one pair on the snout and an erectile protective spine under the eye. Their swim bladder is reduced in size, which makes them negatively buoyant, an appropriate adaptation for bottom-living fishes. In addition there is some indication that the swim bladder makes certain loaches sensitive to atmospheric pressure. The Japanese weatherfish, *Misqurnus anquillicaudatus*, becomes more active as barometric pressure falls. Cobitids are widely distributed in Europe and Asia but are absent from the Americas. Approximately 135 species are known. Loaches are adapted for life on the bottom. Even those which are not worm-like in shape have a flattened ventral surface.

Acanthophthalmus semicinctus – coolie loach

Size – To 8 cm (3 in)
Range – East India.
Feeding – In aquarium: prefer bottom-living organisms such as Tubifex worms and insect larvae; will feed on prepared foods and detritus.

Aquarium care – Do well in a wide range of water conditions but need suitable cover as they tend to spend much time hiding. Temperature-tolerant but 21–25° C (70–77° F) is recommended.

One of several species and subspecies known in the pet market as a "coolie" loach. Other "coolies" include *A. kuhlia, A. myersi* and their subspecies.

51

Cobitididae

Botia macracantha – clown loach

Size – To 30 cm (12 in) in nature but rarely exceeds 15 cm (6 in) in captivity.
Range – Sumatra and Borneo.
Feeding – In nature: bottom feeders; commonly include insect larvae, worms, crustaceans and plant material in their diet. In aquarium: prepared aquarium foods and worms, especially Tubifex worms.
Aquarium care – Do best if three or more are kept together. Require soft water in a planted aquarium with a soft bottom. Keep at 22–26° C (72–79° F). Provide cover.

ORDER SILURIFORMES – FAMILY SILURIDAE

Silurid Catfishes

Catfishes of the family Siluridae belong to the order Siluriformes along with about 30 other catfish families. Like the Characiformes and Cypriniformes, they possess a Weberian apparatus and release an alarm substance when injured, and are included in the superorder Ostariophysi. Catfishes lack scales but may be covered with bony plates; the adipose fin is usually present, and spines are often present at the front of the dorsal and pectoral fins. Barbels are usually present on the jaws. The eyes are usually small. Some species are venomous and contain poison cells in the epidermis of the skin covering the fin spines. Catfishes may get very large; *Siluris glanis* of Europe reaches at least 3.3 m (11 ft); but many catfishes attain less than 12 cm (5 in). The family Siluridae is confined to Europe and Asia in tropical and temperate waters. Only a few species are important to the home aquarist.

Kryptopterus bicirrhis – glass catfish

Size – To 15 cm (6 in)
Range – Indochina and Indonesia.
Feeding – In aquarium: live insect larvae, *Artemia* and other planktonic crustaceans; prepared aquarium foods.
Aquarium care – A peaceful, schooling species. Keep several to many together. Can be kept with other schooling species. Water composition is not critical; keep at 20–26° C (68–79° F).

This is the most transparent of fishes. Its body is highly compressed with a minute dorsal fin containing only one ray, a very long anal fin, an adipose fin, and a pair of large mobile barbels on the upper jaw. A close relative, *Kryptopterus macrocephalus*, is also imported.

ORDER SILURIFORMES – FAMILY CLARIIDAE

Air-breathing Catfishes

These catfishes have a very long dorsal fin and a rounded, separate caudal fin. Four pairs of barbels are present around the mouth. The most distinctive characteristic of the family is the air-breathing labyrinth organ. Derived from the gills, this organ permits the fish to remain out of water for a considerable time or survive in water low in oxygen. Members of the family are found in Africa, the Middle East and Asia. About 100 species are known and included in 13 genera.

Clarias batrachus – walking catfish

Size – To 55 cm (22 in)
Range – Southeast Asia; introduced into Florida.
Feeding – In nature: omnivorous. In aquarium: all kinds of aquarium foods.
Aquarium care – A hardy but voracious species. Only juveniles are suitable for the home aquarist. Keep at 22–27° C (68–81° F) in an aquarium provided with many hiding places. Plants may have to be potted in order to survive.

This is not a highly desirable home aquarium species but is hardy and now widespread. Introduced into the Florida environment, it is sometimes encountered skittering across lawns. The accessory breathing apparatus facilitates its terrestrial sojourns.

ORDER SILURIFORMES – FAMILY MOCHOKIDAE

Upside-down Catfishes

Members of this family possess an unusual adipose fin which contains bony fin-rays, and have an anal fin with no more than nine fin-rays. They are found only in Africa. As is common in catfishes they lack scales. Their dorsal and pectoral fins contain hooked protective spines; three pairs of barbels, sensitive of touch and taste, surround the mouth. They feed by browsing on algae and small aquatic insects. More than 150 species are known.

Synodontis nigriventris – upside-down catfish (black-bellied catfish)

Size – To 10 cm (4 in)
Range – Central Africa.
Feeding – In nature: algae and other plant material, insects, crustaceans. In aquarium: normal aquarium diets including dried foods.

Aquarium care – A good species for the community tank. It has the advantage of helping to keep unwanted algae down. Keep several together at 22–27° C (72–81° F).

As the common and scientific names suggest, this fish has a dark belly and is cryptically colored when in a belly-up position such as on the underside of branches or leaves. It has been spawned in captivity.

Synodontis alberti – Albert's upside-down catfish

Size – To 20 cm (8 in)
Range – Zaire basin, Africa.
Feeding and aquarium care – As for *S. nigriventris*.

This species has the longest barbels of any fish in the genus. For a discussion of other members known in the aquarium trade see Finlay (1980); Sterba (1966); and Van Ramshorst (1978).

Synodontis nigriventris

Synodontis alberti

Electric Catfishes

This small family of catfishes includes only two species, *Malapterurus electricus* and *M. microstoma*, both from Africa. Electric catfishes are thickset, oblong, scaleless, lack a dorsal fin and have pectoral fins without spines. An adipose fin is present, inserted far to the posterior. The lips are thick and fleshy with three pairs of barbels; the eyes are small. Electricity is generated by an electric organ which lies in the skin and covers most of the body muscle system. Shocks up to 350 volts are used to stun prey and to discourage predators. These fishes are not normally kept by the home aquarist because of their large size as adults. They are, of course, of interest to those seeking fishes with special adaptations. Exhibits in public aquaria are sometimes designed to exhibit the electrical properties of fishes, which can be trained to discharge when presented with food. Electrodes in the tank transmit the signal to oscilloscopes, loudspeakers or other devices that display the discharge. Other strongly electric families include the electric eels (family Electrophoridae), the stargazers (family Uranoscopidae), both fresh-water, and the electric rays (family Torpedinidae), which is marine. The electric eels produce the largest shock, over 650 volts, enough to stun a horse. In addition, weak electric fishes produce currents for intraspecific communication or orientation. These include the fresh-water fish families: Mormyridae (elephant fishes), Gymnarchidae, Gymnotidae, Apteronotidae and Rhamphichthyidae.

Malapterurus electricus – electric catfish

Size – To 100 cm (39 in)
Range – Widespread in central Africa including the Congo and Nile basins.
Feeding – In nature: predaceous. In aquarium: worms, strips of meat, fishes.
Aquarium care – A hardy species but not comparable with other fishes. Keep alone in an appropriately sized aquarium at 22–29° C (72–84° F). Water composition is not critical.

Electric catfish are primarily of interest to the aquarist seeking the unusual or to public aquaria. They are nocturnal, spending much of the day inactive or hiding and becoming active at nightfall.

Armored Catfishes

These catfishes have their body covered with two rows of bony plates and their swim bladder is encased with bone; a spine is inserted at the anterior edge of the adipose fin. There are about 130 species in the family. Almost every fresh-water aquarist is familiar with one or more members of the family. Callichthyid catfishes are natives of South America and Trinidad. A number of species have been successfully reared in captivity. Some are bubblenest builders.

Corydoras aeneus

Corydoras aeneus – bronze catfish

Size – To 7 cm (3 in).
Range – Trinidad; South America to La Plata.
Feeding – In nature: omnivorous. In aquarium: worms, insects, prepared aquarium foods containing plant matter.
Aquarium care – A hardy, peaceful, undemanding species whose only problem is that it may uproot plants. Suitable for community tanks. Keep at 19–27° C (66–81° F). For breeding, a large planted tank should be provided. The pH should be approximately 7. The eggs will be laid on the leaves of the plants and hatch in about six days. The fry should be swimming after eight days. They can be started feeding on brine shrimp nauplii.

The bronze catfish is a welcome addition to most community tanks. It is a relatively active species that spends much time cruising about the aquarium testing the bottom and other surfaces with its barbels. Many other species of *Corydoras* have been imported and are good aquarium fishes.

Callichthys callichthys – bubblenest catfish

Size – To 18 cm (7 in)
Range – Tropical South America.
Feeding – In nature: omnivorous, feeds extensively on benthic organisms. In aquarium: insects, worms, prepared foods that sink to the bottom.
Aquarium care – Provide hiding places and use sturdy plants. Hardy and peaceful; water composition is not critical. Keep at 21–26° C (70–79° F).

This is a good species for the community tank as it is peaceful and helps with the housecleaning. In nature it occurs in shallow waters and has an accessory intestinal breathing apparatus that allows it to respire gulped air when oxygen is low in its habitat. It has been bred in captivity. The male builds a bubblenest amongst plants at the surface. After the female has laid her eggs the male will guard the nest. The fry require very fine powdered food.

Callichthys callichthys

Family Loricariidae

The loricariid armored catfishes are similar in some respects to the callichthyids but lack conspicuous barbels around the mouth, which is sucker-like and has three to four rows of bony plates on each side. They occur in the fresh waters of South America, Panama and Costa Rica. A few species are found in brackish waters. About 400 species are known.

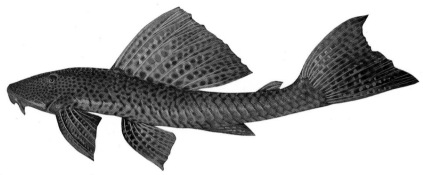

Hypostomus (= Plecostomas) plecostomus – plecostomus

Size – To 30 cm (14 in)
Range – Northern South America including the region from Venezuela to French Guiana.
Feeding – In nature: primarily herbivorous. In aquarium: feeds on surface algae but needs additional foods such as lettuce and prepared aquarium foods rich in plant matter.
Aquarium care – Should do best in a large community tank provided with hiding places. Most active at dawn and dusk. A good tank cleaner. Keep at 20–25° C (68–77° F). Water composition is not critical.

Its popularity as an aquarium fish and use as a food fish have led to extensive collecting and as a result this species could face extinction. The development of successful breeding techniques would be a major contribution to its survival.

Loricaria filamentosa – filamentous catfish

Size – To 25 cm (10 in)
Range – Rio Magdalena, South America.
Feeding – In aquarium: plant material supplemented with normal aquarium foods.
Aquarium care – A good community tank fish. Does best in soft, slightly acid water kept at 21–28° C (70–82° F). Provide hiding places and surfaces for algae growth. It has been bred in captivity.

ORDER GYMNOTIFORMES – FAMILY GYMNOTIDAE

Knife-eels

Knife-eels are a small family of eel-like fishes confined to the fresh waters of Central and South America. They appear to have evolved from the characoid fishes. Only three species are known. They have eel-like, compressed bodies covered with small scales. Locomotion is provided by a very long anal fin which is undulated in a ripple-like manner to produce backward and forward movement. The dorsal, caudal and pelvic fins are lacking. Knife-eels possess weak electric organs which help them orient in murky waters and at night. They also have accessory respiration organs which permit them to gulp air and thus survive in poorly oxygenated waters.

Gymnotus carapo – banded knifefish

Size – To 60 cm (24 in)
Range – Guatemala to Argentina.
Feeding – In nature: carnivorous. In aquarium: feed readily; a diet of chopped fish, beef heart and worms is adequate.
Aquarium care – Easy to care for but aggressive with each other. Keep in a large dim aquarium of 400 liters (100 gal.) or more decorated with hollow tree trunks or roots at 23–28° C (73–82° F). Water quality is not critical.

These fish are only suitable for large aquaria. In spite of being aggressive with their own kind, they do well with other species of large fishes. If the aquarium is kept dimly lit, they can be taught to feed and become active by day.

ORDER CYPRINODONTIFORMES – FAMILY CYPRINODONTIDAE

Killifishes

The killifish family (egg-laying toothcarps, topminnows) contains many species of interest to aquarists. Killifishes are small, seldom over 13 cm (5 in), often colorful, carp-like fishes but unlike the carps possess teeth in both jaws. The head is often flattened, with the mouth terminal or superior and lacking barbels. The single dorsal fin is inserted well back on the body; no adipose fin is present; pelvic fins may be present or absent and the tail is usually rounded. Most males possess ctenoid scales while most females have cycloid scales. The lateral line is confined chiefly to the head. Over 300 species are present world-wide. Several systems of classification have been used. Recently *Cynolebias*, along with several other related genera, have been placed in a separate family, Rivulidae.

DISTRIBUTION AND ECOLOGY. Killifishes are found in the tropical and temperate fresh waters of all continents except Australia. They occur in a wide range of habitats from the extreme conditions of desert cave springs and tropical seasonal ponds, to high mountain lakes, swamps and coastal marshes. Of particular interest to aquarists are the annual or seasonal fishes of temporary ponds in Africa and South America. These fishes include true annuals which spawn in the substrate of seasonal ponds and die as the ponds dry. The eggs, which are resistant to desiccation, survive until the next rainy season when they hatch and repopulate the ponds.

REPRODUCTION. Although killifishes are egg-layers, fertilization is internal. Spawning may take place amongst vegetation or in the substrate depending upon the species. Some undergo normal aquatic incubation in permanent waters; while others require a period of drying in the substrate before they will develop. Intermediate forms have eggs which will tolerate, but do not require drying.

AQUARIUM CARE. Killifishes include species that readily adapt to captivity, such as the topminnows, *Fundulus* spp., as well as other species such as the tropical "annuals" which require special conditions if they are to be successfully maintained and bred. Many killifishes are highly aggressive fish and the hobbyist who specializes in them will have a battery of small, well-planted tanks of 8–15 liters (2–4 gal.), each containing a single male with one or more females.

Cyprinodontidae

Oryzias latipes – Japanese medaka (rice paddy fish)

Size – To 4 cm (1.5 in)
Range – Japan.
Feeding – In aquarium: do best on small live foods; will usually do well on a suitable prepared food.
Aquarium care – Do well in schools or community tanks with peaceful species. Keep in aquaria of 12 liters (3 gal.) or larger supplied with floating plants and slightly alkaline water at 20–25° C (68–77° F).

The Japanese medaka is one of several species of *Oryzias* found throughout southeast Asia in habitats ranging from rice paddies and ditches to mountain streams. The females are courted vigorously by the males. Fertilization is internal; the eggs remain suspended in clusters attached to the female after spawning until she brushes them off on suitable floating vegetation. Closely related genera include *Epiplatys*, *Pachypanchax* and *Aplocheilus*.

Cyprinodon macularis – desert pupfish

Size – To 7 cm (3 in)
Range – California, Arizona and Baja California, Mexico.
Feeding – In nature: omnivorous; primarily small crustaceans and algae. In aquarium: all normal aquarium foods.
Aquarium care – Extremely hardy; survives at temperatures from 9 to 45° C (48–113° F) and salinities approaching 7%.

Found mostly in habitats too extreme for other fishes. Other species of *Cyprinodon* include the devil's hole pupfish *Cyprinodon diabolis*, which is restricted to a single spring in western Nevada, and the sheepshead minnow *Cyprinodon variegatus* of the east coast of North America.

Fundulus chrysotus

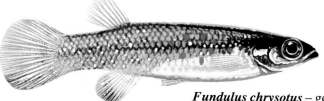

Aphyosemion australe – lyretail

Size – To 5 cm (2 in)
Range – Equatorial West Africa.
Feeding – In aquarium: prepared aquarium foods supplemented weekly with live food such as fruit flies, ants, mosquito larvae, *Daphnia*, etc.
Aquarium care – *Aphyosemion* are usually kept in small aquaria of 7–15 liters (2–4 gal.) in each of which is placed a single male and one or several females. Aeration and heaters are not usually necessary. Temperatures of 20–25° C (68–77° F) are sufficient. Soft, slightly acid water and a boiled peat substrate are recommended. Plants are not necessary but are helpful in providing cover for the females, which without hiding places may be courted to exhaustion by the male.

This is one of many species of *Aphyosemion* successfully kept by aquarists. Lyretails spawn close to the surface, laying 10–12 eggs each day attached to vegetation. The eggs hatch in about 15 days and the fry will feed on brine shrimp nauplii. The male is easily distinguished because he is considerably more colorful than the female. For further information about breeding, see Axelrod (Book 2, 1971) or Scheel (1975).

Fundulus chrysotus – goldenear killifish

Size – To 8 cm (3 in)
Range – South Carolina to Florida.
Feeding – In aquarium: feeds readily on prepared foods.
Aquarium care – Easy to maintain. Keep at 22–26° C (72–79° F). Spawns in vegetation; remove eggs to brood tank immediately.

Other species of *Fundulus* are found in fresh, brackish, and coastal waters of the east, west and south coasts of North America. All are hardy species.

Aphyosemion sjoestedi – blue gularis

Size – To 12 cm (5 in)
Range – Eastern Nigeria and Cameroon.
Feeding – In nature: probably insects. In aquarium: usually requires live food.
Aquarium care – A pugnacious species. Keep a single male with several females in a planted 40-liter (10-gal.) aquarium with or without a substrate. Heaters and filters are not necessary; keep at 17–24° C (63–75° F). Hard water may reduce the incidence of disease. This is a substrate spawner. If the tank bottom is left bare spawning mops can be used. Fish must be well conditioned on live foods to promote spawning, which peaks at about 20 eggs per day. The eggs can be incubated in water and will hatch in about 30 days or in semi-damp peat moss, in which case they will take about twice as long to hatch. The fry will usually accept brine shrimp nauplii.

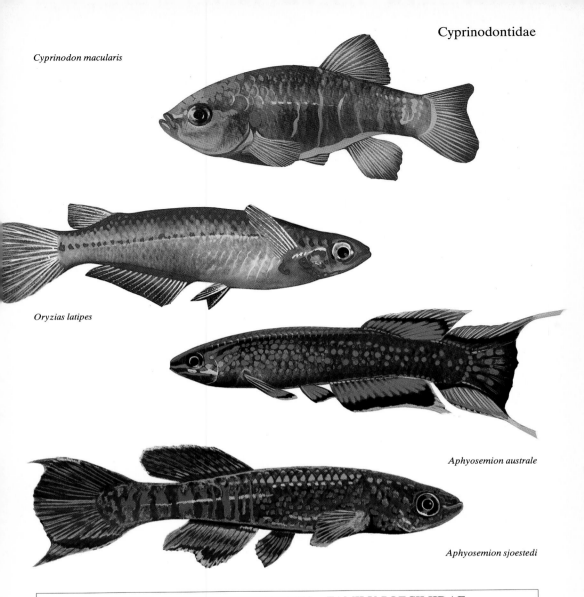

Cyprinodon macularis

Oryzias latipes

Aphyosemion australe

Aphyosemion sjoestedi

ORDER CYPRINODONTIFORMES – FAMILY POECILIIDAE

Live-bearing Topminnows

These small fishes, seldom over 10 cm (4 in), are very similar in appearance to killifishes. The body is stout, usually moderately compressed; the scales are large and cycloid. Fin species are lacking; the single dorsal fin is inserted at mid-body or posterior; the tail is usually rounded. The mouth is terminal, usually upturned, and has teeth in both jaws. The anal fin of males is modified to form a copulatory organ or gonopodium. The third, fourth and fifth anal rays are elongated and form a trough by which sperm packets or spermatophores are inserted into the female. The sperm may be stored and several batches of eggs fertilized from each mating. Males are usually smaller than females. Poeciliids (live-bearers) occur naturally in fresh and brackish waters from the eastern United States to Argentina but only a few species occur south of the Amazon. They are most common in lakes, ponds and along river margins. Some species, especially the

Poeciliidae

mosquitofish *Gambusia affinis*, are very important in mosquito control. Many species have been kept in aquaria. Most are peaceful and hardy aquarium fishes. Many are colorful. Since they exhibit sexual dimorphism (the gonopodium makes the males easy to recognize), selective breeding is much easier and many domestic strains have been produced. The females are often cannibalistic and should be removed after giving birth, or may be kept in a brood cage with a slatted bottom through which the young will fall out of their reach.

Gambusia affinis

Xiphophorus helleri

Gambusia affinis – mosquitofish

Size – Females to 6 cm (2.5 in); males smaller, to 3.5 cm (1.3 in)
Range – Southeast United States, Texas and Mexico; widely introduced elsewhere.
Feeding – In nature: omnivorous. In aquarium: any variety of the normal aquarium foods.
Aquarium care – An aggressive species that nips the fins of other species; best kept in a single-species tank. Hardy; water quality is not critical. Will tolerate temperatures from 10 to 37° C (50–99° F); but 18–24° C (64–75° F) is recommended for the aquarium. Bears 1–130 young. Gestation is three to four weeks. The adults are cannibalistic.

An excellent pondfish for mosquito control.

Xiphophorus maculatus

Xiphophorus helleri – swordtail

Size – Females to 12 cm (5 in); males smaller.
Range – Central America.
Feeding – In nature: omnivorous. In aquarium: prepared foods, worms, insects, crustaceans; include plant matter.
Aquarium care – A peaceful, active species that is popular with novice aquarists. Keep in a planted aquarium, preferably in slightly alkaline water at temperatures from 21 to 26° C (70–79° F). Suitable for community tanks with other peaceful species. Easy to breed. Gestation is four to six weeks. The young will accept brine shrimp nauplii immediately and receive a more varied diet beginning with the second week.

A number of varieties have been produced by selective breeding and hybridization. The "sword" is present only in the males.

Xiphophorus (= Platypoecilus) maculatus – platy (southern platefish)

Size – Females to 6 cm (2.5 in); males smaller.
Range – Central America including Southern Mexico, Honduras, Guatemala.
Feeding – In nature: omnivorous. In aquarium: prepared aquarium foods containing plant matter, insects, etc.
Aquarium care – Does best in slightly alkaline water in a well-planted aquarium. Gestation is about four weeks; 10–50 young are produced and will usually accept brine shrimp nauplii.

This is a highly variable species in the wild and many varieties and hybrids have been produced through selective breeding (e.g. red platy, tuxedo platy, black wagtail and gold platy, etc.).

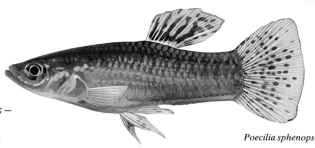

Poecilia sphenops

Poecilia (= Mollienesia) sphenops – shortfin molly

Size – Females to 12 cm (5 in); males smaller.
Range – Neotropics from Texas to Colombia.
Feeding – In aquarium: prepared aquarium foods that include plant matter.
Aquarium care – As for above species but do best in slightly brackish water. Suitable for community tanks. Many varieties have been produced by selective breeding.

Poecilia latipinna

Poecilia reticulata

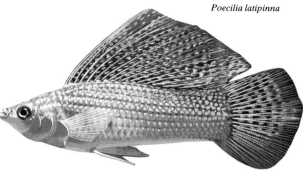

Poecilia reticulata – guppy

Size – Females to 5 cm (2 in); males smaller.
Range – Northern South America, West Indies.
Feeding – In nature: omnivorous, including insect larvae and crustaceans. In aquarium: prepared foods, insects, worms, brine shrimp.
Aquarium care – Easy to keep and breed. Usually a brood cage is used. Keep at 20–28° C (68–83° F).

Many attractive domestic varieties have been produced.

Poecilia (= Mollienesia) latipinna – sailfin molly

Size – To 8 cm (3 in)
Range – Coastal regions from South Carolina to northeastern Mexico; introduced elsewhere including California.
Feeding – In nature: detritus and algae. In aquarium: normal aquarium diets; include plant matter.
Aquarium care – Should have a large, 75-liter (20-gal.) or more, well-planted tank. Keep in pairs or small groups. Water composition is not critical. Keep at 24–28° C (75–82° F). This species is easily bred. The gestation period is eight to ten weeks. Provide a well-planted tank for the 20–80 young which will accept brine shrimp nauplii or other similar live food immediately.

ORDER CYPRINODONTIFORMES – FAMILY ANABLEPIDAE

Four-eyed Fishes

Four-eyed fishes are closely related to the cyprinodonts and poeciliids. They are surface-living fishes with unique eyes adapted for simultaneous aerial and subsurface vision. Each eye has two pupils and a divided cornea. In the fish's normal posture one pupil is above, the other below the water surface. Light rays from above pass through the upper pupil and are focused on the lower retina, via the small end of a single pear-shaped lens; while light rays from the subsurface environment pass through the more sharply curved larger diameter of the lower lens, to focus on the upper retina. Three species of four-eyed fishes are known, all from central and northern

South America. They occur in lakes, rivers, canals and ditches, coastal lagoons, estuaries, and in the case of one species (*Anableps microlepis*) along the coast in full seawater. Water clarity may vary from highly turbid to clear. During the day they travel in schools, apparently feeding on surface organisms and at night they move into very shallow water amongst rocks and plants to feed upon the abundant insects and crustaceans. They are prodigious leapers, and use this ability along with excellent aerial vision to escape birds and other predators from above. Like the poeciliids they are live-bearers with internal fertilization but their genital organs are offset to one side or the other. A male has a well-developed gonopodium which he can move to only one side while females have genital openings which are likewise offset. It is commonly reported that "right-handed" males can only mate with left-handed females and vice versa but this has not been fully verified.

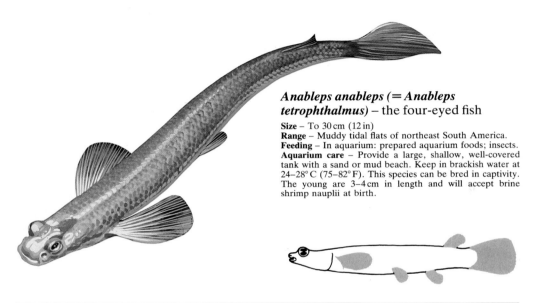

Anableps anableps (= Anableps tetrophthalmus) – the four-eyed fish

Size – To 30 cm (12 in)
Range – Muddy tidal flats of northeast South America.
Feeding – In aquarium: prepared aquarium foods; insects.
Aquarium care – Provide a large, shallow, well-covered tank with a sand or mud beach. Keep in brackish water at 24–28° C (75–82° F). This species can be bred in captivity. The young are 3–4 cm in length and will accept brine shrimp nauplii at birth.

ORDER CYPRINODONTIFORMES – FAMILY GOODEIDAE

Goodeids

Goodeids are set apart from their close relatives the killifishes (*Cyprinodontidae*) and the live-bearing tooth carps (*Poeciliidae*) by their unusual reproduction. As in the poeciliids, fertilization is internal and the young are born alive. However, in goodeids the male does not have a well-developed tubal gonopodium but instead has an intromittent organ, formed from the first few rays of the anal fin which are stiffened and set apart by a notch. The embryos are also unique in that all but one species have ribbon-like extensions of the rectum called trophotaeniae that function like a placenta, allowing the embryos to absorb nutrients and oxygen from the mother and eliminate waste. Goodeids vary from deep-bodied to slender; have terminal mouths with an extended lower jaw and have teeth in each jaw. They have a single dorsal fin, which, along with the anal fin, is posterior in placement; pelvic fins are present; there is no adipose fin and fin spines are absent. The scales are large and cycloid. Most goodeids range in size from 3.5 cm (1.5 in) to about 10 cm (4 in). About 35 species occur, all confined to the highlands of central Mexico. At least 20 species have been successfully maintained by hobbyists. Goodeids are found in habitats ranging from stony mountain creeks, with little vegetation, to polluted village streams with muddy bottoms rich in organic material including algae. After fertilization the brood period averages 45 days, ranging from four to eleven weeks depending on species and temperature. Brood sizes range from fewer than 10 to more than 40. The young will usually survive on good-quality, prepared fry foods.

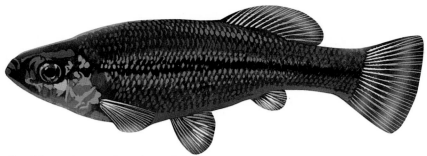

Ilyodon furcidens – bass-colored goodeid

Size – To 10 cm (4 in)
Range – West central Mexico.
Feeding – In nature: omnivorous. In aquarium: provide both live and prepared aquarium foods including brine shrimp nauplii.

Aquarium care – This species does best in aquaria of 60 liters (15 gal.) or larger with surface plants and dark surroundings. Water should be slightly alkaline. Keep between 24 and 27° C (75–81° F). Keep two males with three to eight females in a single-species aquarium.

ORDER SCORPAENIFORMES – FAMILY COTTIDAE

Fresh-water Sculpins

Fresh-water sculpins are small bottom-living fishes. Their large flattened heads, large pectoral fins and lack of a swim bladder adapt them well for living on the bottom and remaining stable in areas of surge or current. The mouth is large, usually terminal, and the eyes dorsally placed. The scales are ctenoid, usually in a few rows but they may be reduced to prickers or absent. The spinous and soft-rayed parts of the dorsal fin are divided. Most sculpins are marine, and fresh-water sculpins usually tolerate high salinities. Some sculpins spend part of their life in both environments. Oviparous; fertilization is internal. Males have a large conspicuous genital papilla. Sculpins are primarily cold-water fishes; they are abundant in North America, Europe and Asia. Single species occur in New Zealand, Australia and Argentina. About 65 genera are known with nearly 300 species.

Cottus gobio – miller's thumb

Size – To 17 cm (7 in)
Range – Europe and Asia
Feeding – In nature: carnivorous; aquatic insects and benthic invertebrates. In aquarium: accepts most aquarium foods but prefers live food.

Aquarium care – Requires cool water. Set up a 75-liter (20-gal.) or larger aquarium with a gravel bottom and rocks for cover. It may be best to keep one male with several females. Spawns under rocks. The male guards the nest. The miller's thumb prefers clear slow-moving streams with rocky bottoms. It spends the day hiding amongst the rocks and feeds most actively at dawn and dusk.

63

Sticklebacks

Sticklebacks are well known for their nest-building and reproductive behavior. They include five genera but only about eight species which are found in North America, Europe and northern Asia. Sticklebacks are small fishes with slender spindle-shaped laterally compressed bodies and upturned terminal mouths. They are covered with a series of bony plates rather than scales and are further protected by a series of spines along the back and pelvic fins that take the form of lateral spines. Typically they live amongst heavy vegetation in quiet waters and may be freshwater, marine or anadromous. The reproductive behavior of sticklebacks has been the subject of extensive observation and study. At sexual maturity, the male adopts breeding coloration highlighted by a bright red belly and constructs a tunnel-like nest of plant material which is held together by a sticky substance that he secretes. A female that is ready to spawn will be courted by the male and eventually encouraged to enter the nest with several nudges. After she lays her eggs they are fertilized by the male who usually repeats this process with several females. Once spawning is complete, the male defends the nest vigorously and fans the eggs until they hatch, usually in six to eight days. He will continue to guard the fry until they are active enough to survive on their own.

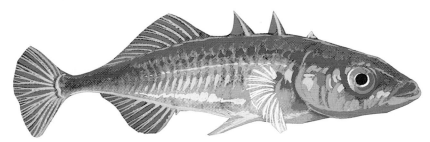

Gasterosteus aculeatus – the three-spine stickleback

Size – To 8 cm (3 in)
Range – Widely distributed from Europe across Russia to Japan and Korea and along both coasts of North America.
Feeding – In nature: fresh-water populations feed on benthic organisms and organisms living on plants. Migratory populations feed more on pelagic organisms (zooplankton, etc.). In aquarium: will thrive on a wide variety of aquarium foods.
Aquarium care – Keep at room temperature in water approximating the salinity of the area from which the fish are collected. Provide a sand bottom and bits of vegetation for nest-building. Use subsand or outside filters. Breeds readily in captivity if a large enough tank and suitable nest material are provided.

This is a hardy temperate-zone species found in fresh water, brackish water or seawater. Although not particularly striking in appearance, its reproductive behavior makes it an interesting aquarium species. Sticklebacks usually spawn in late spring. The male scoops out a depression and constructs a tunnel-like nest in a mass of plant material. He may court and mate with several females but guards the eggs and fry by himself.

Sunfishes

Centrarchids include sunfishes and basses, many of them important gamefishes. Relatively large, they are usually kept in ponds by the aquarist. Indigenous only to North America, they include nine genera and about 30 species. They are elongate to deep-bodied and moderately to highly compressed. The undivided dorsal fin includes spines and rays; the posterior soft-rayed portion is symmetrical with the large anal fin. The mouth is terminal, the upper jaw protractile, and the teeth small. Scales are ctenoid and the lateral line complete. Opportunistic carnivores, they typically dwell in still or slow-moving waters and construct nests for the protection of eggs and young.

Lepomis macrochirus – bluegill

Size – To 40 cm (16 in)
Range – Indigenous to eastern North America from Mexico to Canada; widely introduced elsewhere.
Feeding – In nature: opportunistic carnivore. In ponds: prepared foods such as trout pellets; vary with worms, insects, etc. if desired.

Aquarium care – Keep in ponds or large aquaria of 1,000 liters (250 gal.) or more. Water quality is not critical. Keep at 15–25° C (59–77° F) but will tolerate temperatures from near freezing to the high 20s° C (80s° F).

These are popular gamefish and easy to keep in ponds. They may hybridize with close relatives including the redear sunfish (*L. microlophus*), the pumpkinseed (*L. gibbosus*) and the green sunfish (*L. cyanellus*).

ORDER PERCIFORMES – FAMILY CENTROPOMIDAE

Glassfishes and Snooks

The centropomids include two groups of fishes, apparently diverse, the snooks and glassfishes, but they have a number of features in common including a lateral line which extends onto the tail. The snooks are large shovel-nosed fishes with divided dorsal fins. They occur on both coasts of the tropical Atlantic and along the east coast of the tropical Pacific. They enter both estuarine and fresh waters. Also included in the family is the Nile "perch" *Lates niloticus* which reaches nearly 100 kg (220 lb). This very large species is usually only kept in institutional aquaria. Of most interest to the home aquarists are the much smaller "transparent" glassfishes of the genera *Chanda* and *Gymnochanda*.

Chanda (= Ambassis) wolffi – Indonesian glassfish

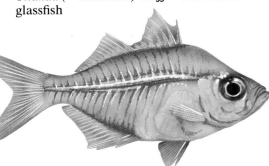

Size – To 10 cm (4 in) in captivity; 20 cm (8 in) in nature.
Range – Indonesia, Thailand.
Feeding – In nature: browses on small planktonic organisms. In aquarium: requires live food; feed *Daphnia* and other small crustaceans, mosquito larvae, white worms, etc.
Aquarium care – Suitable in a community tank with peaceful species. Provide fine-leaved plants for cover. Keep at 20–29° C (68–84° F).

The smaller Indian glassfish *Chanda ranga* is probably better known to aquarists and, unlike *C. wolffi*, is frequently but not easily bred in captivity. *C. ranga* does best in dilute brackish water.

Tripletails

The tripletails are distinguished by large rounded dorsal and anal fins which, along with a rounded caudal fin, give the fishes the appearance of having three tails. The body is deep and strongly compressed. Both jaws are toothed. The dorsal fin is long and undivided. The scales are ctenoid; the lateral line is arched and complete. The tripletails are found in most warm seas and extend into brackish and fresh waters. Two genera are known with four species.

Datnioides spp. – Siamese tigerfish

Size – To 40 cm (16 in)
Range – Southeast Asia from India to New Guinea.
Feeding – In nature: carnivorous. In aquarium: start with live fish if necessary but convert to whole dead fish then to chopped fish, clams, etc.

Aquarium care – Suitable in a community tank of 400 liters (100 gal.) or more with other large peaceful species. Use rocks and sunken wood to provide cover. Vegetation is desirable but leave adequate swimming space. Water quality is not critical but many aquarists prefer to use slightly brackish water, for example 20 g. of sea salts per 10 liters of water (two parts per thousand).

Archerfishes

Archerfishes are capable of shooting a jet of water with sufficient force, and accuracy, to knock down insects a meter (3 ft) or more above the water. They are moderate-sized surface fishes with a deep compressed body and a dorsal profile that is almost straight. The mouth is large, terminal and highly protractile; the eyes are large and placed well forward. The dorsal fin is continuous; the pectoral fins are strong and well developed for maneuvering. The lateral line is complete; the scales are ctenoid. Archerfishes are native to coastal waters of the tropical Indo-Pacific from the Red Sea to Polynesia. The young are found in both brackish and fresh waters; the adults are primarily marine-dwelling and spawn on coral reefs.

Toxotes jaculator – archerfish

Size – To 24 cm (9 in)
Range – From the coasts of the Red Sea, India and Sri Lanka to Australia and Melanesia.
Feeding – In nature: primarily insects. In aquarium: insects, worms, chopped meat and fish.
Aquarium care – Provide a tall aquarium of 125 liters (30 gal.) or more partially filled with sea-, brackish or fresh water and with suitable hiding places. Mangrove roots and terrestrial plants can be used to provide an aesthetic and naturalistic habitat. Keep at 22–28° C (72–82° F).

Archerfish will learn to shoot down chopped meat and fish stuck to the glass. Very difficult to breed in captivity.

Toxotes jaculator

ORDER PERCIFORMES – FAMILY MONODACTYLIDAE

Moonfishes

Moonfishes (fingerfishes) are extremely deep-bodied, highly compressed, disk-shaped fishes similar in appearance to butterflyfishes. They have a large eye and a small mouth with fine teeth. Unlike butterflyfishes, they have dorsal and anal fins with few spines. The fins are nearly equal in size. The pelvic fins are reduced. The scales may be either cycloid or ctenoid; the lateral line is complete. Moonfishes are found in coastal and brackish waters of the tropical eastern Atlantic and Indo-Pacific Oceans. They usually occur in schools and are common around mangrove roots, docks, and anchored ships; also in rivers. Three genera with five species are recognized. As a group, they are excellent aquarium fishes and have been reared in captivity.

Monodactylus argenteus – fingerfish (silver batfish)

Size – To 25 cm (10 in)
Range – East coast of Africa to the tropical western Pacific.
Feeding – In nature: omnivorous. In aquarium: does well on a mixed diet of live and prepared foods.

Aquarium care – Very young specimens can be kept in fresh water but require increasing salinity as they grow; adults require seawater. Keep several together in a large aquarium of 500 liters (125 gal.) or more and leave ample swimming space. Preferred temperature 24–28° C (75–85° F).

The fingerfish is an aquarium favorite because of its attractiveness and adaptability to captivity, but it is difficult to breed in the aquarium.

67

Scats

Scats (argus fishes) are a small family of fishes, similar in appearance to butterflyfishes, but which differ in having a nonprotractile mouth and a deeply notched dorsal fin with the spinous and soft-rayed portions almost divided. There are no noticeable sexual differences. Natives of the tropical waters of southeast Asia, scats are found in marine, brackish or fresh waters but apparently spawn only in seawater. The family name means scat or feces-eater and refers to their unappealing habit of feeding on animal waste. As might be expected, scats are abundant around sewage outfalls. In spite of their unsanitary habits in nature, scats make attractive aquarium fishes.

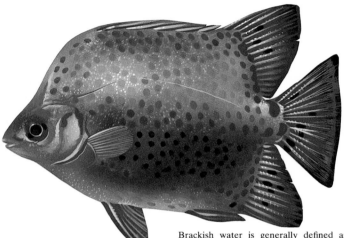

Scatophagus argus – scat (argus fish)

Size – To 30 cm (12 in), but remain smaller in captivity.
Range – Tropical Southeast Asia.
Feeding – In nature: omnivorous. In aquarium: prepared foods including plant material; supplement with live foods.
Aquarium care – Suitable in either community or single-species tanks. Keep several together in as large an aquarium as possible. Provide a sand bottom with a few rocks for decoration and no vegetation. A subsand filter is advised, supplemented with extra outside filtration as the fish produce excessive waste. Brackish water is best.

Brackish water is generally defined as dilute seawater ranging from 0.5 parts per thousand of dissolved salts to just under 30 parts per thousand. For most brackish water, fishes use about 60 g (or 2 oz) of sea salts per 10 liters (2.5 gal.) of fresh water. This results in a mixture that is equivalent to about one-fifth seawater. Keep at 20–28° C (68–82° F).

Scats are normally schooling fishes and should not be kept alone. They are rather nervous fishes and should be placed in the part of the room where they will be the least disturbed.

Leaffishes

Leaffishes are small, deep-bodied, compressed fishes noted for their camouflage and mimicry. The head and mouth are large; the jaws are highly protrusible. The dorsal fin is continuous and contains both spiny and soft rays; the caudal fin is rounded. The lateral line is incomplete or absent. They have no external sex differences. They live in shallow water where they may use their camouflage to hide among the reeds, sunken limbs and roots and to await prey. Or, they may swim slowly on their sides mimicking a floating or sinking leaf as they stalk an unsuspecting fish. About 10 species are known, placed in seven genera. They are found in South America, west Africa and southern Asia. Several species are available to hobbyists.

Badis badis

Monocirrhus polyacanthus

Badis badis – badis (chameleon fish)

Size – To 8 cm (3 in)
Range – India to Burma and Thailand.
Feeding – In nature: preys on small crustaceans, worms and insect larvae. In aquarium: prepared foods but live foods are required to bring fish into spawning condition.
Aquarium care – Badis is best suited for single-species aquaria but can be kept in a well-planted community tank which includes good hiding places. Place a 20-liter (5-gal.) or larger aquarium in a dimly lit area. Build caves of natural rock or use flower pots for cover. The bottom should be dark sand or gravel. Soft to slightly brackish water is recommended. Keep at 21–26° C (70–79° F).

Although shy and secretive when kept alone, *Badis badis* makes an interesting aquarium species when kept in pairs. Males have a concave ventral profile; females convex. Reproduction is similar to that of gouramis.

Monocirrhus polyacanthus – South American leaffish

Size – To 10 cm (4 in)
Range – Amazon and Rio Negro basins, Guyana.
Feeding – In nature: predators; prey on tetras and other small fishes. In aquarium: guppies and other small fishes.
Aquarium care – Keep in a single-species tank of 75 liters (20 gal.) or more, well planted, with soft, slightly acid water, at 22–26° C (72–79° F).

The leaffish reproduces much like cichlids. Spawning occurs with little courtship. The male selects a site on the underside of a leaf, stone or (in the aquarium) a flower pot and cleans it thoroughly. The female carefully attaches adhesive eggs to the spawning site, after which the male sprays them with milt. He then guards them until they hatch (three to four days) and are free-swimming, about another week. A close relative, *Polycentrus schomburgki*, can be kept in the same manner.

69

Cichlids

Cichlids are among the best known and most popular of fresh-water aquarium fishes. They are of interest as much for their complex behavior as for their beauty. Many aquarists believe them to be the "most intelligent" of all fishes. In appearance and structure, cichlids are reminiscent of their close relatives, the marine damselfishes (family Pomacentridae) and share with them a territorial and aggressive nature which must be taken into account if cichlids are to be kept successfully. Cichlids are typically robust, deep-bodied and compressed, with conspicuous, moderate to large scales which are usually ctenoid and only partially cover the head. The lateral line is usually divided into an upper anterior portion and a separate lower posterior portion. The dorsal and anal fins include both spiny rays and soft rays. The soft rays of the dorsal, anal or pelvic fins are extended in some species to produce long trailing margins. The caudal fin is usually rounded or truncate; the adipose fin is absent. The mouth is protractile. The teeth are commonly conical but vary greatly with feeding habits. Like the damselfishes, cichlids have only a single nostril opening on each side of the snout. Approximately 1,000 species of cichlids are recognized. They are indigenous to Africa (where most species occur), South America, and North America as far north as Texas, where one species occurs; but are absent from Europe, Australia, and most of Asia. As might be expected in a group this large, and with many species in remote areas, the taxonomy of cichlids is both difficult and subject to change. Cichlids are most common in still or slow-moving waters and where rocks or vegetation provide cover. Most species are territorial and defend their territories with vigor. They are commonly predatory on small fishes and insects. However, many specialized feeding types have evolved including plankton and deposit feeders, algae scrapers, leaf choppers, mollusc and zooplankton eaters, scale pluckers and even one species that specializes in attacking the eyes of other fishes. In the aquarium cichlids usually feed voraciously. Cichlids are egg-layers (oviparous) and well known for the extended care they provide to their eggs and young. Several patterns of reproduction have evolved as described by Fryer and Iles (1972):

1. Substrate spawners: a) Eggs laid in a pit or attached to a hard surface; both parents tend eggs and young; e.g. Jack Dempsey, *Cichlasoma octofasciatum*. b) Eggs guarded; female broods young in her mouth; e.g. eartheater *Geophagus jurupari*.
2. Mouthbrooders: a) Mouth brooding of eggs and young by both parents; e.g. *Tilapia galilaea*.
   b) Mouth brooding of eggs and young by female; e.g. Egyptian mouthbrooder, *Hemihaplochromis* (= *Pseudocrenilabrus*) *multicolor*.
   c) Mouth brooding of eggs and young by male; e.g. block-chinned mouthbrooder, *Tilapia macrocephala*.
   d) Mouth brooding of eggs by male with mouth brooding of young by both parents; e.g. Guenther's African mouthbrooder, *Chromidotilopia guentheri*.

In typical substrate spawners, such as many of the *Cichlasoma*, the fish pair up and thoroughly clean a flat-rock surface, onto which small batches of eggs are laid and fertilized. The eggs hatch in two to five days, after which the newly hatched fry are transferred by the parents to a previously prepared shallow pit where they are protected until the yolk sac is absorbed. By this time they are free-swimming and have begun to feed (four to ten days). Depending on the species, parental care continues for varying periods of time after the fry hatch. While some cichlids spawn in the open, others spawn in shelters such as holes or caves. Details are given below under the various species. More highly evolved spawning behavior is exhibited by the mouthbrooders. Typically the male digs a pit in which the eggs are laid. The female picks up the eggs, which in some species are fertilized in her mouth by the male as she nibbles him in the genital area, attracted there by dummy eggs on his anal fin, or "tassels" near his vent. After fertilization the female departs and carries the eggs in her mouth until they hatch, about six to ten days. She usually continues to shelter the young until they are large enough to fend for themselves. Many cichlids are polygamous and spawn with more than one male during a single reproductive period. Permanent or temporary sexual dimorphism and dichromatism are common in cichlids. In many species the males become intensely colored when in spawning condition (dichromatism). Mature males may also differ in body shape as the result of deposition of fatty deposits, especially in the head area (dimorphism). Some cichlids lack external sexual differences but sometimes the sexes can be determined during breeding when the genital papilla becomes visible. In males it tends to be more conical and pointed than in the females. Cichlids, as is typical of fishes with extended parental care, lay relatively few eggs.

AQUARIUM CARE – Because of their aggressive nature, and tendency to dig, cichlids are more troublesome to maintain than some aquarium fishes. Many of the difficulties can be overcome by using a large aquarium provided with a suitable habitat and by judiciously selecting the specimens to be kept together. The tank should be large enough to provide swimming space and a choice of several hiding places. Tanks of 250 liters (65 gal.) or more are recommended for most species. The habitat should be constructed to restrict disruption by digging. Large rocks and large pieces of bogwood should be utilized to provide hiding places and can be cemented together to help stabilize them. A gravel bed is usually more satisfactory than sand. Floating plants will do best, although with many species of cichlids hardy plants will survive if they are planted in pots and anchored with rocks. Some species such as discus and angelfish normally use plants for cover and should be provided with them in the aquarium. Water quality is not critical with most cichlids but it is wise to approximate their natural conditions. South American cichlids tend to be found in soft, slightly acid water, while African lakes are usually alkaline and vary in the amounts and composition of dissolved salts. Efficient filtration should be supplied. Outside filtration with a one-to-two-hour turnover rate is generally quite satisfactory. Temperatures vary with the species, but most do well between 21 and 27°C (70–81°F).

REARING CICHLIDS – In nature cichlids extend diligent parental care to their young, which, in aquaria, can often be raised with their parents. This has two important advantages. It allows the aquarist the opportunity of observing parental-care behavior, and helps to ensure that the capability of providing natural parental care is retained in future generations. Sometimes the first batch of young is eaten, but under proper conditions subsequent batches are reared successfully. In species where only one parent cares for the young it may be best to remove the parent not involved in the rearing. The fry normally become active and begin feeding when the yolk sac is absorbed and will usually accept brine shrimp nauplii readily. If it is essential to maximize the production of young in substrate spawners, the eggs may be raised alone in brood tanks. The most difficult task facing the would-be cichlid breeder is the formation and maintenance of compatible pairs. One approach is to raise a group of juveniles together and let them establish their own pairs. This usually works well with unaggressive species. Alternatively, a procedure that works well with many aggressive substrate spawners is to separate the pair with a glass partition that is raised slightly above the bottom so that the milt can pass underneath but the fish cannot. As long as the fish can see each other and have a suitable substrate, they should proceed to court and spawn and extend egg care.

Apistogramma agassizi – Agassiz's dwarf cichlid

Size – To 8 cm (3 in)
Range – Amazon region including upper Rios Paraña and Paraguay.
Feeding – In nature: primarily carnivorous. In aquarium: live foods preferred such as small crustaceans, worms, insect larvae.
Aquarium care – Does best in soft, slightly acid water that has been filtered through peat. Keep several females with a male in a large tank with plenty of hiding places including caves (small flower pots will do). Plants can be maintained. Keep at 21–25° (70–77°F).

This is a harem species in which one male will include several females in his territory. Spawning usually takes place in a cave at a spawning site prepared by the male. The female cares for eggs and recently hatched young while the male guards the overall territory.

Microgeophagus (= Apistogrammus) ramirezi – Ramirez dwarf cichlid (Ram)

Size – To 5 cm (2 in)
Range – Venezuela.
Feeding – In nature: aquatic insects, crustaceans. In aquarium: live foods supplemented with prepared foods.
Aquarium care – Peaceful. Provide a planted aquarium of 40 liters (10 gal.) or more with plenty of hiding places. Soft, acid water preferred. Keep near 25°C (77°F).

Easy to breed in the aquarium. Spawns on flat surfaces or in pits; both parents tend young. The first batch of spawn is commonly eaten. The use of a dither fish such as small zebra danios to distract parents may promote egg protection. When free-swimming the fry will accept brine shrimp nauplii.

Microgeophagus ramirezi

Astronotus ocellatus

Astronotus ocellatus – Oscar

Size – To 30 cm (12 in)
Range – Northern South America.
Feeding – In nature: predatory or small fishes and insects. In aquarium: feed a varied diet including such items as crustaceans, worms, meat and insects. They will usually thrive on prepared foods.
Aquarium care – Keep in a single-species tank. Small specimens may get by in an aquarium of 75 liters (20 gal.), but since adults normally reach 30 cm (12 in) or more, a tank of 200 liters (50 gal.) is preferred. Although hardy in captivity, Oscars can be highly aggressive, especially toward members of their own species. Oscars do well at temperatures between 20 and 27°C (68–81°F); water quality is not critical but ample filtration is required. Since this species is a relentless digger, it is usually not practical to keep plants. Use rocks and bogwood for cover and provide a gravel bottom. Breeds readily in captivity.

Oscars are among the most popular of all aquarium species. They are long-lived and tame readily. Color varies extensively among the strains available, including "red Oscars". Oscars spawn in the open, usually on a smooth rock. The eggs hatch in three to four days and the parents move the fry to a shallow pit until they become free-swimming (five to six days later). It is common practice to remove the parents at this time but better practice to allow parental care. The fry normally accept brine shrimp nauplii.

Symphysodon **spp.** – discus

Size – To 15 cm (6 in)
Range – Amazon region.
Feeding – In nature: omnivorous. In aquarium: live foods plus plant matter supplemented with prepared foods and beef heart.
Aquarium care – Delicate species. Discus require large, well-planted aquaria with soft, slightly acid water and frequent water changes to keep total dissolved solids low. Single-species tanks are recommended, but community tanks with other peaceful species such as tetras and angelfish are feasible. Paint the ends and sides of the aquarium black to reduce stress and use a branch or stump to provide cover near the center of the tank. Do best from 25 to 28°C (77–82°F).

Two species of *Symphysodon* are generally recognized, *S. discus* and *S. aequifasciata.* Each shows considerable variation, depending upon the habitat and water quality. A number of subspecies have been described but their validity remains uncertain. Several color forms are available to the hobbyist; many of them have resulted from selective breeding. A unique feature of discus is their brooding of the young, which are initially nourished by mucous secretions from the skin of the parents. Successful rearing is difficult in aquaria. Condition adults with a varied diet including live foods. Provide a vertical piece of slate for substrate; young should soon accept brine shrimp nauplii and by four weeks should eat freeze-dried foods. Leave both parents with eggs and young.

Pterophyllum scalare – Amazon angelfish

Size – To 15 cm (6 in)
Range – Amazon region.
Feeding – In nature: small living organisms including crustaceans and insect larvae. In aquarium: crustaceans, insects and worms; prepared foods.
Aquarium care – Provide a large, deep aquarium with vegetation around the margins (e.g. *Echinodorus*). Water should be neutral to slightly acid and at 25–27°C (77–81°F). Keep several angelfish together and allow them to select their own mates. They will spawn on slate or flat rocks which can be removed to a brood tank. The eggs may also be left in the care of the parents but since most angelfish available to the hobbyist have been produced through many generations of artificial brooding, adequate parental care is unlikely. Begin feeding the young on squeezed boiled egg yolk followed by the nauplii of brine shrimp. Angelfish are suitable in a community tank with other peaceful species.

Three species of angelfish are recognized: *Pterophyllum scalare*, *P. altum*, and *P. dumerilii*. In addition many varieties, including "albinos," have been produced by selective breeding.

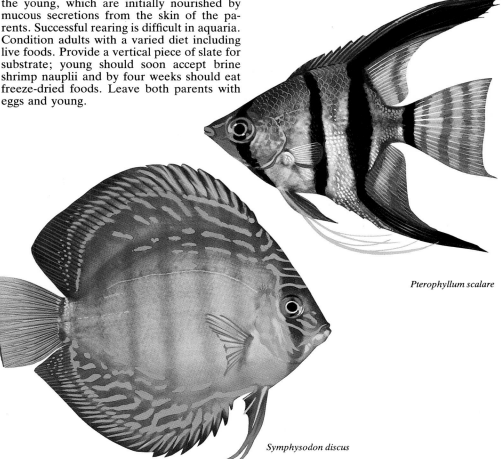

Pterophyllum scalare

Symphysodon discus

Geophagus jurupari – geophagus (eartheater)

Size – To 24 cm (9 in)
Range – Northern South America.
Feeding – In nature: sifts bottom material to obtain invertebrates and other organic material. In aquarium: prepared foods which contain some plant material; supplement with live foods if needed.
Aquarium care – Provide an aquarium of at least 75 liters (20 gal.) with a sand bottom and flat rocks. Hardy plants may be included, but bear in mind that this species is by nature a digger. Water quality is not critical; keep at 21–27°C (70–81°F). Outside filtration is desirable since the fish are constant diggers.

Geophagus jurupari is an interesting breeder. Spawning occurs on a flat rock. The eggs are adhesive and are left attached for about two days, at which time a mouthful of eggs is picked up by the female and incubated. The female will continue to brood the fry for some time after they hatch. The fry will accept brine shrimp nauplii once they are free-swimming.

Cichlasoma octofasciatum (= biocellatum) – Jack Dempsey

Size – To 20 cm (8 in)
Range – Amazon and Rio Negro basins.
Feeding – In nature: omnivorous. In aquarium: accepts and does well on conventional aquarium diets.
Aquarium care – Usually aggressive; best kept alone or in pairs. Tends to uproot vegetation during breeding. Water quality is not critical. Keep near 24° (75°F).

This popular aquarium fish is well named after a famous boxer; it is particularly aggressive during the spawning period. The male becomes more brightly colored and develops fatty deposits on the head when sexually mature; its dorsal and anal fins are more pointed. The female spawns on stones or pieces of wood which have been cleaned by the parents, both of which tend the eggs and fry. Easy to rear.

Cichlasoma meeki – firemouth

Size – To 15 cm (6 in)
Range – Central America.
Feeding – In aquarium: usual aquarium foods.
Aquarium care – Provide an aquarium of at least 75 liters (20 gal.) which may be planted with hardy plants. Does best in hard water with a pH of 7.5 to 8. The firemouth will dig in search of food if given the opportunity. Does well from 20 to 26°C (68–79°F). Provide flat stones for spawning.

A colorful and popular aquarium species that is reputed to be peaceful but sometimes is not. Usually it is best to keep firemouths in single-species tanks. The firemouth is a substrate spawner; both parents tend the eggs and fry, which will accept brine shrimp nauplii when they become free-swimming. The fry and parents may be left together, usually without harm to the young. *Cichlasoma* is a large genus with approximately 60 species known in South and Central America. Many species have been kept successfully.

Aequidens curviceps – flag cichlid

Size – To 8 cm (3 in)
Range – Amazon basin.
Feeding – In nature: all variety of invertebrates. In aquarium: conventional live foods; prepared aquarium foods.
Aquarium care – A peaceful species that does well in a community tank. Several can be maintained in an aquarium as small as 55 liters (15 gal.). Tolerates plants. Cover back and ends of the aquarium and provide hiding places. Water composition is not critical. Keep at 18–27°C (64–81°F). Male has longer, more pointed dorsal and anal fins. A substrate spawner; both parents tend eggs and young.

The genus *Aequidens* includes approximately 30 species, most of which are medium-sized, peaceful, and suitable for community tanks. Other popular species include the blue acara *Aequidens pulcher* (= *A. latifrons*), the key-hole cichlid *A. maroni*, and the port acara *A. portalegnensis*.

Asian Cichlids

Etroplus maculatus – orange chromide

Size – To 10 cm (4 in)
Range – India and Sri Lanka.
Feeding – In nature: omnivorous. In aquarium: include both live food and plant matter in the diet.
Aquarium care – A brackish-water species. Add sea salts or seawater to fresh water to keep specific gravity between 1.005 and 1.025. This is a peaceful species that can be kept in community tanks. Provide a planted aquarium with a sand bottom, flat rocks placed vertically, and bogwood. Keep between 21 and 28°C (70–82°F).

Etroplus is the only genus of cichlids in Asia and includes only two species. The male selects the spawning site, which may be a vertical or overhanging rocks to which the eggs are attached. Both parents tend the eggs and fry. Initial food for the fry includes mucus secreted by the parents. The fry are soon able to include brine shrimp nauplii in their diet.

African cichlids

The majority of cichlids occur in Africa. The most striking feature of their biology is their explosive speciation in the rift lakes of east Africa, each of which has its own distinctive fauna. In Lake Malawi alone over 200 species of cichlids occur, the greatest number of species of fishes for any lake in the world. Almost all of the cichlids of Lake Malawi are endemic; only four species are found elsewhere. Many factors have contributed to the extensive speciation of African lake cichlids, including the size and age of the lakes, the diversity of habitats and the plasticity of the ancestral cichlids. In contrast, the east African rivers have relatively few cichlid species. African cichlids range in size from 4 cm (1.5 in) to 80 cm (31.5 in). Generally only the smaller species are of interest to aquarists. Rock-dwelling species, such as the mbuna or rock cichlids of Lake Malawi, tend to be more colorful than sand-dwelling species. The mbuna have the added interest of being sexually dimorphic mouthbrooders. As in the case of their South and Central American cousins, African cichlids may tolerate a relatively wide variation of water quality, but many aquarists feel they need a rather specific set of salts and high pH, with frequent changing of water. Most species may do best under moderately alkaline conditions. For a physical description of the great lakes and a wealth of biological information see Fryer and Iles (1972).

Pelvicachromis pulcher (= *Pelmatochromis kribensis*) – African dwarf cichlid (Krib)

Size – To 10 cm (4 in)
Range – West Africa, delta of the Niger River.
Feeding – In aquarium: prefers live foods including worms, insects and crustaceans. Probably will do well on a diet of prepared aquarium foods, supplemented occasionally with live foods.
Aquarium care – Peaceful, can be kept in a planted community tank of 55 liters (15 gal.) or larger. Use rocks and roots to provide caves.

This is a cave-spawning species in which both parents may tend the eggs and young. Aquarists often provide a flower pot, placed on its side, as a spawning nest. The male is larger

Male

Female

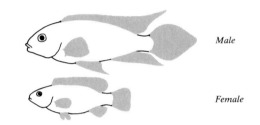

than the female and usually has a more pointed tail with two or three spots on the upper lobe. The pH of the water apparently affects the sex of the young; highly acid water gives rise to a high percentage of females while neutral pH gives rise to a high percentage of males.

Hemichromis guttatus – jewel cichlid

Size – To 15 cm (6 in)
Range – Widespread in tropical Africa.
Feeding – In nature: carnivorous. In aquarium: live foods recommended; otherwise dried foods supplemented with insects, worms, chopped meat and fish.
Aquarium care – An aggressive species. Keep in a large single-species tank provided with hiding places and designed to withstand digging activity. Water quality is not critical. Keep between 22 and 28°C (72–82°F). Provide efficient outside filtration.

Commonly misidentified as *Hemichromis bimaculatus*, this is a well-studied aquarium favorite that is easy to keep and breed. Color is variable; sexually mature males are more reddish. Domestic all-red varieties are available. The jewel cichlid is a substrate spawner well known for its parental care. Both parents continue to tend the fry until they are 1 cm (0.4 in) or more. Eggs hatch in about two to three days; the fry are then transferred by mouth to a pit. They begin to swim and feed three to five days later.

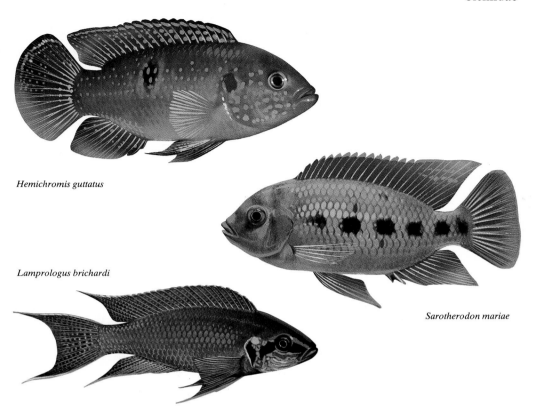

Hemichromis guttatus

Lamprologus brichardi

Sarotherodon mariae

Lamprologus brichardi (= *L. savoryi elongatus*) – lyretail lamprologus (Brichard's lamprologus)

Size – To 10 cm (4 in)
Range – Lake Tanganyika.
Feeding – In nature: browses on small crustaceans and other invertebrates. In aquarium: live foods preferable; supplement with frozen euphausiids to enhance color; or feed flake and freeze-dried food supplemented with chopped shrimp, worms, etc.
Aquarium care – A sociable species. A pair can be kept in an 80-liter (20-gal.) aquarium; community tanks should be 250 liters (66 gal.) or larger. Provide a gravel bottom and rock cover with many hiding places; plants unnecessary. Water should be hard and alkaline and kept stable; temperatures from 23 to 28°C (73–82°F). Efficient filtration with good bio-filtration is required. Keep well covered.

Lamprologus is the most common genus in Lake Tanganyika with approximately 40 species ranging in size from 4 to 31 cm (1.5–12 in). A number of them are good aquarium species, including the lyretail lamprologus. It is a substrate spawner in which the female prepares the nest and guards the eggs. Both parents tend the fry. The fry will usually accept small brine shrimp nauplii, but may require infusoria or other smaller food initially.

Tilapia mariae – Maria's tilapia (tiger cichlid, zebra cichlid)

Size – To 15 cm (6 in)
Range – West Africa.
Feeding – In nature: primarily herbivorous. In aquarium: vegetable matter supplemented with live food; prepared foods.
Aquarium care – Provide a large aquarium with rock and wood cover constructed to resist digging; include caves with overhead flat rocks. Water quality is not critical; slightly acid is best. Keep at 24–27°C (75–81°F).

The tiger cichlid is a substrate spawner in which the female attaches the eggs, usually about 1,200, to the underside of a rock. Following fertilization the female guards the eggs while the male guards the territory. After two days the female transfers fertile eggs to a prepared pit where they hatch a few hours later. The young begin to swim when the yolk sac is absorbed, five to six days later, and will accept brine shrimp nauplii.

Cichlidae

Astatotilapia (= *Haplochromis*) *burtoni* – Burton's mouthbrooder

Size – To 12 cm (5 in)
Range – Lake Tanganyika and associated rivers.
Feeding – In nature: carnivorous. In aquarium: prefers live foods, worms, etc. but will survive on prepared foods.
Aquarium care – Can be kept in a large community tank but pairs should be removed to a single-species tank during reproduction. Keep in an aquarium with a sand bottom, vegetation around the margins and numerous hiding places constructed of rocks and wood. Water quality is not critical but hard alkaline water is best. Keep at 24–27°C (75–81°F).

A classic mouthbrooder. Males have well-defined egg spots on the anal fin. The eggs are quickly picked up by the female after laying and are fertilized as she picks at the dummy eggs on the male's anal fin. The female carries the eggs in her mouth until they hatch and are free-swimming (10–20 days). The genus *Haplochromis* has recently been split into a number of separate genera, including *Astatotilapia*.

MBUNA

Mbuna are small, rock-dwelling cichlids, ranging in size from 7 to 20 cm (3–8 in) that are found only in Lake Malawi, where they form dense aggregations. They exist primarily as isolated communities, with most species living in relatively shallow water. The majority feed on algae scraped from rocks and plants. Some feed on insects and other invertebrates found in the algae mat, but one zooplankton-feeding species and one scale-eating species have also evolved. At least one species occurs as deep as 64 m (210 ft). The mbuna are an exceptional example of explosive adaptive radiation and include 10 genera with at least 29 species. They are believed to have evolved from a common ancestor through isolation of various populations along the rocky shores of Lake Malawi. Some species, such as *Pseudotropheus livingstoni*, use shells as cover. The mbuna are maternal mouthbrooders and exhibit both sexual dichromatism (males more colorful than females) and polychromatism (several different color forms within a single species). The genera include *Pseudotropheus*, *Melanochromis*, *Gephyrochromis*, *Cyathochromis*, *Petrotilapia*, *Labeotropheus*, *Genyochromis*, *Cyanotilapia*, *Labidochromis* and *Iodotropheus*. All are believed to be polygamous. For further information see the references cited under the family description, and Jackson and Ribbinck (1975).

Pseudotropheus zebra – zebra mbuna

Size – To 13 cm (5 in)
Range – Lake Malawi.
Feeding – In nature: scrapes algae from rocks. In aquarium: provide prepared foods rich in plant material supplemented with live foods.
Aquarium care – Keep one male with two or more females in a tank of 400 liters (100 gal.) or more. Provide rock caves, or flower pots, etc. for cover for the female. Water quality is not critical but slightly alkaline and hard is best. Keep at 28–30°C (82–86°F).

Reproduction is typical of other mbuna. The female picks up the eggs immediately after laying them, seeks out the male and nips his vent to initiate release of the sperm. Fertilization takes place in her mouth, where she carries the eggs until they hatch (about 20 days) and continues to take care of the fry. The male will continue to worry the female after spawning but can be distracted from her by providing other females. *P. zebra* is a polychromatic species with several aquarium-produced varieties.

Gobies

Gobies are bottom-living fishes, often sedentary; but many are excellent and interesting aquarium species. The pelvic fins are distinctively fused together to form a sucking disk for attachment to hard surfaces or for resting on soft surfaces. Gobies are small, elongate, cylindrical fishes, usually with two clearly separate dorsal fins, the first supported by spines, the other by soft rays. The caudal fin is usually rounded. The mouth is terminal and the lips prominent. The gill opening is small. Scales may be cycloid or ctenoid but are occasionally absent. The swim bladder is usually absent, making the fish negatively buoyant and helping it hold position on the bottom in currents or surge. Gobies are the largest family of marine fishes with over 800 species; there are also brackish and fresh-water species. Most are tropical but many others are temperate. Many gobies live in the sand, in burrows or tubes. Many others live in rocky habitats in holes or crevices. Gobies usually lay stalked, elongate eggs which they attach to rocks, coral or the sides of their burrows. Many species tend the eggs until they hatch. Both parents may share the duty.

Brachygobius xanthozona – bumblebee goby

Size – To 4 cm (1.5 in)
Range – Indonesia.
Feeding – In nature: benthic invertebrates. In aquarium: will accept a wide variety of live foods; may survive well on good-quality prepared foods.
Aquarium care – A shy species; best kept in a small single-species tank. Requires brackish water; use dilute seawater or sea salts to produce brackish water that is about 20% of normal seawater. Provide a sand bottom with rocks for cover and (if desired) salt-tolerant plants. Recommended temperatures 24–28° C (75–82° F).

Many species of gobies are found in brackish or fresh water, although most of the 800 or so known species are marine. Fresh-water gobies include the pygmy goby (*Pandaka pygmaea*) from the Philippines, the smallest known fish, which reaches only 1.8 cm (about 0.5 in). Difficult to breed. Eggs are attached to roof or walls of shelter and are guarded by the male. Female should be removed. Infusoria or other small live food is required by fry. *B. nunus* is similar to *B. xanthozona* in appearance but differs slightly in anatomy.

LABYRINTH FISHES

Labyrinth fishes include two families of importance to aquarists: Anabantidae and Belontiidae. These fishes are characterized by having an accessory apparatus called the labyrinth organ, which enables them to extract oxygen from the air and thus to survive in oxygen-poor waters. An enlargement in the upper region of the branchial chamber contains folded and crenulated plates, well supplied with blood vessels, and adapted for absorbing atmospheric oxygen. Most species are obligate air-breathers. Labyrinth fishes are commonly found in the still waters of weedy rivers, swamps, irrigation ditches and polluted ponds. There are about 70 species in the suborder. In an aquarium they require breathing room above the surface.

ORDER PERCIFORMES – FAMILY ANABANTIDAE

Climbing Perches

Anabantids are relatively deep-bodied, compressed fishes with a large mouth and strong conical teeth in both jaws. They have long-based dorsal and anal fins, both with spines as well as rays; the tail is rounded and the pelvic fins are placed forward in the thoracic position. There are three genera with a total of approximately 40 species. Only the climbing perch is an important aquarium fish.

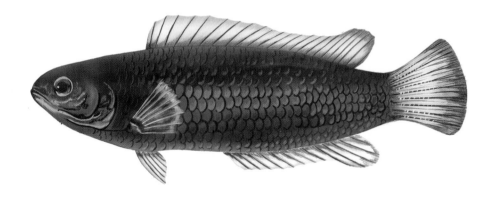

Anabas testudineus – climbing perch

Size – To 25 cm (10 in)
Range – Widely distributed from India and Ceylon through southeast Asia to China and the Philippines.
Feeding – In nature: carnivorous. In aquarium: normal aquarium foods.
Aquarium care – Provide a well-covered, planted aquarium, only partially filled, and include a branch or rocks that extend above the surface. Climbing perch are obligate air-breathers and will suffocate if kept submerged. Water quality is not critical. Keep at 20–30° C (68–86° F). A subsand filter is suitable.

This species is somewhat drab in appearance and attains a rather large size for an aquarium fish. It is primarily of interest to aquarists because of its ability to climb out of water and wander overland. It can survive out of water for several hours. The climbing perch is shy but can be pugnacious with its tank-mates.

Gouramies and their Relatives

These labyrinth fishes include such aquarium species as the paradise fishes, betas, and gouramies, many of them long-time aquarium favorites. They possess the usual anabantoid features, described earlier, and are characterized by: protrusible upper jaws; dorsal fins with a short base, anal fins with a long base; and pelvic fins often with a long hair-like ray. Ten genera and about 30 species are included, ranging from west Africa through India and southeast Asia to Korea. They are generally easy to maintain in aquaria, which should include at least floating vegetation and usually a dark bottom. Temperatures as low as 20° C (68° F) are acceptable for temperate species and up to at least 27° C (81° F) for tropical species. Although most feed on small living organisms they will usually thrive on dried foods. In most species the male constructs a bubblenest that may include plant material, under which he entices the female. Courtship may be elaborate and include displays, butting, chasing and nipping. It culminates in a spawning embrace with the male wrapped around the female. The eggs usually float and may find their own way into the nest. Otherwise they are gathered and placed in the nest by the male. The eggs are tended by the male and hatch in one to two days. The female should be removed for her protection after spawning and the male when the fry become free-swimming. The fry will usually accept liquid and paste fry foods upon hatching but may require infusoria.

Trichogaster leeri – pearl gourami (mosaic gourami)

Size – To 11 cm (4 in)
Range – Southeast Asia from Thailand to Borneo and Sumatra.
Feeding – In nature: carnivorous on small living aquatic organisms. In aquarium: worms, insects, brine shrimp, chopped shrimp, etc.; prepared foods.
Aquarium care – Provide an aquarium of 40 liters (10 gal.) or more that is well planted and includes floating plants. Keep at 23–30° C (73–86° F).

The pearl gourami is a peaceful species, easy to maintain, and well suited to community tanks. However, it is best bred in single-species tanks. Feed live foods to promote breeding conditions. The male is distinguished by an elongate dorsal fin. Both sexes may develop bright red-orange ventral coloration when they are ready to spawn, although it is much less pronounced in the female. Reproduction as described for the family.

Trichogaster trichopterus – blue gourami (three-spot gourami)

Size – To 13 cm (5 in)
Range – Southeast Asia from Thailand through Sunda Islands.
Feeding – In nature: insects, crustaceans, worms and other small invertebrates. In aquarium: prepared foods supplemented with live foods such as mosquito larvae, worms, *Daphnia*.
Aquarium care – May be kept in community tanks and in a group of the same species, but a pecking order will develop. Provide a planted aquarium of 40 liters (10 gal.) or more. Water quality is not critical; temperatures 24–29° C (75–84° F).

This is another very popular aquarium species because of its attractiveness, generally peaceful nature, and its breeding behavior. Males have longer and generally more pointed fins. The male builds a bubblenest which does not include plants. He then becomes very dark, ready to spawn. Courtship, spawning and rearing generally follow the family pattern.

Trichogaster trichopterus

Trichogaster leeri

FIGHTING FISHES

Although historically bred for fighting in public contests upon which wagers were placed, fighting fishes (Bettas) are now of interest to the hobbyist primarily for the variety of beautiful colors and elaborate fin shapes that can be produced by selective breeding. Serious Betta fanciers may wish to belong to a society such as the International Betta Congress (c/o W. P. Hart, 142 E. 7th Ave., Ft. Pierre, S.D.). Excellent articles by Gene A. Lucas appear regularly in the Freshwater and Marine Aquarium magazine. Bettas are elongate, compressed fishes, characterized by a very long anal fin, a short dorsal fin that begins far back on the body, and an almost round caudal fin. Many richly colored varieties have been developed including blues, purples and goldens. Male Bettas are highly aggressive and attack not only other males but also unreceptive females. It is common practice to raise males alone in small containers. Since they are air-breathers, no aeration is required. About 17 species of Bettas are recognized. They include both mouthbrooders and bubblenest builders. Mating follows the usual pattern of gouramies.

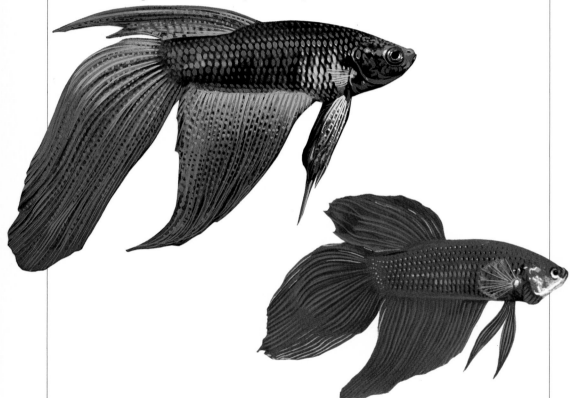

Betta splendens – Siamese fighting fish

Size – To 6 cm (2.5 in)
Range – Indochina and Malaysia.
Feeding – In nature: a wide variety of small fresh-water organisms.In aquarium: usual aquarium foods including prepared or live foods.
Aquarium care – A single male with one or two females can be kept in a community tank or single-species tank of 40 liters (10 gal.) or more. Water quality is not critical but breeding appears to be stimulated by keeping the water level low, such as 15 cm (6 in) or less. Provide floating vegetation and keep at 26–30°C (79–86°F).

Betta splendens is a bubblenest builder and reproduces readily in captivity. Following courtship which involves rubbing, butting, and circling, the male embraces the female by forming a "U" around her. After spawning the female should be removed. The young hatch in 24–36 hours and will accept rotifers and infusoria once they become free-swimming, at which time the male should be separated.

Macropodus opercularis – paradise fish

Size – To 10 cm (4 in)
Range – Warm-temperate and tropical regions of southeast China, Korea, Vietnam and Taiwan.
Feeding – In nature: carnivorous, including insects and other invertebrates. In aquarium: accepts most aquarium foods including worms, crustaceans and prepared foods. Will accept flatworms.
Aquarium care – Will survive in tanks as small as 10 liters (3 gal.) but tanks of 40 liters (10 gal.) or more are preferred. Aggressive, they are acceptable in community tanks but only with larger, hardy fishes. Water quality is not critical. Provide vegetation including floating plants. Keep at 15–24° C (59–75° F).

Reproduce readily; sexes difficult to distinguish; male builds a bubblenest. After spawning the female should be removed. The fry are easy to raise; once free-swimming, they will accept brine shrimp nauplii, infusoria, etc.

ORDER PERCIFORMES – FAMILY HELOSTOMIDAE

Kissing Gourami

Although closely related to the family Belontiidae, this species differs in mouth structure and has a long-based dorsal fin. It is therefore placed in a separate family.

Helostoma temmincki – kissing gourami

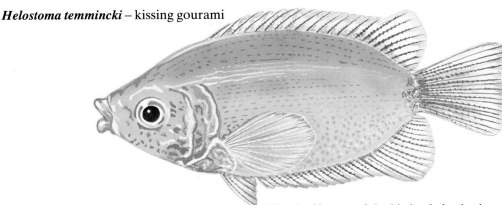

Size – To 30 cm (12 in)
Range – Indochina peninsula through Indonesia.
Feeding – In nature: primarily herbivorous. In aquarium: prepared foods; supplement with live foods and plant material to promote spawning. Feed two to three times per day.
Aquarium care – Easy to keep and a good community tank fish; requires a 75-liter (20-gal.) aquarium or larger. Keep at 24–30° C (75–86° F).

Kissing gouramies in the wild are silvery green; the pink variety available to the hobbyist is a domestic strain. Sexual differences are not apparent except when the female is ripe.

The significance of the kissing behavior is not understood and may not be sex-related since it often takes place between fish of the same sex. Kissing gouramies spawn without building a nest. The eggs are laid during the typical gourami embrace, usually at dusk, and float to the surface where they hatch in about 24 hours. The parents may eat the eggs and should be removed after spawning. Initially the fry need fine food and can be started on infusoria, ground egg yolk or prepared fine fry food. After one week they should accept brine shrimp nauplii.

Puffers

Fishes of this order are characterized by having fused incisor-like teeth. The major propulsion is usually provided by the pectoral fins or the dorsal and anal fins. The premaxillary and maxillary are fused so that the mouth is not protrusible. Pharyngeal teeth are often present and well developed. The scales are modified to form spines or plates but may be absent; the lateral line and swim bladder may be present or absent. Many species produce sound. The order is divided into eight families including the porcupine fishes, triggerfishes and sunfishes; there are 65 genera and about 320 species. In the puffers the stomach is modified to inflate (normally by gulping water) which greatly enlarges the appearance of the fish and helps to discourage predators. Puffers have strong jaws with the teeth fused to form four beak-like incisors. The dorsal and anal fins have soft rays only; the pelvic fins are absent. The pectoral fins combine with the dorsal and anal fins to provide the main propulsion. By using their pectoral fins puffers can swim backwards with relative ease. The scales may be modified as prickles or absent. The viscera, especially the gonads, may contain toxin. The puffers are a large family with 10 genera and over 100 species.

Tetraodon palembangensis – striped puffer (figure-eight puffer)

Size – To 20 cm (8 in)
Range – Southeast Asia.
Feeding – In nature: carnivorous. In aquarium: does best if snails are included in the diet; also include worms, crustaceans, insects.

Aquarium care – Keep in single-species tanks in brackish water that is about 20% of normal seawater. Provide conventional filtration and a sand bottom with some flat rocks. The striped puffer spawns on flat rocks. The male guards and fans the eggs until they hatch, usually in six to eight days. The young are small and difficult to rear. Try feeding them rotifers (e.g. *Brachionus*) followed by brine shrimp nauplii. Keep at 23–28° C (73–82° F).

Several species of puffers may be imported, including the green puffer *T. fluviatilis* from southeast Asia which may be less aggressive, and *T. mbu* from Lake Tanganyika.

MARINE FISHES

Cartilaginous Fishes

The cartilaginous fishes include sharks, skates, rays and chimaeras (ratfishes, etc.) but are generally of little interest to the home aquarist because of their large size. Only a few species are small enough to include in home aquaria. The cartilaginous fishes have in common a skeleton composed of cartilage, not bone, internal fertilization by means of pelvic claspers associated with the pelvic fins of the male, no swim bladder, intestines with a spiral valve and blood high in urea which helps to raise the osmotic pressure to that of the surrounding sea. The class includes six orders and about 625 species.

SUBCLASS ELASMOBRANCHII

The elasmobranchs include the sharks, skates and rays. They have five to seven gill slits on each side of the head and possess denticle-like placoid scales, unique to the class Chondrichthyes.

ORDER HETERODONTIFORMES – FAMILY HETERODONTIDAE

Horn Sharks

Horn sharks are relatively small and inactive, and usually adapt well to captivity. They have a stocky body with a squarish, blunt head; a subterminal mouth with small teeth; and two dorsal fins each preceded by a stout spine. The horn sharks are oviparous with internal fertilization; the egg is protected by a horny case which differs with each species.

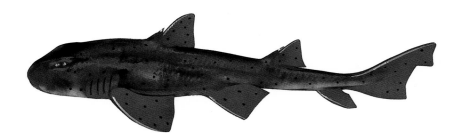

Heterodontus francisci – California horn shark

Size – To 96 cm (38 in)
Range – Central California to the Gulf of California.
Feeding – In nature: carnivorous; feeds on crabs, other benthic invertebrates and small benthic fishes. Most active at night. In aquarium: feeds readily on chopped fish, squid, crustaceans, etc.
Aquarium care – Very hardy. Water quality is not critical. Only young specimens are usually suitable for the home aquarium. Provide a tank at least three times as long as the fish. Keep at 13–24° C (55–75° F).

The California horn shark mates and reproduces readily in captivity. Courtship may include much fin biting by the male. Unreceptive females should be removed to minimize damage to them. During copulation the male holds the female by the back with his teeth and curls around her to insert his claspers into her cloaca. The eggs are laid in a horny, spiral-shaped case. Gestation is about nine months at 20° C (68° F).

Requiem Sharks

This is a large family of sharks of various sizes with most species found in the tropics, where they may be abundant. The family includes most species known to be dangerous to humans. Requiem sharks are fusiform in shape, with a pointed profile, two dorsal fins, and a caudal fin with an enlarged upper lobe. The spiracles are small or absent. Most species are nomadic. Those that have been maintained in captivity are usually active. Fertilization is internal; most species are viviparous. About 150 species are known. At least one species, the bull shark, *Carcharhinus leucas*, ventures into fresh water.

Triakis semifasciata – leopard shark

Size – To 200 cm (84 in)
Range – Oregon, U.S.A. to the Gulf of California, Mexico.
Feeding – In nature: carnivorous: benthic invertebrates, crustaceans, etc., small benthic fishes. In aquarium: feeds readily on fresh or frozen fish and squid.
Aquarium care – Only young specimens are suitable for the home aquarium. Provide an aquarium at least three times the length of the shark. Keep at 13–24° C (55–75° F).

Carcharinid sharks are generally not suited for the home aquarium, but for the aquarist who desires to keep one the leopard shark is an excellent choice. It is a hardy species, active much of the time; but unlike many other active sharks seldom injures itself by colliding with the tank walls. This species and its other close relatives are sometimes placed in their own family (Triakidae).

Bony Fishes

This class includes all the living fishes except the sharks, rays, skates and ratfishes. It is divided into 424 families containing over 18,000 species. The large infraclass Teleostei is the most abundant of all vertebrate groups and contains the vast majority of fishes of interest to aquarists. The classification of the bony fishes used in this book is modified from Nelson (1984); many other schemes exist. The bony fishes have a skeleton containing true bone; single gill openings on each side; and usually possess a swim bladder.

ORDER ANGUILLIFORMES (TRUE EELS)

True eels have an elongate, often snake-like body. The pelvic fins and usually the pectoral fins are absent; the anal fin is elongate, and with the dorsal fin is continuous with the tail. The gill openings are small. Eels possess a characteristic ribbon-like larva, the leptocephalus, unique to the order. The order includes 22 families and over 600 species.

Moray Eels

Eels with no pectoral or pelvic fins; gill openings small and round; lateral-line pores only on the head. Scales are absent and the skin is usually leather-like and smooth. The moray eels are all marine; most are tropical but some occur in temperate seas. About 100 species are known, placed in 12 genera.

Gymnomuraena zebra – zebra moray

Size – To 76 cm (30 in)
Range – Indo-west Pacific; tropical eastern Pacific.
Feeding – In nature: small benthic invertebrates, especially crustaceans. In aquarium: does well on squid, chopped shrimp, etc.
Aquarium care – A hardy species. Provide rocky crevices for cover. Often secretive during the day except when feeding. Preferred temperature 20–24° C (68–75° F) but will tolerate 17–30° C (63–86° F).

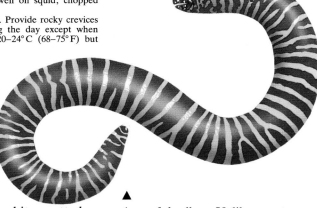

▲

A reef-dweller. Unlike most morays, the zebra moray has rounded molar-like teeth well adapted for grinding small hard-shelled organisms. It is most active at night and is rarely seen by divers during the day.

Gymnothorax meleagris – white-spotted moray eel (guinea-hen moray eel)

Size – To 100 cm (42 in)
Range – Tropical Indian and Pacific Oceans from Africa to Polynesia.
Feeding – In nature: carnivorous. In aquarium: chopped squid, fish and shrimp.
Aquarium care – A hardy species. Well suited to community tanks except with small bite-size fishes. Provide crevices for cover. Keep at 22–28° C (72–82° F).

Like many morays this species is a nocturnal predator and relies heavily on olfaction for locating prey. It is common on coral reefs

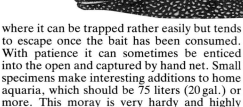

where it can be trapped rather easily but tends to escape once the bait has been consumed. With patience it can sometimes be enticed into the open and captured by hand net. Small specimens make interesting additions to home aquaria, which should be 75 liters (20 gal.) or more. This moray is very hardy and highly resistant to disease.

Muraena pardalis – dragon-face moray (leopard moray)

Size – To 100 cm (36 in)
Range – Indo-Pacific from southern Japan to Polynesia.
Feeding – In nature: carnivorous; prefers bottom-living crustaceans and octopuses but also eats small fishes. In aquarium: chopped seafood.
Aquarium care – Small specimens are suitable in community aquaria of 75 liters (20 gal.) or more. They are hardy, long-lived and usually do not bother other fishes unless they are bite-size. Keep at 22–28° C (72–82° F) in a tank with suitable rocky crevices.

Like most morays the dragon-face moray is active at night but in captivity learns to feed by day. The horny-appearing structures above the eyes are actually tubular extensions of the posterior nostrils. A close relative, *M. lentiginosa*, the Cortez leopard moray or jewel moray, is common in the Gulf of California and southward along the tropical eastern Pacific coast to Peru and the Galápagos Islands. Although not usually available to the hobbyist it too is an excellent aquarium fish.

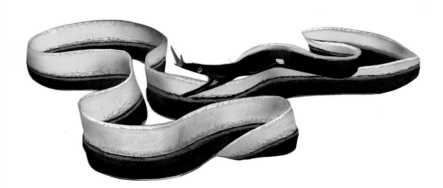

Rhinomuraena amboinensis – blue ribbon eel

Size – To 125 cm (48 in)
Range – Tropical western Pacific Ocean.
Feeding – In nature: carnivorous; includes crustaceans and fishes in its diet. In aquarium: chopped seafood supplemented with small live fishes.
Aquarium care – Provide holes and crevices for cover and a dark tank bottom. Keep light level low and turn off at night. Satisfactory in a community tank but don't keep it with aggressive nibblers such as territorial damsels or with small bite-size fishes. Aquarium should be 125 liters (30 gal.) or more and kept at 24–29° C (75–84° F). It must be tightly covered. Although popular with aquarists, these

morays are more difficult to maintain than other species. Be sure to provide an abundance of holes and crevices for them to hide completely. Diet should be varied and include small live fishes and if possible small live crustaceans.

The blue ribbon eel is usually encountered in shallow lagoons and corals.

Conger Eels and Garden Eels

This family includes the garden eels, which from a distance look somewhat like plants swaying in the breeze. They live in burrows in sand and other soft or loose substrate, from which they partially emerge and face toward the current to feed upon benthic zooplankton that drift by. At night or when approached they retreat completely into the sand for protection. Even when mating they emerge only partially, just far enough to intertwine their bodies and bring their vents into close proximity for spawning. Garden eels often form huge colonies, some of which in the Gulf of California, for example, number into the millions. Four genera and eight species of garden eels are known, while the family Congridae as a whole includes about 100 species.

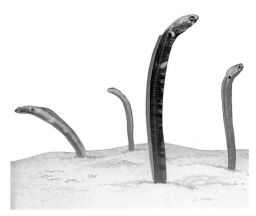

Taenioconger digueti – Cortez garden eel

Size – To 76 cm (30 in)
Range – Gulf of California, Mexico.
Feeding – In nature: benthic zooplankton. In aquarium: live adult brine shrimps supplemented with other living plankton and worms; may accept dead organisms when well adapted to captivity.
Aquarium care – Provide a large high aquarium of at least 400 liters (100 gal.) equipped with a subsand filter. Cover the bottom with loose substrate material such as coral sand to a depth of 15 cm (6 in) or more.

In the Gulf of California two species of garden eels are common at depths from 4 to 20 m (13–66 ft). The second species, *T. canabus*, is slenderer but otherwise similar to *T. digueti* except in minute anatomical details.

Catfish Eels

Catfish eels are elongate, somewhat eel-like fishes, with barbels around their mouths. They have two dorsal fins; the first one, along with the anal fin, is confluent with the pointed tail. Sharp serrated spines, capable of causing severe injury, precede the first dorsal fin and the pectoral fins. Scales are absent. Catfish eels are bottom-living species usually associated with soft substrates and often occurring in aggregations. About 30 species are known from the marine and brackish waters of the tropical Indian and Pacific Oceans and adjoining fresh waters.

Plotosus anguillaris (= P. lineatus) – striped catfish

Size – To 70 cm (28 in)
Range – Indo-Pacific from East Africa to Polynesia.
Feeding – In nature: soft, bottom-living organisms and organic matter. In aquarium: chopped fish and meat, worms; prepared foods.
Aquarium care – Only the young are suitable for the home aquarium. Keep several together in an aquarium provided with a sandy area; can be kept in community tanks. Hardy; keep at 20–30° C (68–86° F).

This is an estuarine species that is found widely distributed in coastal waters of the Indo-Pacific. Adults are an important food fish in many regions.

Toadfishes

Toadfishes are robust, sluggish, bottom-dwelling fishes with large broad heads, wide mouths, strong teeth, and dorsally placed eyes. Scales are usually lacking but the body is well coated with mucus. One or more lateral lines are present. The first dorsal fin is short, and supported by a few strong spines; the second dorsal fin is long-based and supported by rays. The pelvic fins are inserted anterior to the pectoral fins. In some species the fin and opercular spines contain toxins that can cause painful wounds. The swim bladder is present and is used to produce sounds, particularly during courtship. Toadfishes are primarily coastal marine bottom-living fishes found in the temperate and tropical waters of the Atlantic, Pacific and Indian Oceans. Two species are fresh-water. They can live in waters low in oxygen and will survive for some time out of water. About 55 species are known.

Opsanus tau – Atlantic toadfish (oyster toadfish)

Size – To 25 cm (10 in)
Range – Maine to Florida.
Feeding – In nature: carnivorous. In aquarium: whole and chopped fish, squid, etc.
Aquarium care – Easy to maintain, but don't keep with fish small enough to be eaten. Provide fish-sized caves, pots, or tubes for spawning. Keep at 18–24° C (64–75° F).

Toadfishes are primarily of interest because of their sound production during courtship, which includes a variety of grunts, hums, croaks, and whistles. They spawn in shallow water, often laying their eggs inside old tin cans, or shells and other shelters. The male guards the eggs for 10–25 days until they hatch.

Frogfishes

In the fishes of this order, the first ray of the dorsal fin is modified to form a line and lure (illicium and esca) for attracting prey close enough to the mouth to be sucked in and swallowed. The frogfishes or anglerfishes of this family are globe-shaped with saggy skin that lacks scales but is sometimes covered with denticles. Some species such as the sargassum fish (*Histrio histrio*) are highly ornamented and mimic their environment, rendering them extremely cryptic. The gill openings are small and positioned near the pectoral fins. Anglerfishes move very slowly and may utilize the pectoral and pelvic fins to "walk" along the bottom. About 60 species are known ranging in size from 3 cm (1 in) to 36 cm (14 in). They occur in all tropical and subtropical seas.

Antennarius hispidus – zebra frogfish

Size – To 20 cm (8 in)
Range – Tropical Indian and western Pacific Oceans.
Feeding – In nature: carnivorous. In aquarium: small living fishes and any fresh or frozen seafood they will accept.
Aquarium care – Although they can be included in a suitable community tank, they are best displayed in a single-species tank and supplied with live prey. Keep at 24–29° C (75–84° F).

The zebra frogfish is variable in color and may be yellowish to brown with zebra-like stripes. Its usual habitat is quiet areas on the coral flat where it can attract a wide variety of passing fishes.

Antennarius sanguineus – sanguine frogfish

Size – To 9 cm (3.5 in)
Range – Gulf of California to Peru.
Feeding – In nature: small fishes and bottom-swarming crustaceans. In aquarium: small live fishes, adult brine shrimp supplemented with chopped squid, shrimp, or fish.
Aquarium care – Suitable for the community tank but care must be taken to ensure that it has adequate opportunity to feed. Keep at 20–24° C (68–75° F) in an aquarium provided with low-relief, rocky hiding places.

The sanguine frogfish is a common inhabitant of dark crevices along rocky shores. It is best located by means of a strong underwater light.

Histrio histrio – sargassum fish

Size – To 20 cm (7.5 in)
Range – Tropical Atlantic and western Pacific Oceans among drifting *Sargassum* weed.
Feeding – In nature: carnivorous; small fishes. In aquarium: provide small living fishes to initiate feeding; may accept chopped fish, shrimp and squid once adapted to captivity.
Aquarium care – If possible provide floating *Sargassum* weed for cover; otherwise try a floating imitation. Keep at 20–27° C (68–81° F).

This highly cryptic anglerfish mimics *Sargassum* weed in color, pattern and form; it seldom if ever leaves its shelter, where it feeds on an abundance of small prey.

ORDER LOPHIIFORMES – FAMILY OGCOCEPHALIDAE

Batfishes

These odd-shaped anglerfishes swim poorly but can walk along the bottom on specialized, arm-like pectoral and pelvic fins. Their bodies are highly depressed, possess tubercle-like scales and lack a first dorsal fin other than a modified retractible spine that remains present as a line and bait (illicium and esca). The 55 described species have been placed in eight genera. Most species live on soft bottoms in deep water and are rarely kept by aquarists. They are found in both temperate and tropical waters.

Zaleutes elater – Cortez batfish

Size – To 15 cm (6 in)
Range – Southern California to Peru.
Feeding – In nature: carnivorous; includes fishes, crustaceans, worms and molluscs in its diet. In aquarium: live brine shrimp and chopped shrimp, clams and squid.
Aquarium care – Provide an aquarium with a moderately fine sand bottom and subdued light. A 10 cm specimen should have at least a 100-liter (25-gal.) aquarium. Keep at 18–21° C (64–70° F).

The ogcocephalid batfishes are found in subtropical and tropical regions of the Atlantic, Pacific and Indian Oceans. Most are captured by trawlers in water over 100 m (330 ft) deep, incidental to their normal catch. However, some batfishes (for example *Ogcocephalus radiatus*) are found at depths of less than 10 m (33 ft). A number of species have been kept in aquaria.

Flashlight Fishes

The fishes of the order Beryciformes are usually considered to be intermediate between the lower or soft-rayed fishes and the higher fishes which possess both spiny and soft fin-rays. As might be expected, characteristics of both groups are found in this order. Typically, beryciform fishes have a well-developed spiny first dorsal fin partially separated from the soft dorsal fin by a notch; pelvic fins relatively large and posterior to the pectoral fins; ctenoid or cycloid scales; and an open or closed swim bladder (sometimes absent). They occur in all oceans and occupy habitats ranging from shallow tropical reefs to the deepsea and open ocean. About 140 species are known in approximately 40 genera placed in 15 families. This small but unusual family includes four species, each of which possesses a large light-producing organ (containing luminescent bacteria) under each eye. The light organs are unique in that they can be "turned off" either by raising a flap of skin to cover the organ (*Photoblepharon*), rotating the organ inward (*Anomalops*) or by a combination of both methods (*Kryptophanaron*). Flashlight fishes live in the darkness of deep water or shallow caves. They are sensitive to light and move into surface waters only on the darkest of nights. They apparently use their lights to locate prey as well as for intraspecific communication. Because they flee when a diver with a light approaches, flashlight fishes remained unknown to divers until it was discovered that they could be located by diving without a light on moonless nights and watching for the flash of their bean-shaped light organs. The diver can then switch on his light, which momentarily causes the fish to freeze and be captured with a hand net. By using this method the Caribbean flashlight fish (*Kryptophanaron alfredi*) has now been captured at Grand Cayman Island, Puerto Rico and Curacao at depths ranging from 20 m (60 ft) to 45 m (150 ft), while in the Red Sea *Photoblepharon palpebratus* have been caught at considerably shallower depths. The latter species was successfully captured alive at the Comoro Islands, north of Madagascar, during a Steinhart Aquarium expedition to capture the coelacanth (*Latimeria*) and was successfully placed on display. It subsequently became known as the "petite Peugeot." It has proven to be quite amenable to display. Unfortunately the less hardy *Anomalops katoptron* from the Philippines is the species most frequently available to North American aquarists.

Photoblepharon palpebratus – the petite Peugeot

Size – To 9 cm (3.5 in)
Range – Red Sea and Indian Ocean.
Feeding – In nature: carnivorous; pelagic crustaceans and small fishes. In aquarium: live brine shrimp and other swimming crustaceans, frozen krill.
Aquarium care – As for *Anomalops*.

Photoblepharon is easily distinguished from the other species by its single dorsal fin. It

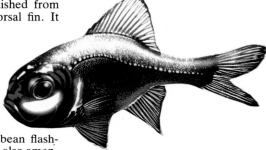

does well in captivity. The Caribbean flashlight fish *Kryptophanaron alfredi* is also amenable to captivity, but its eastern Pacific counterpart *K. harveyi* is known from only one specimen and has not been maintained in captivity.

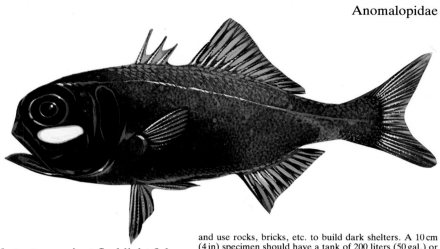

Anomalops katoptron – giant flashlight fish

Size – To 30 cm (12 in)
Range – Widespread in the Indo-Pacific, full range unknown.
Feeding – In nature: carnivorous; small fishes and crustaceans. In aquarium: live brine shrimp, small living fishes.
Aquarium care – Provide an unlit aquarium in a dark area of the room. Cover the back and sides with opaque paper and use rocks, bricks, etc. to build dark shelters. A 10 cm (4 in) specimen should have a tank of 200 liters (50 gal.) or more. Keep at 20–24° C (68–75° F).

Small specimens of *Anomalops* collected in the Philippines have been exported for the aquarium trade. This species is less hardy than *Photoblepharon* and its lights tend to become dim in captivity.

ORDER BERYCIFORMES – FAMILY MONOCENTRIDAE

Pineconefishes

Pineconefishes, or knightfishes, are prized by the marine aquarist because of their unique appearance and adaptability to captivity. They are stocky, oblong, moderately compressed fishes, with large mouths and eyes, covered with large, distinctive bony scales, each of which has a sharp central spine.

Monocentris japonicus – pineconefish

Pineconefish are among the more uncommon fish kept by the home aquarist. If available, they are strongly recommended since they are hardy, exhibit very little aggression, and are unique and interesting in appearance. In addition to *M. japonicus* the Australian knightfish, *Cleidopus gloriaemaris*, is sometimes available and is equally desirable. A third species, *Monocentris reedi*, is known from San Felix Island off the coast of Chile but is rarely captured.

Size – To 13 cm (5 in)
Range – Indo-Pacific; wide ranging but undetermined.
Feeding – In nature: uncertain. In aquarium: usually accepts whole shrimp, chopped shrimp and clams readily.
Aquarium care – Easy to maintain. Keep several together in a single-species tank. Provide a well defined, dimly lit cave with an open swimming space at the front. Does well at 20–22° C (68–72° F).

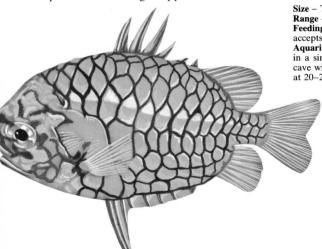

Squirrelfishes

The squirrelfishes are moderately compressed, moderately deep-bodied fishes that are usually reddish in color; they have large eyes, strong, sharp fin spines, and prickly scales. They are primarily nocturnal and spend the day in caves and crevices in relatively shallow water along rocky shores, usually in less than 30 m (100 ft). Many species are excellent aquarium fishes. Hardy and active, they quickly adjust to feeding by day; they are not aggressive toward other fishes of the same or other species, nor are they subjected to aggression. Seventy species are known, all tropical marine. They occur in the Pacific, Atlantic and Indian Oceans, with most species in the Indo-Pacific region.

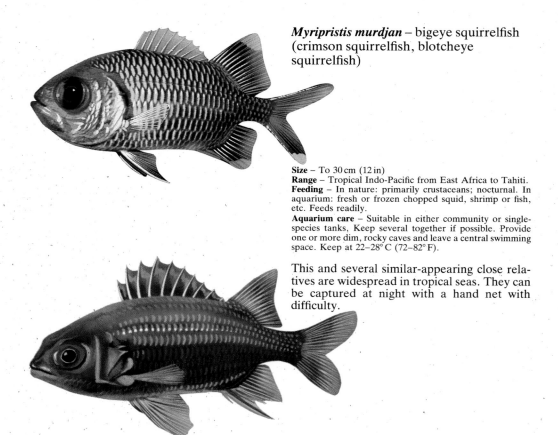

Myripristis murdjan – bigeye squirrelfish (crimson squirrelfish, blotcheye squirrelfish)

Size – To 30 cm (12 in)
Range – Tropical Indo-Pacific from East Africa to Tahiti.
Feeding – In nature: primarily crustaceans; nocturnal. In aquarium: fresh or frozen chopped squid, shrimp or fish, etc. Feeds readily.
Aquarium care – Suitable in either community or single-species tanks, Keep several together if possible. Provide one or more dim, rocky caves and leave a central swimming space. Keep at 22–28° C (72–82° F).

This and several similar-appearing close relatives are widespread in tropical seas. They can be captured at night with a hand net with difficulty.

Adioryx (= Holocentrus) suborbitalis – tinsel squirrelfish (candil, brassy squirrelfish)

Size – To 25 cm (10 in)
Range – Gulf of California, Mexico, to Ecuador.
Feeding – In nature: carnivorous; feeds primarily on small crustaceans. In aquarium: does well on chopped shrimp, squid and fish.

Aquarium care – A good community tank species. Provide caves and crevices for cover. Keep at 20–27° C (68–81° F) but will tolerate greater extremes.

This species hides in caves and crevices during the day, usually in water less than 3 m (10 ft). It emerges at night and is easy to capture with scuba and a hand net.

Holocentrus rufus – white-tip squirrelfish

Size – To 20 cm (8 in)
Range – Bermuda to the Lesser Antilles.
Feeding – In nature: carnivorous; primarily crustaceans. In aquarium: feeds readily on chopped squid, fish and shrimp.
Aquarium care – Easy to maintain in community or single-species tanks. If possible keep several together. Tank should be at least 375 liters (100 gal.) and provided with a rocky cave. Keep at 18–25° C (64–77° F).

During the day this species is found in dimly lit areas under overhangs or in caves at depths from the surface to 30 m (100 ft).

ORDER SYNGNATHIFORMES – FAMILY CENTRISCIDAE

Shrimpfishes

This order includes pipefishes, seahorses, trumpetfishes, coronetfishes and snipefishes, all of which possess a small mouth at the end of a tube-like snout; the upper jaw is not protractile. Shrimpfishes are unusual in both structure and behavior. Elongate and highly compressed, their bodies are encased in bony plates that form a razor-thin ventral margin. They have no teeth or lateral line. The first dorsal-fin spine has been displaced to become terminal in position where it serves an obvious protective function. They swim vertically with their heads down, forming aggregations amongst the long species of sea urchins, or amongst sea grasses where they become almost totally inconspicuous. Shrimpfishes are delicate but, if transported with care, they can adapt successfully to aquarium life. They form an interesting and unique exhibit. Only four species are known, all tropical Indo-Pacific and ranging from East Africa to Hawaii. The closely related snipefish, family Macrorhamphosidae, are somewhat similar in appearance and behavior although more conventional in structure. They are also desirable aquarium fishes.

Aeoliscus strigatus – striped shrimpfish

Size – To 15 cm (6 in)
Range – Indo-Pacific from the Persian Gulf to Hawaii.
Feeding – In nature: carnivorous. In aquarium: newly hatched and adult brine shrimp, small worms and zooplankton; prepared foods.
Aquarium care – Keep several together in a single-species tank of at least 75 liters (20 gal.) with a sand bottom, planted with real or imitation sea grass and, if desired, long-spined sea urchins. Cover the sides and back of the tank to minimize disturbances. Keep at 22–28° C (72–82° F).

These aquarium fish are very attractive. They are delicate, but if captured and transported with care, they can adapt well to aquarium life.

97

Pipefishes and Seahorses

Syngnathids are elongate or "S"-shaped fishes with tubesnouts and bodies armored with a series of bony rings. The gill openings are very small. Only a single dorsal fin is present; the pelvic fins are lacking and the anal fin is very small. The eggs are brooded by the male in a ventral pouch. There are about 150 species of pipefishes but only 24 species of seahorses. Most species inhabit shallow water. Pipefishes occur in marine or brackish water with some in fresh water and are common in both tropical and temperate regions. Seahorses are marine and primarily tropical, rarely temperate. The largest seahorse is the giant Pacific seahorse which reaches 30 cm (1 ft).

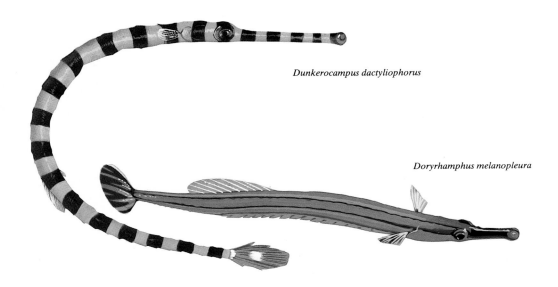

Dunkerocampus dactyliophorus

Doryrhamphus melanopleura

Dunkerocampus dactyliophorus – banded pipefish (harlequin pipefish)

Size – To 18 cm (7 in)
Range – Central tropical Indo-Pacific including the East Indies and Melanesia.
Feeding – In nature: carnivorous; bottom-swarming crustaceans, larvae, fishes, etc. In aquarium: live brine shrimp, newly hatched guppies, small worms; prepared foods.
Aquarium care – Suitable in the community tank but only with non-aggressive species. Care must be taken to see that it receives adequate food. Keep at 22–28° C (72–82° F).

This is usually considered to be the most attractively colored of the pipefishes. It is one of the few species of pipefishes that is normally of interest to the aquarist. It occurs on coral reefs and can be captured with a fine-meshed hand net. Egg care is given by the male, who carries the eggs on the ventral surface of his abdomen.

Doryrhamphus melanopleura – fantail pipefish

Size – To 7.5 cm (3 in)
Range – Tropical Indian Ocean to tropical eastern Pacific.
Feeding – In nature: probably bottom-swarming crustaceans and larval organisms. In aquarium: brine shrimp nauplii; prepared foods; feed at least once per day, twice is preferred.
Aquarium care – Keep with other small fishes. Provide crevices for cover. Keep at 20–29° C (68–84° F).

This delicate little creature is one of the few rocky reef fishes that occur on both sides of the tropical Pacific. It is usually found under dark ledges or in dark crevices on vertical faces and rarely ventures far from its shelter. It is not aggressive but will defend its territory against other members of its species.

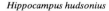

Syngnathus leptorhynchus – bay pipefish

Size – To 24 cm (9 in)
Range – Alaska to southern Baja California, Mexico.
Feeding – In nature: carnivorous; feeds primarily on small crustaceans including amphipods, copepods and crab larvae. In aquarium: feed live brine shrimp, including both adults and nauplii and other live zooplankton.
Aquarium care – Keep only with non-aggressive species or in single-species tanks which should be 75 liters (20 gal.) or more. Keep at 10–22° C (50–72° F).

This species has one of the longest north–south ranges of Pacific Coast shore fishes. It is most commonly encountered in bays and sloughs in eelgrass beds where it orients parallel with the grass in order to remain unseen.

Hippocampus hudsonius

Hippocampus kuda – golden seahorse

Size – To 25 cm (10 in)
Range – Tropical Indo-Pacific.
Feeding and care – As for Florida seahorse.

Seahorses are usually among the more difficult species to maintain. They need plenty of live food and should be given as much variety as possible in order to provide optimal nutrition.

Hippocampus hudsonius – Florida seahorse

Size – To 15 cm (6 in)
Range – Tropical and temperate western Atlantic from Florida to New York.
Feeding – In nature: browses on zooplankton. In aquarium: live brine shrimp; include newly hatched nauplii as adults. Try to supplement with other living crustaceans and tiny fishes such as newborn guppies.
Aquarium care – Keep with other peaceful species such as pipefishes and shrimpfishes or keep in a single-species tank. Provide vegetation or slender coral for attachment.

This species occurs in a variety of color phases including gray, brown and red. It is relatively easy to keep and has been bred in captivity.

Rockfishes and Scorpionfishes

The fishes in this order are characterized by a unique bone, known as the suborbital stay, which extends under the eye and across the cheek. The body shape varies from cylindrical to compressed; the head and body are often spiny; the pectoral fin is rounded, the tail fin rounded or square. The order includes 21 families, 260 genera and about 1,000 species. Scorpaenids vary from active to sedentary. Sedentary species are often cryptic. The body is cylindrical to compressed, the head large and often spiny; the mouth is usually large. The pectoral fins are nearly always large and rounded; the tail is square or round. Fertilization is internal; development may be external (oviparous) or internal (ovoviviparous).

Scorpaena guttata – California scorpionfish

Size – To 43 cm (17 in)

Range – Central California to the Gulf of California.

Feeding – In nature: carnivorous; an opportunistic feeder that preys on a variety of benthic organisms. In aquarium: chopped fish, squid, etc.

Aquarium care – Only small specimens are usually kept by the home aquarist. Sedentary; requires little space. Suitable for community tanks but do not keep with aggressive nibblers such as damselfishes. Keep at 15–25° C (59–77° F).

Scorpionfishes have poisonous dorsal spines and must be handled with care. If an injury occurs, treat the site with very hot water; since the toxin is a protein that is inactivated by heat. These fishes are sedentary and cryptic in nature, and somewhat of a hazard to divers since they are difficult to see. Once observed they are easy to collect with a hand net. Since they lack a swim bladder, they can be easily brought to the surface alive from deep water. Fertilization is internal and the eggs are laid in a gelatinous mass. The larvae are small and difficult to rear. These fishes are primarily of interest to aquarists who wish to specialize in temperate-water fishes.

Pterois volitans

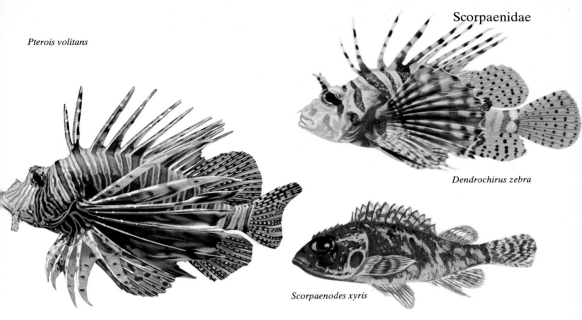

Dendrochirus zebra

Scorpaenodes xyris

Pterois volitans – lionfish (turkeyfish, red firefish, dragonfish)

Size – To 30 cm (12 in)
Range – Tropical Indo-Pacific except Hawaii.
Feeding – In nature: carnivorous; crustaceans and fishes. In aquarium: shrimp, chopped fish and squid; live fish if desired.
Aquarium care – Easy to maintain but grow very rapidly and should be kept in a tank of at least 200 liters (50 gal.). Suitable in a single-species tank where several can be kept together, or in a community tank with larger than bite-size fishes. Keep at 22–30° C (72–85° F).

The lionfish inhabits lagoons, channels and partially protected reefs down to depths of 35 m (115 ft) or more. It is usually observed under ledges where it preys on small fishes and crustaceans. *DANGER!* Its beautiful flowing fins are supported by sharp venomous spines which are used in defense and can cause extremely painful, though non-fatal injuries. If injury does occur a prompt, extremely hot bath, as hot as you can bear, will often give relief. A physician should be consulted promptly.

Dendrochirus (= Brachirus) zebra – zebra lionfish (dwarf lionfish, zebra firefish)

Size – To 18 cm (7 in)
Range – Widespread in the tropical Indo-Pacific but absent from Hawaii.
Feeding – In nature: carnivorous. In aquarium: pieces of fish, squid and shrimp. Provide live fish if required to initiate feeding.
Aquarium care – As for *Pterois volitans* but a 75-liter (20-gal.) tank is adequate.

This species is widespread on coral reefs and is easy to capture, but care must be taken to avoid its toxic spines. A close relative, *D. barberi* (= *D. brachypterus*) occurs in Hawaii but appears to prefer caves and ledges. Several other species of lionfishes have been kept including: *Pterois sphex* from Hawaii, *Pteropterus* (= *Pterois*) *antennata* and *Pterois russelli* (= *P. lunulata*) from the western Indo-Pacific region.

Scorpaenodes xyris – rainbow scorpionfish

Size – To 18 cm (7 in); rarely more than 10 cm (4 in)
Range – Southern California to Peru.
Feeding – In nature: opportunistic carnivore; feeds on small crustaceans and fishes, etc. In aquarium: chopped fish, squid, shrimp.
Aquarium care – Easy to maintain and suitable in community tanks except with very small, bite-size fishes. Keep at 20–27° C (68–81° F).

This small scorpionfish is highly cryptic and relatively inactive, but it is extremely hardy and a useful addition to community tanks. It is common along rocky shores, usually in crevices. Once observed it is easy to collect with a hand net and probe. For unknown reasons the largest specimens are found at the northern extreme of its range.

Sebastes rubrivinctus

Sebastes rosaceus

Sebastes rubrivinctus – flag rockfish (barberpole rockfish)

Size – To 36 cm (14 in)
Range – Southern California and northern Baja California, Mexico.
Feeding – As for the rosy rockfish.
Aquarium care – Provide rocks for cover. Adults require an aquarium of 1,000 liters (250 gal.) or more. Temperatures below 15° C (59° F) preferred but it can acclimate to temperatures perhaps as high as 23° C (73° F).

A close relative, the treefish (*S. serriceps*), occurs in shallower water and is easily taken with scuba, which permits it to be degassed at the time of capture. Young treefish are found in association with floating kelp and are relatively easy to capture at this time. The treefish is an attractive fish with narrow black bars over a yellow background. It can easily be kept at temperatures up to 23° C (73° F).

Sebastes rosaceus – rosy rockfish

Size – To 36 cm (11 in)
Range – California to central Baja California, Mexico.
Feeding – In nature: carnivorous. In aquarium: chopped squid, fish, shrimp.
Aquarium care – Suitable for single-species or community tanks. Adults require an aquarium of 1,000 liters (250 gal.) or more. Provide rocks for cover along the back and one end of the bank but leave plenty of swimming space. Several can be kept together. Keep at 15–20° C (57–68° F).

The rosy rockfish is frequently caught by sportfishermen; usually at depths greater than 15 m (50 ft); to bring to the surface alive, it must have its swim bladder degassed with a hypodermic needle (or be decompressed). Many do not survive capture by hook and line from the surface but those that do make excellent aquarium fishes.

Stonefishes

Stonefishes are the most venomous of all fishes. Because of their danger they are not recommended for the home aquarist. (However, an antivenin is available.) Importation and possession of them is subject to regulations which vary from country to country; check with local authorities. Their bodies are moderately elongate and normal appearing, but their heads, covered with ridges, spines and concavities, appear misshapen and grotesque. They have very large pectoral fins and a single dorsal fin with sharp anterior spines. Poison glands are present at the base of each spine. Scales are absent as is the swim bladder. Stonefish are cryptically colored and usually lie partially submerged in the mud or among rocks or corals. Since they often occur in very shallow water it is easy to step on them when wading or bump into them while swimming. The resultant injury is extremely painful and often leads to respiratory distress, sometimes death. About 20 species are known. All are tropical shallow-water marine species, rarely brackish, and occur from South Africa to the Society Islands including the Red Sea and Australia. They are absent from Hawaii and the eastern Pacific.

Synanceia verrucosa – reef stonefish

Size – To 33 cm (13 in)
Range – Tropical Indo-Pacific from East Africa to Tahiti, including the Red Sea but absent from Queensland and Hawaii.
Feeding – In nature: carnivorous; small fishes and crustaceans. In aquarium: live fishes and fresh or frozen fish and shrimp.

Aquarium care – Use a tightly covered tamper-proof aquarium. Suitable in a community tank with fish larger than "bite-size." Stonefish are sedentary and require little space. A 25 cm (10 in) specimen can be kept in a 75-liter (20-gal.) aquarium. Keep at 22–28° C (72–82° F).

Several other species of stonefishes have been maintained including *Synanceia horrida*, *Inimicus didactylus* (the demon stinger), etc. They are all dangerous to handle and keep.

Sculpins

The sculpins are a large family of cold-water bottom fishes closely related to the rockfishes. Most are relatively small, have a cylindrical body with a large head and taper to a narrow peduncle. The eyes are usually high on the head, the mouth and lips large. The dorsal fin is usually long with the spinous portion wholly or partially separated from the soft-rayed portion; the anal fin is usually long; the pectoral fins are large and fanlike, and the tail rounded or square. Scales may cover the body, occur in rows or patches, as bony plates or prickles, or be absent. Most species possess cirri, some have many. The swim bladder is lacking, an adaptation which facilitates the

103

sculpins' bottom-dwelling existence. Spawning occurs in winter or spring, fertilization is internal; eggs are usually laid in relatively small numbers and guarded by the male. Most species occur in shallow water, some in moderately deep water, some in fresh water and some function anadromously. The sculpins include about 70 genera and 300 species.

Nautichthys oculofasciatus – sailfin sculpin

Size – To 20 cm (8 in)
Range – Alaska to Central California.
Feeding – In nature: carnivorous; feeds extensively on crustaceans. In aquarium: live adult brine shrimp, chopped shrimp, chopped squid.
Aquarium care – A delightful fish in the cold-water aquarium. Provide a good-sized cave. Keep several together at temperatures of 10–13° C (50–55° F).

The sailfin sculpin is most active at night. By day scuba divers find it in small caves, often hanging upside down on the roof. The long anterior dorsal fin is used as a primitive lure to attract swimming crustaceans, etc. When food is present the sculpin waves its dorsal fin back and forth to attract prey, then lowers the fin near its mouth where the prey can be engulfed.

Nautichthys oculofasciatus

Rhamphocottus richardsoni – grunt sculpin

Size – To 7 cm (3 in)
Range – Alaska to Central California.
Feeding – In nature: carnivorous; feeds on small benthic and bottom-swarming crustaceans. In aquarium: live adult brine shrimp and other living crustaceans, chopped shrimp and chopped squid.
Aquarium care – Provide a rocky habitat with holes, caves and crevices. Keep in a single-species tank of 75 liters (20 gal.) or more, or in a community tank with other peaceful species. Temperatures below 15° C (59° F) are recommended.

The grunt sculpin occurs primarily along rocky shores from tidepools down to about 30 m (100 ft), but it has been found on sandy bottoms and at depths as great as 165 m (540 ft). It uses its pectoral fins for perching and crawling and is capable of conventional swimming. Reproduction usually occurs in winter; yellow or orange eggs are laid in small numbers on a rocky surface.

Jordania zonope – longfin sculpin

Size – To 15 cm (6 in)
Range – Alaska to Central California.
Feeding – In nature: browses on small crustaceans and other benthic invertebrates. In aquarium: live brine shrimp, chopped shrimp and other crustaceans.
Aquarium care – Does best in an aquarium chilled to below 10° C (50° F) but will adjust to temperatures as high as 20° C (68° F). Provide large rocks with flat vertical surfaces for perching, and crevices for hiding.

The longfin sculpin is very abundant in southern British Columbia and Washington at depths of 6–15 m (20–50 ft). It favors vertical rock faces covered with algae and attached invertebrates where in spite of its bright coloration it is highly cryptic. It can be collected with a fine-mesh monofilament hand net or a "slurp" gun. Fertilization is internal. Eggs are usually laid in the fall in small clusters. The young are relatively large and should be easy to rear.

Jordania zonope

Sea Basses and Groupers

Serranids are characteristically robust, large-mouthed fishes with strong teeth and bodies, usually moderately compressed and moderately deep-bodied. The spiny dorsal fin is joined to the soft-rayed portion with or without a notch; the caudal fin may be rounded, truncate, lunate or moderately forked. The mouth is subterminal with the lower jaw often projecting beyond the upper jaw. Scales are usually ctenoid; the lateral line is complete; the gas (swim) bladder is present and closed. Most serranids are bottom-dwellers and all are carnivorous. Many can undergo rapid color changes that involve a change of pattern as well as hue or shade. Most serranids are hermaphroditic, usually sequential, being first male then changing to female. Serranids tend to be large as adults and of little interest to the aquarist. A number of smaller species and juveniles make interesting additions, especially to community tanks. About 370 species of serranids are known. They range in size from about 10 cm (4 in) to over 3 m (10 ft) and to weights greater than 400 kg (800 lb). The majority of species are tropical marine; some are warm-temperate but only a few are found in cold-temperate waters; a few species are fresh-water.

Cromileptes altivelis – panther grouper

Size – To 65 cm (25 in)
Range – Central Indo-Pacific from India to the Philippines.
Feeding – In nature: carnivorous. In aquarium: feeds readily on pieces of fish, squid, shrimp, clams or almost any edible marine animal.
Aquarium care – Usually kept in a community tank. Provide a coral-reef habitat with some rocky holes and crevices. Use as large a tank as possible. Keep at 22–28°C (72–82°F).

This is one of the most commonly kept members of the grouper family. Although it may reach more than 65 cm (25 in) as an adult, juveniles grow slowly in captivity, are peaceful, and may remain a suitable size for the home aquarium for several years. In nature, panther groupers are predatory bottom fishes that usually lie partially concealed amongst rocks or coral waiting to ambush prey.

Cephalopholis miniatus

Cephalopholis argus

Cephalopholis miniatus – red grouper (coral trout)

Size – To 45 cm (18 in)
Range – Tropical Indo-Pacific from the Red Sea to Tahiti; absent from Hawaii.
Feeding – In nature: carnivorous. In aquarium: fish, squid and crustaceans.
Aquarium care – Suitable in a community tank with larger than bite-size fishes. Provide some rock cover and, if desired, coral. Keep at 21–28° C (70–82° F).

This is a colorful species that can add a lot to a community tank. In nature the red grouper is rather secretive. Although it may be common on coral reefs, it is rarely caught by hook and line. Several species are similar in appearance, including the leopard cod (*Plectropoma maculatum*) and the fairy cod (*Variola louti*), both of which, however, lack the rounded tail.

Cephalopholis argus – blue-spotted grouper (peacock rock cod, jewel grouper)

Size – To 40 cm (16 in)
Range – Tropical Indo-Pacific from South Africa to the Tuamotu Archipelago, and Hawaii (introduced).
Feeding – In nature: carnivorous; feeds on small fishes and crustaceans during both the day and night. In aquarium: fish, squid and crustaceans.
Aquarium care – Easy to keep and suitable for community tanks with larger fishes. Provide as large a tank as possible. Furnish with rock and coral cover. Keep at 20–30° C (68–86° F).

This species is most commonly encountered in areas of thick coral growth. Adults occur from the surface down to 40 m (130 ft) or more. Juveniles usually occur in shallow protected areas. They are relatively slow-growing in captivity and will survive for many years under proper aquarium conditions. The blue-spotted grouper was first introduced into Hawaii in 1956 (from the Society Islands).

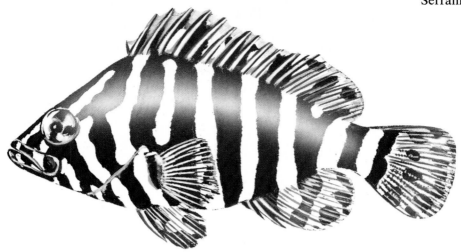

Epinephelus (= Dermatolepis) dermatolepis – leatherback bass

Size – To 100 cm (36 in)
Range – Gulf of California to Ecuador, including Galápagos Islands and other offshore islands.
Feeding – In nature: carnivorous. In aquarium: feeds readily; accepts chopped shrimp, squid, fish, etc.
Aquarium care – Only the juveniles are suitable for the home aquarium. In spite of their carnivorous nature, they are peaceful aquarium fishes and do well in community tanks except with bite-size fishes. Provide a large tank and keep at 18–24° C (64–75° F).

Juvenile leatherback bass hide amongst the spines of the sea urchins *Diadema* and *Centrostephanus* where their black-barred pattern renders them inconspicuous. They can easily be taken in shallow water by snorkelers as well as scuba divers by means of a hand net. Once they outgrow the home aquarium they are usually eagerly accepted by public aquaria.

Liopoproma (= Chorististium) rubre – Swissguard basslet

Size – To 9 cm (3.5 in)
Range – Gulf of Mexico and South Florida to the Lesser Antilles; Yucatan.
Feeding – In nature: unknown, possibly small crustaceans. In aquarium: live brine shrimp, chopped shrimp, squid, clams; prepared foods.
Aquarium care – Suitable in the community tank. Provide caves and crevices for cover. Keep in an aquarium of 75 liters (20 gal.) or more at temperatures from 20 to 24° C (68–75° F).

In nature this is a secretive species that is usually found in deep holes or caves and in the hollows of coral heads. It generally becomes tame in the aquarium: but if it persists in hiding it may be necessary to reduce the available cover. Swissguard basslets are not usually combative with other species, nor are they bothered by any except the most aggressive of species.

Serranidae

Serranus tabacarius – tobaccofish

Size – To 15 cm (6.5 in)
Range – Bermuda to the Lesser Antilles.
Feeding – In nature: carnivorous. In aquarium: pieces of fish, squid, shrimp and clams; small live fishes.
Aquarium care – Suitable in the community tank with fish the same size or larger. Provide some rocky cover. Keep at 21–24°C (70–75°F).

This species varies considerably in color and may be quite drab. It is hardy in captivity and is one of the smaller serranids available to the hobbyist. The tobaccofish is a solitary species commonly found near the coral reef, hovering just above the bottom. It has been taken at depths ranging from 1 to 40 m (3–125 ft).

Serranus fasciatus – Cortez harlequin bass (barred serrano)

Size – To 11 cm (4.5 in)
Range – Gulf of California to Peru; Galápagos Islands.
Feeding – In nature: carnivorous; apparently feeds on small fishes and crustaceans. In aquarium: feeds readily on chopped seafood.
Aquarium care – A hardy species that is relatively inactive and peaceful. Best suited for the community tank but avoid placing it with small fishes. Keep at 20–25°C (68–77°F).

This is a shallow-water species found along rocky shores and in areas with vegetation for cover. It is relatively easy to capture and since it can be found at less than 6 m (20 ft), it does not require degassing. Since it tends to be inactive it should not be kept with aggressive damselfishes. Several other species of *Serranus* occur, many of them small, including the harlequin bass *Serranus tigrinus* from the tropical Atlantic and the orangeback bass *S. annularis*, also of the Atlantic. The latter is very colorful and is easy to keep.

Liopoproma fasciatus – Cortez rainbow basslet

Size – To 18 cm (7 in)
Range – Gulf of California.
Feeding – In nature: unknown, possibly bottom-swarming organisms. In aquarium: chopped shrimp, squid and fish; supplement with live adult brine shrimp, krill, etc.
Aquarium care – An excellent community tank species. Provide caves and crevices over a sand bottom for cover. Keep at 19–22°C (66–72°F).

This species is rarely observed in nature even by scuba divers. It is most commonly found below the surface thermocline at depths exceeding 25 m (80 ft), hovering in the entrance of caves which have a coarse sand bottom. Since it has a closed swim bladder it should be "degassed" at the depth of capture with a hypodermic needle before being brought to the surface.

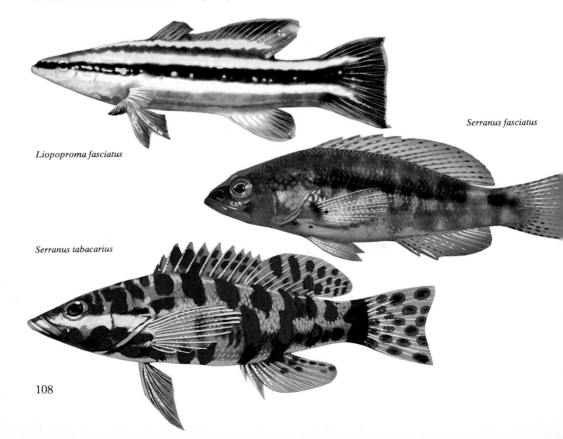

Liopoproma fasciatus

Serranus fasciatus

Serranus tabacarius

HAMLETS

The hamlets, *Hypoplectrus* spp., have been a difficult group taxonomically. As the result of recent biochemical studies, a number of species that were previously recognized are now considered to be color morphs of the same species, *H. unicolor*.

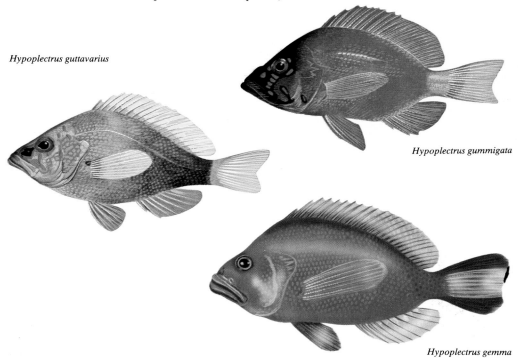

Hypoplectrus guttavarius

Hypoplectrus gummigata

Hypoplectrus gemma

Hypoplectrus unicolor (formerly *H. gemma*) – the blue hamlet

Size – To 13 cm (5 in)
Range – Florida to Central America.
Feeding – In nature: carnivorous, primarily shrimp, crabs and small fishes. In aquarium: shrimps and small fishes, minced.
Aquarium care – Young fish adapt best to captivity. Suitable in a community tank of 75 liters (20 gal.) or more. Provide numerous places to hide. Keep at 21–25° C (70–77° F).

Unlike most serranids, hamlets are often brightly colored and conspicuous on the reef. The blue hamlet mimics the blue chromis (*Chromis cyaneus*), which apparently allows the hamlet to approach and capture prey, not preyed on by the blue chromis. The two species, kept together in coral habitat, make an attractive exhibit.

Hypoplectrus unicolor (formerly *H. gummigata*) – golden hamlet

Also known as the blueface hamlet, this is the most sought-after of the hamlets because of its attractive color and its rarity in captivity. It prefers deeper water than the better-known hamlets and is usually encountered at depths exceeding 20 m (70 ft), where it is more difficult to collect than the shallower species.

Hypoplectrus unicolor (formerly *H. guttavarius*) – shy hamlet

This color morph is common on well-developed reefs. It appears to be a mimic of the rock beauty angelfish (*Holacanthus tricolor*), which may allow it to approach shrimp closely enough to capture them, since the rock beauty is primarily a sponge feeder and not a predator of shrimp.

109

Soapfishes

These close relatives of the serranids produce a soapy protective mucus. About 17 species are known. They occur in the Atlantic and Indo-Pacific.

Grammistes sexlineatus – golden-striped grouper (six-lined perch)

Size – To 30 cm (12 in)
Range – Tropical Indo-Pacific from East Africa to Tahiti; absent from Hawaii.
Feeding – In nature: carnivorous. In aquarium: fish, squid, beefheart, etc.
Aquarium care – This is a risky fish to keep since it can exude toxic mucus when handled or frightened. It is capable of killing itself as well as other fishes in the aquarium. Never transport this species with other fish. If you wish to keep the golden-striped grouper, try introducing it into an oversize aquarium by itself and leave it undisturbed until it acclimatizes itself. Then add other fish. Be sure they are larger than the grouper! Keep at 22–27° C (72–81° F).

This species is found on coral reefs and in tidal pools. It is very shy and seeks cover when approached. In the aquarium, however, it usually becomes quite tame.

Dottybacks

These small active fishes are closely related to the serranids, from which they differ principally by having an interrupted lateral line. The family includes several colorful aquarium fishes.

Pseudochromis porphyreus – purple dottyback

Size – To 6 cm (2 in)
Range – Tropical Indo-Pacific.
Feeding – In nature: bottom-swarming plankton. In aquarium: live brine shrimp, small worms, krill and prepared foods.
Aquarium care – Suitable for the community tank but they require areas of dense cover amongst rocks and coral. Keep two or three in a 75-liter (20-gal.) tank at 22–28° C (72–82° F).

This species is usually found on steep faces of coral reefs at depths of 15 m (50 ft) or more. There may be a space of several feet between each fish. It is difficult to capture even with a fish anesthetic.

Pseudochromis flavivertex

Pseudochromis porphyreus

Pseudochromis flavivertex – orange-striped dottyback (orange-back pseudochromis)

Size – To 10 cm (4 in)
Range – Tropical Indo-Pacific.
Feeding – In nature: plankton. In aquarium: live adult and newly hatched brine shrimp plus prepared foods.

Aquarium care – Suitable in community tanks; be sure to provide numerous small cavities amongst rocks and coral for cover. Keep at 22–28° C (72–82° F).

This is a peaceful, active species that does much to liven up the aquarium. Several should be kept together.

ORDER PERCIFORMES – FAMILY TERAPONIDAE

Tigerperches

These small serranid-like fishes are confined to the Indo-Pacific where they occur in marine, brackish and fresh waters. They differ from the serranids in technical anatomical details. Most are striped. At least 15 species are known.

Terapon jarbua – crescent tigerperch (tiger bass)

Size – To 25 cm (10 in)
Range – Tropical Indo-Pacific from East Africa to Melanesia and Taiwan.
Feeding – In nature: carnivorous. In aquarium: pieces of fish, squid, clams, shrimp; provide prepared foods and small live fish if desired.
Aquarium care – Easy to keep. Do well in schools in a single-species tank but are also suitable for community tanks. Keep at 22–28° C (72–82° F). They can be kept in brackish or even fresh water.

The tigerperch is well suited to captivity but because of its rather ordinary appearance is not a highly popular species with the aquarist. Tigerperches are common to bays and estuaries where they prey on small fishes and other soft-bodied organisms. They are relatively easy to capture by seine or cast net and can also be taken by hook and line. They have been spawned and raised in captivity.

Aholeholes

Aholeholes (reef trout, flag-tails) are moderately deep-bodied, compressed, silvery, perch-like fishes, with large eyes, an oblique mouth, dorsal fins that are deeply notched, and a forked tail. They occur in a variety of habitats from coral reefs to mangroves and from seawater to fresh water. Some species prefer the shelter of overhanging rocks. They are valued both as food fish and bait fish. Little is known about their reproduction but they appear to spawn throughout the year, the young move into shallow water. About 12 species are known, ranging from East Africa throughout the tropical Indian and Pacific Oceans.

Kuhlia taeniura – aholehole

Size – To 30 cm (12 in)
Range – Tropical Indian and Pacific Oceans from East Africa to the Revillagigedo Islands.
Feeding – In nature: feed at night, primarily on free-swimming crustaceans. In aquarium: readily accept all manner of aquarium foods including chopped fish, squid, clams, and shrimp.
Aquarium care – Suitable in either single-species or community tanks. Keep several together in a spacious tank with a sand bottom and some rock or coral cover, but be sure to leave plenty of swimming space. Does well at temperatures from 21 to 24° C (70–75° F).

The young of this species can be found in tidepools where they are easily captured. Adults form schools along the outer edges of reefs. Although they normally occur in aggregations, they will do well singly in the aquarium.

Cardinalfishes

Cardinalfishes are small, reddish to bronze, nocturnal fishes. They have large heads with large eyes and mouths, two dorsal fins completely separated and similar in size, and large conspicuous scales which are usually ctenoid but sometimes cycloid. Only the largest species reach 20 cm (8 in); most are 10 cm (4 in) or less. About 170 species are known, placed in 20 genera. They are found worldwide in tropical seas. Nearly all are marine, shallow-water species, found in association with coral reefs. Some occur in tidepools, a few in deep water. Most species hide by day in darkened areas, such as caves and crevices, where they often form aggregations. At night they emerge and disperse to feed on plankton. Some species seek shelter in other organisms such as sponges or gastropods. Cardinalfishes are usually mouthbrooders. In most species the male tends the eggs and young; in some species it is the female, and in others it is both sexes. Most species appear to be short-lived; some may be annuals. In the aquarium they are usually peaceful and feed readily. They all require hiding places. Most species can be collected at night with scuba and using a hand net.

Apogon retrosella – barspot cardinalfish (cardenal)

Size – To 10 cm (4 in)
Range – Gulf of California to Oaxaca, Mexico.
Feeding – In nature: primarily small crustaceans, nocturnal. In aquarium: live adult brine shrimp with chopped shrimp, clams or squid; also krill and prepared foods.
Aquarium care – Suitable in the community tank with peaceful species. Should have one or more secluded caves for cover. Keep at 20–23° C (68–73° F).

Like other cardinalfishes, members of this species are nocturnal and hide by day in caves or crevices, which they often share with the Panama squirrelfish, *Myripristis leiognathos*. They are found on rocky reefs from near the shoreline to at least 60 m (200 ft). At night cardinalfish emerge to feed on planktonic crustaceans. On moonless nights they may venture into the midwater region, a considerable distance from shelter. In common with other cardinalfish, *A. retrosella* is a mouthbrooder and has been observed carrying eggs in September.

Apogon maculatus – flamefish

Size – To 13 cm (5 in)
Range – Tropical western Atlantic; strays north as far as New England; occurs south to Brazil.
Feeding – In nature: plankton, primarily crustaceans. In aquarium: feeds readily. Does well on prepared foods supplemented with chopped shrimp and live brine shrimp.
Aquarium care – Very adaptable to captivity. Several can be kept together in a single-species tank or in a community tank. Provide cover and crevices. Keep at 22–28° C (72–82° F).

This species is distinguished from closely related species by the dark markings on the caudal peduncle and the two white stripes through the eye. It is the most common shallow-water cardinalfish in the western Atlantic. Nocturnal, it hides in caves and crevices on the reef by day and emerges to feed at night. It is a mouthbrooder and breeds in early summer. It is found from the shoreline to at least 120 m (400 ft).

Apogon retrosella

Apogon maculatus

Apogonidae

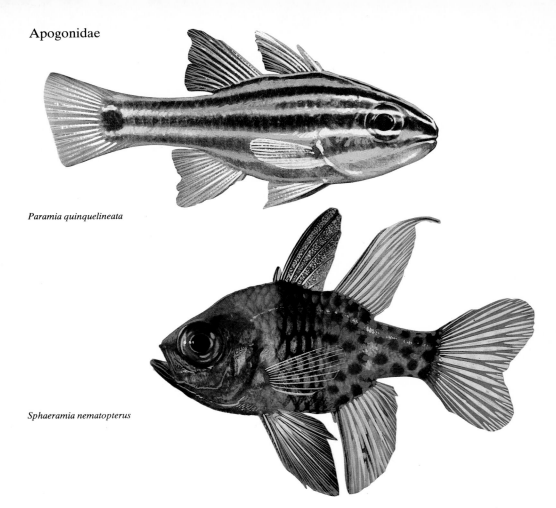

Paramia quinquelineata

Sphaeramia nematopterus

Sphaeramia nematopterus (= Apogon orbicularis) – pajama cardinalfish

Size – To 10 cm (4 in)
Range – Tropical Indo-Pacific from East Africa to Fiji.
Feeding – In nature: small fishes and large plankton. In aquarium: chopped shrimp, squid and fish; krill, live brine shrimp; prepared foods.
Aquarium care – Peaceful. Keep several together in a tank furnished with hiding places amongst rocks and coral. Delicate and probably best suited to the single-species tank. Keep at 22–28° C (72–82° F).

This species requires more delicate handling during capture and transportation than most cardinalfishes and should only be kept with peaceful species. It is common in inner protected lagoons amongst coral and in mangrove swamps. The young have a bright yellow coloration with red spots which fade as the fish grow. A mouthbrooder; the males carry the young. Females have a prolonged second dorsal fin and more distinctive markings.

Paramia quinquelineata (= Cheilodipterus quinquelineatus) – five-lined cardinalfish

Size – To 10 cm (4 in)
Range – Tropical Indo-Pacific from East Africa to the Line Islands. Not known from Hawaii.
Feeding – In nature: carnivorous; feeds on small fishes and crustaceans. In aquarium: usually feeds readily; provide a varied diet of live brine shrimp, krill, chopped shrimp; prepared foods.
Aquarium care – Keep several together in a single-species or community tank of 75 liters (20 gal.) or more. Provide caves and crevices plus shelter among coral. Keep at 22–28° C (72–82° F).

This is a common species on reef flats, in lagoons, and on seaward reefs to depths of at least 40 m (130 ft). It usually occurs in small schools near shelters and is most active at night. A mouthbrooder, the male carries the eggs until they hatch. The five-lined cardinalfish is easily captured at night but is delicate and must be handled carefully.

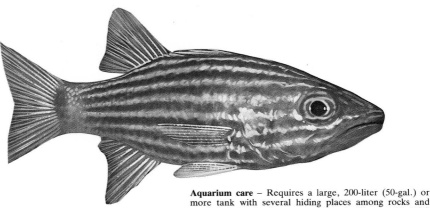

Aquarium care – Requires a large, 200-liter (50-gal.) or more tank with several hiding places among rocks and coral. Suitable in the community tank. Keep at 22–28°C (72–82°F).

Cheilodipterus macrodon – big-toothed cardinalfish

Size – To 20 cm (8 in)
Range – Tropical Indo-Pacific from the East Indies to the Society Islands; absent from Hawaii.
Feeding – In nature: small fishes, large planktonic animals and soft-bodied benthic animals. In aquarium: chopped fish, squid, clams, and shrimp supplemented with small live fish such as guppies.

This genus, and especially this species, is distinguished by its prominent canine teeth. Since *C. macrodon* is one of the larger cardinalfishes, it is not imported as frequently as many other species. It occurs on coral reefs and in lagoons and is easy to capture with a hand net while diving at night.

ORDER PERCIFORMES – FAMILY HAEMULIDAE

Grunts and Sweetlips

The family Haemulidae includes species that in other references may be classified in the families Pomadasyidae, Pristipomatidae, Gaterinidae or Plectorhynchidae. They differ from the snappers in dentition, primarily in the lack of enlarged canine teeth in the jaws. The inside of the mouth of many species is brightly colored and it is displayed during courtship or territorial behavior. Many grunts grind their pharyngeal teeth to produce sounds which are amplified by the gas bladder. A few species have abnormally large, conspicuous lips. Juveniles usually differ greatly from the adults and are more colorful and boldly marked. Grunts typically aggregate on reefs by day and disperse to hunt at dusk on soft bottoms or grassy flats, where they seek shrimps, clams, worms and other invertebrates. Approximately 175 species are known, distributed in 21 genera. Only a few species, which have brightly colored juveniles, are of interest to aquarists.

Gaterin (= Plectorhynchus) chaetodonoides – harlequin sweetlips

Size – To 45 cm (18 in)
Range – Tropical Indo-Pacific from the East Indies to Tahiti.
Feeding – In nature: omnivorous. In aquarium: chopped fish, clams and squid, plus some plant matter if desired.
Aquarium care – The young are excellent community tank species but should be provided with many hiding places. Keep at 22–28°C (72–82°F).

Only the young, which differ greatly from the drab, spotted adults, are normally of interest to the aquarist. The juvenile color pattern remains until the fish reach at least 13 cm (5 in) in length.

Haemulidae

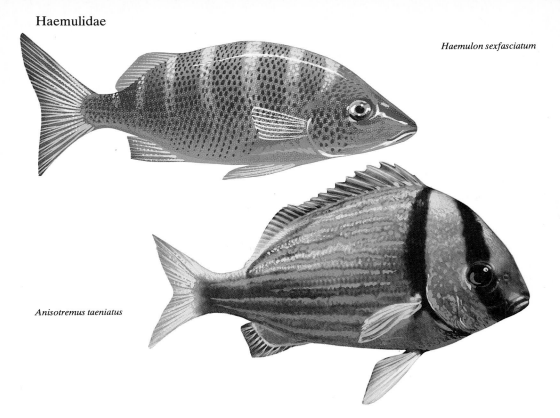

Haemulon sexfasciatum

Anisotremus taeniatus

Haemulon sexfasciatum – graybar grunt (burro almejera)

Size – To 30 cm (12 in)
Range – Gulf of California to Panama.
Feeding – In nature: carnivorous; benthic animals including small fishes, crustaceans, molluscs and worms. In aquarium: chopped seafoods.
Aquarium care – Juveniles are suitable in tanks of 75 liters (20 gal.) and larger. Adults are normally kept only in public aquaria. Keep at 20–23° C (68–73° F). This species is long-lived in captivity.

Graybar grunts form schools around the edge of reefs by day and disperse to feed at night, at which time they can be seined near rocky areas and gravel beaches.

Anisotremus taeniatus – porkfish

Size – To 30 cm (12 in)
Range – Cabo San Lucas, Mexico to Panama.
Feeding – In nature: worms, brittle stars, crustaceans and molluscs; nocturnal. In aquarium: shrimp, chopped squid and clams. Feed in the evenings.
Aquarium care – The young do well in most community tanks. Adults require a tank of 1,000 liters (250 gal.) or more and are not normally kept by the home aquarist. Keep at 20–23° C (68–73° F).

Juveniles differ in color from adults and are yellowish with two black stripes and two dusty bars on their sides. They sometimes act as cleanerfish. A sibling species, *A. virginicus*, occurs in the western Atlantic.

ORDER PERCIFORMES – FAMILY CARANGIDAE

Jacks and Pompanos

Carangids are fast-swimming predators; only a few of them, usually juveniles, are kept by hobbyists. Most species are displayed only in public aquaria. They usually have silvery or shiny blue bodies with deeply forked or sickle-shaped (lunate) tails preceded by a narrow peduncle. Many species have sharp bony scutes along the side, especially toward the tail. They vary in shape from shallow-bodied to extremely deep and are usually covered with small cycloid scales. The anal fin usually has three strong anterior spines, the first two of which are detached, an important diagnostic character. Carangids are roving fishes, usually found in schools. They occur in a wide range of habitats from the open ocean to bays and estuaries, with a few species penetrating fresh water. They usually move offshore to spawn. Juveniles often associate with flotsam such as *Sargassum* or kelp patties. Some seek the shelter of large organisms such as jellyfish, others may associate with larger fishes and feed opportunistically on the scraps of their prey, as is the case with pilotfish (*Naucrates ductor*) and sharks. About 200 species are known, distributed in 24 genera. They are found worldwide in tropical and temperate waters. Many carangids are important food fishes but a number of them, especially large species, have been known to cause ciguatera or fish poisoning. Consult local authorities before eating.

Selene vomer – lookdown

Size – To 30 cm (12 in)
Range – Tropical eastern and western Atlantic.
Feeding – In nature: primarily piscivorous; nocturnal. In aquarium: small fish and shrimp; pieces of fish, squid and clams.
Aquarium care – Provide a tank of 400 liters (100 gal.) or larger and a sand bottom with a few rocks for aesthetics. Cover the sides and back to minimize disturbances. Keep at 22–28° C (72–82° F).

Lookdowns usually swim in schools at the surface over open sand bottoms, sometimes near rocks. Their silvery bodies make them very hard to see and when they turn head on, or away, they virtually disappear. Their skin is very delicate but, once they have recovered from the initial injuries of capture and transport, they do well in captivity in single-species tanks, or in community tanks with peaceful species. A sibling species, *S. peruviana* (= *S. brevoorti*), occurs in the tropical western Pacific.

Vomer declivifrons – Pacific moonfish

Size – To 25 cm (10 in)
Range – Southern California to Peru; Galápagos Islands.
Feeding – In nature: primarily piscivorous; nocturnal. In aquarium: chopped clams, fish, shrimp and squid.
Aquarium care – As for the species lookdown.

The moonfish usually occurs inshore in bays. Its sibling, the Atlantic moonfish (*V. setapinnis*), occurs in the coastal waters of both shores of the Atlantic Ocean.

Vomer declivifrons

Selene vomer

Gnathanodon speciosus

Gnathanodon speciosus – yellowjack (golden trevally)

Size – To 100 cm (40 in)
Range – Tropical Indian and Pacific oceans from the Red Sea to Panama; also Hawaii.
Feeding – In nature: feeds on benthic invertebrates on sand bottoms and amongst algae on rock surfaces. In aquarium: chopped fish, shrimp, squid and clams.
Aquarium care – The young are attractive and excellent aquarium fishes. Provide a 200-liter (50-gal.) or more aquarium with a sand bottom and plenty of swimming space. Keep at 20–28° C (70–82° F).

Juvenile yellowjacks may be found around floating objects such as logs and buoys. When less than 5 cm (2 in) in length, they sometimes live symbiotically amongst the tentacles of jellyfish. Those over 5 cm (2 in) often associate with large fishes such as sharks and groupers. Adults lack teeth and feed primarily by digging invertebrates out of the soft bottoms of bays and lagoons. They also venture on to the reef to forage for small fishes. Reproduction is by spawning, usually in shallow water. In Palau, large spawning aggregations are observed from November to May. In the Gulf of California the young are easily captured around floating objects in early autumn.

Trachinotus rhodopus – gafftopsail pompano

Size – To 60 cm (24 in)
Range – California to Peru; also the Galápagos Islands.
Feeding – In nature: carnivorous; diurnal. In aquarium: feeds readily on a variety of fish and other seafoods.

Trachinotus rhodopus

Aquarium care – As for the species lookdown but a larger tank is required. It should be at least 2,000 liters (500 gal.). Keep at 20–23° C (68–73° F).

Most commonly found in sandy areas near rocks. This, and the young of several other small carangids such as the threadfin pompanos (*Alectis* spp.) make attractive displays in large tanks.

Snappers

Snappers are moderate-sized fishes, seldom exceeding 100 cm (36 in) in length. They are similar in appearance to groupers and sea basses. They are more or less compressed and vary from deep-bodied to elongate. Some species such as the fusiliers (sometimes placed in a separate family, Caesionidae) are distinctly fusiform. The dorsal fin is continuous and has strong spines; the caudal fin is forked to emarginate. The body is covered with moderate to large ctenoid scales. The lateral line is complete. The gill cover is usually serrated, and sometimes has a very sharp edge. Snappers usually differ from groupers in having a longer snout, a long sloping forehead and a thin-appearing upper lip which is the result of the upper jawbone (maxilla) sliding under the cheek bone. Strong enlarged canines are usually conspicuous in the jaws. Most snappers are bottom-living, nocturnal or crepuscular predators, that prey on fishes and crustaceans. The fusiliers, however, are plankton feeders. As far as is known, all snappers produce pelagic eggs. The juveniles of many species are found inshore and often differ in color and pattern from the adults. Some species make extensive use of mangroves as nursery areas. Snappers occur worldwide in warmer seas. About 230 species are known, distributed in 23 genera. Many are important food fishes although a few species in some areas are known to cause ciguatera poisoning. Although many species are colorful, few are of interest to aquarists because of their large size as adults.

Lutjanus sebae – emperor snapper (red emperor)

Size – To 90 cm (36 in)
Range – Entire Indo-Pacific except Hawaii.
Feeding – In nature: carnivorous. In aquarium: chopped seafoods.
Aquarium care – Provide a rocky habitat with a swimming area over sand. Keep at 22–28° C (72–82° F).

Juveniles of this species are popular with home aquarists. They are good community tank species when kept with fishes larger than bite-size. Adults pale and lose markings with age.

Lutjanidae

Lutjanus viridis – blue-lined snapper

Size – To 30 cm (12 in)
Range – From Cabo San Lucas, Mexico and adjacent areas to Peru.
Feeding – In nature: carnivorous. In aquarium: chopped fish, squid, clams and shrimp.
Aquarium care – A good community tank species for large aquaria. Provide a rocky habitat with a large swimming area over a sand bottom. Keep at 20–24° C (68–75° F).

Spawning aggregations form in the rocky areas of bays during the autumn, at which time this species can be easily driven into barrier nets by scuba divers.

ORDER PERCIFORMES – FAMILY PRIACANTHIDAE

Bigeyes

The "bigeyes" (or catolufas), as the name implies, have large conspicuous eyes. Primarily nocturnal predators, they are usually reddish in color but can change rapidly from uniform coloration to develop a pattern of bars, spots or blotches. They are found worldwide in warmer waters, usually in association with the bottom.

Pristigenys (= Pseudopriacanthus) serrula – popeye catalufa (ojoton)

Size – To 33 cm (13 in)
Range – Southern California to Peru.
Feeding – In nature: carnivorous. In aquarium: chopped shrimp, squid, clams and fish.
Aquarium care – Provide dark caves for cover. A peaceful species suitable for community tanks. Keep at 18–22° C (64–72° F).

These colorful fishes are excellent aquarium fishes once adapted to captivity. Although nocturnal by nature they soon learn to feed by day. They occur in relatively deep water, usually over 30 m (100 ft), both on rocky reefs and over sand bottoms. They are occasionally observed by scuba divers and are not uncommonly caught by shrimp trawlers. Some are taken during sportfishing for other species.

Croakers and Drums

Drums and croakers are more or less elongate, moderately compressed fishes, usually silvery in color as adults. A few species are fusiform in shape. They are most easily distinguished from other fishes by their lateral line, which extends along the entire side of the fish and onto the tail. Most croakers have inferior mouths, an adaptation to bottom feeding, but some have terminal mouths with protractile jaws. Many have a single barbel or patch of small barbels under the chin. Like the snappers, they have have a thin-appearing upper lip. The dorsal fin is deeply notched, sometimes completely divided; the caudal fin is rounded to truncate. The scales may be either cycloid or ctenoid. A special feature of the croakers is the swim bladder, which is highly modified to enhance sound production. It usually has many branches and is resonated by muscles attached to its walls, thus producing a croaking or drumming sound. In a few species, a bladder is lacking, in which case sound is produced by grinding the pharyngeal teeth. Sound production in croakers may be used for navigation as well as for intraspecific communication. Approximately 160 species are known, distributed in 28 genera. They are found worldwide, mostly in the warmer waters. They are largely confined to the continental margins. None occur in Hawaii. Many species are primarily estuarine; a few are fresh-water dwellers. The juvenile of several species of croakers are of interest to aquarists.

Equetus lanceolatus – jackknife fish

Size – To 23 cm (9 in)
Range – Tropical western Atlantic from Bermuda to Brazil.
Feeding – In nature: omnivorous; nocturnal. In aquarium: usually require live food such as live adult brine shrimp. Supplement with krill, chopped shrimp or plankton.
Aquarium care – Provide coral and crevices for cover. Do best in a single-species tank. Can be kept in a community tank only with very peaceful species. Keep at 22–24° C (72–75° F).

The jackknife fish is generally a deep-water species found below 15 m (50 ft). The highhat or cubbyu (*Equetus acuminatus*) is more common and more familiar to aquarists but it is less attractive. Both species are nocturnal.

Pareques viola – rock croaker (gungo)

Size – To 25 cm (10 in)
Range – Gulf of California to Panama.
Feeding – In nature: carnivorous; primarily crustaceans. Nocturnal. In aquarium: chopped shrimp, squid and clams. Provide live brine shrimp and frozen krill or other whole crustaceans to juveniles.
Aquarium care – Only the juveniles are of interest to the home aquarist. They are delicate fish which seek secure cover during the day and will only flourish with peaceful tank-mates.

The striped juveniles appear in schools during the summer. Adults are very secretive during the day and rarely emerge from crevices and ledges, except at night when they feed.

121

Fairy Basslets

These small, colorful fishes are close relatives of the serranids but differ in having a lateral line that is interrupted or absent. About nine species are known from the tropical west Atlantic and Indo-Pacific.

Gramma loreto – royal gramma (fairy basslet)

Size – To 8 cm (3 in)
Range – Widely distributed in the tropical western Atlantic from Bermuda to Venezuela but absent from Florida.
Feeding – In nature: plankton. In aquarium: live brine shrimp, krill and other small crustaceans plus prepared foods.
Aquarium care – This species is at its best in a single-species tank. Several can be kept together but each should have its own "cave" and a surrounding territory. Keep at 24–27° C (75–81° F).

The royal gramma is most abundant on reefs at between 12 and 24 m (40–80 ft) deep. It may be found as shallow as 3 m (10 ft), but shallow-water specimens are usually in caves where they may be found swimming upside down close to the roof.

Spadefishes

Spadefishes (batfishes, leaffishes) are highly compressed deep-bodied fishes similar in appearance to butterflyfishes, from which they differ by having a divided dorsal fin with only a small spinous portion. Adults are usually silvery with black bars. Juveniles may be coppery to reddish. Some juveniles appear to mimic dead leaves and other vegetation in order to escape detection by predators. Others utilize their dark barred pattern to conceal themselves amongst the spines of sea urchins. Adult spadefishes usually occur in schools and may be found in a wide range of habitats, from deep reefs to shallow flats and mangrove areas. At night they may be seen in harbors browsing on invertebrates attached to piling and floats. Approximately 12 species are recognized, distributed in six genera. They occur worldwide in tropical waters, some in temperate regions. In the aquarium spadefishes are peaceful and usually hardy and easy to maintain. Apparently they have not been reared in captivity.

Chaetodipterus zonatus – spadefish

Size – To 65 cm (25 in)
Range – San Diego to Peru.
Feeding – In nature: omnivorous. In aquarium: pieces of fish, squid, clams or shrimp.
Aquarium care – Suitable in community tanks. Adults should have a tank of 2,000 liters (500 gal.) or more. Provide a sand bottom and decorate with a few rocks if desired. Keep at 20–23° C (68–73° F).

Spadefish are hardy and peaceful aquarium fishes. Juveniles are a favorite of home aquarists. Spadefish usually occur in schools in bays with sandy or rubble bottoms. They range from shallow water to depths of 46 m (150 ft).

At night they often move inshore where they can be seined, or amongst docks and piling where they browse on attached organisms and can sometimes be captured with scuba, a light and hand net. Spadefish reproduce by spawning, apparently in pairs just below the surface. A closely related species, *C. faber*, occurs in the Atlantic.

Platax orbicularis – round batfish

Size – To 50 cm (20 in)
Range – Tropical Indo-Pacific; absent from Hawaii (and eastern Pacific).
Feeding – In nature: omnivorous; including garbage. In aquarium: accept common aquarium foods. A suitable diet is chopped seafood supplemented with prepared aquarium foods.
Aquarium care – Require space to grow. May be timid in captivity at first but usually tame readily. Do not keep them with "fin-nipping" species. Keep at 22–28° C (72–82° F).

The round batfish is a coastal species frequently found in bays and harbors. The young mimic dead leaves and lie or float on their sides to escape detection.

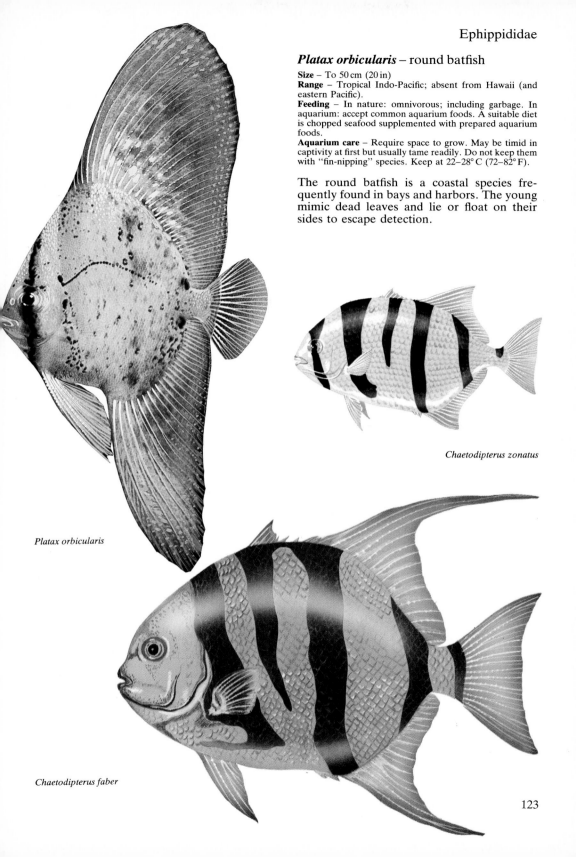

Chaetodipterus zonatus

Platax orbicularis

Chaetodipterus faber

Goatfishes

Goatfishes are most easily recognized by the pair of long barbels under the chin. They have elongate, slightly compressed bodies covered with large ctenoid scales. The lateral line is complete. The head is blunt with a terminal, ventrally placed mouth and protractile jaws that contain small conical teeth. There are two widely spaced dorsal fins; the first is spiniferous, the second soft-rayed; the caudal fin is forked. Goatfishes are bottom-living fishes, usually associated with soft bottoms. They use their feelers, which contain taste buds, to locate such food as small invertebrates which live in the sand or mud. Most goatfishes are brightly colored and able to undergo rapid color changes, either in response to light or to emotional state. Some appear to change color in order to help cleaning fishes find external parasites. Little is known about the reproductive behavior of goatfishes, other than that the eggs and young are pelagic. The young are attracted to a light at night, where they can be dip-netted and then reared as aquarium fishes. Approximately 55 species are known, distributed in six genera. They are found worldwide in tropical seas, most often in shallow waters. Many goatfishes are suitable in the home aquarium, but they can cause a problem by constantly disturbing the sand. They tend to be delicate.

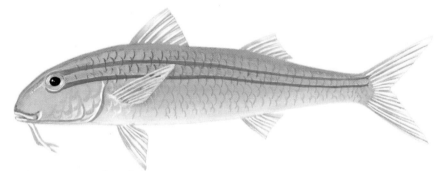

Mulloidichthys dentatus – Mexican goatfish (salmonete)

Size – To 30 cm (12 in)
Range – Southern California (rare) to Peru.
Feeding – In nature: forages on soft bottoms for small crustaceans, molluscs, and worms. In aquarium: chopped squid, clams, and shrimp.
Aquarium care – Small specimens are suitable for a community tank of 75 liters (20 gal.) or more (the bigger the better!). Provide as large a sand area as possible. Food is most readily accepted in the evening. Keep at 20–23° C (68–73° F).

Goatfish form densely packed schools during the day and tend to disperse somewhat at night during feeding. They can be chased down with a hand net at night or, perhaps more profitably, driven into a barrier net. During the day this goatfish often solicits cleaning by the blacknosed butterflyfish or "el barbero." It indicates its receptiveness to cleaning by posing with its head inclined toward the bottom and changing to a darker hue. A sibling species, the yellow goatfish, *M. martinicus*, occurs in the western Atlantic. Other species reach the hobbyist market from the Indo-Pacific.

Butterflyfishes

Butterflyfishes are colorful, active, and among the most popular of aquarium fishes. They are deep-bodied, oval-shaped, highly compressed fishes and have small mouths with bristle-like teeth. Their dorsal fins are continuous, sometimes notched, and contain both spiny and soft rays. Their body is covered with ctenoid scales which are smaller on the head and extend onto the bases of the soft-dorsal and anal fins. Juvenile and adult coloration is usually similar. They are distinguished from the angelfishes by the absence of a well-developed preopercular spine and presence of a distinctive armored larvae stage (tholichthys larva). Over 100 species have been described and are divided into 10 genera (Burgess 1978). Some authorities place butterflyfishes in the same family as the angelfishes but Burgess (1978) and other recent authors consider them a separate family, the Chaetodontidae.

DISTRIBUTION AND ECOLOGY. Butterflyfishes are found in all tropical seas, most at depths above 20 m (approx. 70 ft). A few species live in deeper water, to 200 m (approx. 650 ft) and a few species are known from temperate waters. Most species are found in association with coral reefs but some occur on rubble slopes, others on cliff faces. They may occur singly, in small groups or, in some species, in large aggregations. Butterflyfishes are usually conspicuous, but the reason for their bright coloration is not clearly understood. Facilitation of intraspecific recognition, courtship, territoriality, and warning coloration to predators have been proposed by various behaviorists. Five major types of feeding behavior have been described (Allen 1979): hard coral, soft coral, benthic invertebrates, zooplankton and omnivorous. In addition cleaning behavior, the removal and eating of parasites and diseased tissue from other fishes, has been observed by many investigators. Butterflyfishes reproduce by spawning. Pairing has been observed in a number of species, suggesting at least temporary monogamy. Little else is known about their courtship and spawning. The eggs, often numbering 3,000–4,000, float to the surface where, in the species studied to date, they develop rapidly and hatch in approximately a day. The larvae feed in the plankton and may remain there for several weeks or even months before settling to the bottom.

AQUARIUM CARE. Many species of butterflyfishes can be successfully kept by the home aquarist. Some species, however, are difficult to maintain because of special feeding requirements (e.g. coral polyps), aggressiveness or, conversely, timidity. The species in this book have been chosen because of their attractiveness, availability and suitability to the home aquarium; but a few species not commonly kept have been chosen for those seeking the rare or unusual. Omnivorous species and crustacean feeders are generally the easiest to maintain; sponge- and algae-feeders are more difficult, while polyp (coral)-eaters usually will not survive for very long. Butterflyfishes feed constantly in nature and should be fed a minimum of twice per day but preferably three to four times in order to thrive. Most species of butterflyfishes do well at temperatures between 20 and 24° C (68–74° F). Deeper-water and temperate species prefer 15–20° C (59–68° F). Species from the warmest habitats may do best at temperatures in excess of 24° C (75° F); but at temperatures above 28–30° C (82–86° F) the solubility of oxygen in water is low and the aquarist must take care to see that oxygen does not become insufficient. Important sources of information on butterflyfishes are Burgess (1978), Steene (1977) and Allen (1979).

Chaetodon falcifer – scythe butterflyfish

Size – Mature adults 13–18 cm (5–7 in)
Range – Southern California (rare) to Galápagos Islands.
Feeding – In nature: apparently feeds on bottom-swarming organisms in rocky areas including cliff faces. In aquarium: thrives on a mixed fish and shellfish diet with occasional brine shrimp; also accepts prepared aquarium foods.
Aquarium care – An extremely hardy aquarium species. Does well between 13 and 21° C (60–70° F). Specimens at Scripps Aquarium continue to thrive after eight years in captivity.

This is a cool-water species and in the tropic region is usually found at depths of more than 35 m (120 ft) in the cool water below the thermocline, but can be found closer to the surface in the cool temperate portion of its range. Large aggregations have been observed below 75 m (250 ft) at the tip of Baja California, Mexico, the center of its range (but it can be collected as shallow as 16 m (50 ft) at the San Benito Islands and Guadalupe Island in the temperate waters off central Baja California).

125

Chaetodontidae

Heniochus acuminatus – pennant butterflyfish (longfin bannerfish, featherfin coralfish)

Size – To 25 cm (10 in)
Range – Widespread in Pacific and Indian Oceans including Hawaii, Japan, Indonesia, Australia, South Africa and the Red Sea.
Feeding – In nature: omnivorous. In aquarium: most common aquarium foods including flake foods; variety is recommended.
Aquarium care – Recommended for medium or larger aquaria kept from 21 to 28° C (70–82° F). May do best with others of the same species.

This species shows considerable variation over its range and there may turn out to be a complex of several very similar species. It usually occurs near the reef surface, singly, in pairs or small groups. The closely related *H. diphreutes* is often encountered in large schools in midwater (Allen, 1979), below 12 m (40 ft) and down to 150 m (500 ft). It is easily trapped and is a particularly good species for aquaria.

Johnrandallia (= Heniochus) nigrirostris – black-nosed butterflyfish (el barbero)

Size – Adults to about 20 cm (8 in)
Range – Gulf of California to Gulf of Panama and Galápagos Islands.
Feeding – In nature: bottom-swarming and encrusting organisms including crustaceans, gastropods and some algae. In aquarium: feed a mixed diet of shrimp and squid supplemented with brine shrimp; flake food.
Aquarium care – Does well between 20 and 24° C (68–74° F).

Some individuals act as cleaner fish and aggregate at specific locations or "cleaning stations", where larger (host) fishes gather to receive their services. Usually found between the surface and 12 m (40 ft), this species is encountered down to at least 40 m (130 ft). Black-nosed butterflyfish occur alone, in small or large aggregations. At night pairs, apparently mates, are often observed. This species is easy to collect at night with scuba and a light.

Hemitaurichthys polylepis – pyramid butterflyfish

Size – To about 18 cm (7 in)
Range – Widespread in East Indies, central and western Pacific including Hawaii and the Great Barrier Reef.
Feeding – In nature: mostly plankton. In aquarium: chopped shrimp, brine shrimp and other crustaceans; flake food.
Aquarium care – Does best kept in association with several of its kind in 300-liter (70-gal.) tanks or larger. Temperature range: 24–28° C (75–82° F).

Chelmon rostratus – copper-banded butterflyfish

Size – To 20 cm (about 8 in)
Range – Tropical Indian and western Pacific oceans including Australia, Philippines, India, South Africa.
Feeding – In nature: feeds on crevice organisms, including crustaceans, worm and other small invertebrates. In aquarium: chopped shrimp, chopped squid tentacles, krill, worms, flake food, brine shrimp; may require live food initially.
Aquarium care – Easily available. Usually aggressive toward members of the same species but is usually compatible with other species in a community tank. Prefers temperatures from 24 to 28° C (75–82° F).

This attractive species has the long snout typical of butterflyfish that feed on invertebrates that lie in crevices and coral interstices. Usually found on coral reefs at 1–10 m (3–33 ft). Prefers live food such as brine shrimp, worms and plankton but can usually be converted to eating dead food.

Chaetodon humeralis – Cortez banded angelfish

Size – Adults 10–15 cm (4–6 in); maximum 25 cm (10 in)
Range – Gulf of California to Peru and Galápagos Islands; rarely north to California.
Feeding – In nature: omnivorous. In aquarium: chopped shrimp and squid, flake foods with chopped fish plus brine shrimp for variety.
Aquarium care – Has a wide temperature tolerance; 20–24° C (68–74° F) is recommended.

The most common species in the eastern Pacific, this butterflyfish usually occurs in pairs or small groups and is found on shallow reefs, around wharves, and will venture over open sand. Normal depths range from 1 to 12 m (3–40 ft). Adults and juveniles are similar in coloration. This species is easily captured at night using scuba and a diving light. It is frequently captured by shrimp trawlers.

This is a schooling species usually encountered between 5 and 25 m (about 15–80 ft) and is primarily a plankton-feeder. For unknown reasons, perhaps stress or lighting, the black head coloration may disappear in captive specimens. A closely related species, *H. zoster*, occurs in the Indian Ocean (Burgess 1978) but both its anterior and posterior body regions are dark brown.

Chaetodontidae

Chaetodon humeralis

Hemitaurichthys polylepis

Heniochus acuminatus

Chelmon rostratus

Johnrandallia nigrirostris

127

Chaetodon lunula – raccoon butterflyfish

Size – To 21 cm (8 in)
Range – Tropical Indo-Pacific from East Africa to Hawaii and the Marquesas Islands. Not in the Red Sea.
Feeding – In nature: omnivorous. In aquarium: feed a varied diet including the traditional foods.
Aquarium care – This is a hardy species. For example, it is commonly kept for seven years or more at the Steinhart Aquarium in San Francisco. Keep in a 200-liter (50-gal.) or larger aquarium at temperatures from 22 to 28°C (72–82°F).

The raccoon butterflyfish is usually found in shallow water of 1–5 m (3–26 ft) on inner reefs. It is timid in nature and may be seen singly, in pairs or in aggregations. It is most easily captured by diving at night but will also enter traps.

Chaetodon tinkeri – tinker's butterflyfish

Size – To 15 cm (6 in)
Range – Hawaii.
Feeding – In nature: a variety of planktonic and benthic animals. In aquarium: usually feeds readily on a variety of foods: shrimp, other invertebrates, fish, flake food.
Aquarium care – Keep in an aquarium of at least 300 liters (70 gal.) or larger, at 20–24°C (68–76°F).

This deep-water species is not frequently observed or captured but like *Chaetodon falcifer* it usually does well in captivity. Found at 40–75 m (130–250 ft), it can be kept at normal room temperatures. It should be carefully degassed with a hypodermic needle at its depth of capture and brought to the surface in a plastic bag filled with ambient seawater in order to avoid decompression injuries and temperature shock as it is brought through the thermocline to the surface.

Chaetodon rafflesi – latticed butterflyfish (Raffle's butterflyfish)

Size – To 15 cm (6 in)
Range – Indo-Pacific from Sri Lanka to the Society Islands.
Feeding – In nature: coral polyps and small invertebrates. In aquarium: will survive well without coral polyps; use a varied diet including brine shrimp, chopped shrimp, squid, etc.; flake and freeze-dried food.
Aquarium care – Keep in a 250-liter (60-gal.) or larger aquarium at 24–28°C (75–82°F).

This is a relatively shallow-water species usually found in association with corals at 1–10 m (3–35 ft).

Chaetodon ornatissimus – ornate butterflyfish

Size – To 18 cm (7 in)
Range – Indo-Pacific from Hawaiian Islands to Sri Lanka.
Feeding – In nature: coral polyps. In aquarium: feed a varied diet; try brine shrimp, flake foods, chopped shrimp and squid, food blocks; include coelenterates.
Aquarium care – Keep in a large aquarium of 400 liters (100 gal.) or larger at 24–28° C (75–82° F). Very delicate. Recommended for the advanced aquarist only.

This beautiful but shy species occurs on coral reefs down to 15 m (30 ft). It feeds on coral polyps and is extremely difficult to keep. It needs to be fed frequently, two to three times per day, and may benefit by having food blocks regularly available. The aquarist who maintains this species successfully can be justifiably proud of his accomplishment.

Chaetodon kleini – Klein's butterflyfish

Size – To 13 cm (5 in)
Range – Indo-Pacific from South Africa to Hawaii including the Red Sea.
Feeding – In nature: omnivorous. In aquarium: will usually accept a variety of fresh, frozen, and living fish and invertebrates; flake food.
Aquarium care – Once adapted to captivity this species is often long-lived. Keep in an aquarium of 200 liters (50 gal.) or larger, at 24–28° C (75–82° F).

Adults are usually found between 25 and 55 m (90–180 ft) in Hawaii but occur much shallower in the Philippines. Juveniles are usually found in shallows in both regions. Although not highly colorful, its small size, active nature, and hardiness make this an aquarium species to be preferred. It can be aggressive, however.

Chaetodon ulietensis – saddled butterflyfish (Pacific double-saddled butterflyfish)

Size – To 15 cm (6 in)
Range – Australia, New Guinea and western Pacific including Tahiti and Fiji.
Feeding – In nature: omnivorous. In aquarium: accepts a wide variety of foods; include occasional live food.
Aquarium care – Same as for the tinker's butterflyfish.

This species has frequently been mistaken for its close relative *Chaetodon falcula*, which is restricted to the Indian Ocean (Burgess, 1978). Although not frequently seen in the aquarium trade, it is an excellent species for the home aquarist to obtain. Usually found in association with coral at depths of 5–10 m (16–33 ft).

129

Chaetodon ocellatus

Chaetodon collare

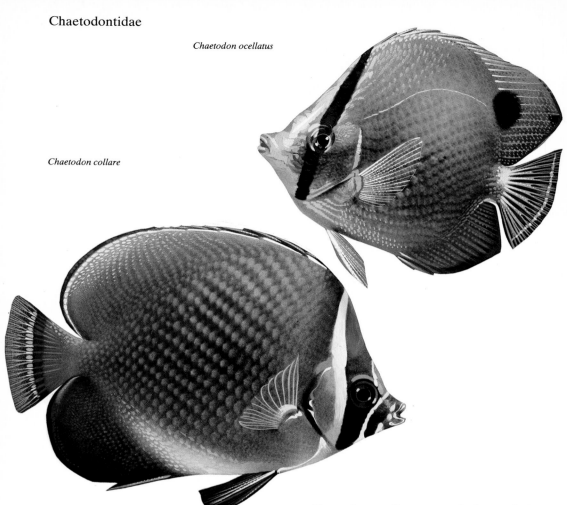

Chaetodon collare – collare butterflyfish (red-tailed butterflyfish)

Size – To 16 cm (6.5 in)
Range – Indo-Pacific from the Arabian Gulf to Philippines, not found in Australia.
Feeding – In nature: coral polyps and coral-dwelling invertebrates. In aquarium: feed a varied diet including crustaceans and provide a food block if possible.
Aquarium care – Provide a large aquarium, 400 liters (100 gal.) or larger, and keep at 24–28° C (77–82° F).

This species may be found in both coral and rocky areas at depths from 4 to 15 m (13–50 ft). Individuals captured on rocky reefs may do better in captivity than those found on coral reefs where diet in nature consists extensively of coral polyps.

Chaetodon ocellatus – spotfin butterflyfish

Size – To 16 cm (6.5 in)
Range – Tropical west Atlantic from Florida to Brazil; seasonally strays as far north as Massachusetts and Nova Scotia.
Feeding – In nature: omnivorous. In aquarium: will accept a variety of foods, fresh, frozen, freeze-dried or live.
Aquarium care – A hardy species; small individuals have been kept in aquaria as small as 80 liters (20 gal.) but an aquarium of at least 200 liters (50 gal.) is preferred. Keep at temperatures from 20 to 26° C (68–79° F).

This Atlantic species has long been popular with American aquarists because of its availability and hardiness. Many aquarists have enjoyed capturing their own specimens. During summer and early fall this species is often found north of its normal range, having been carried there as eggs or larvae by the Gulf Stream. Juveniles may reach 4–5 cm (2 in) in the north before being killed by seasonal cooling. Juveniles are characterized by a posterior black bar which is reduced to a spot on the dorsal fin in the adult.

Chaetodon paucifasciatus

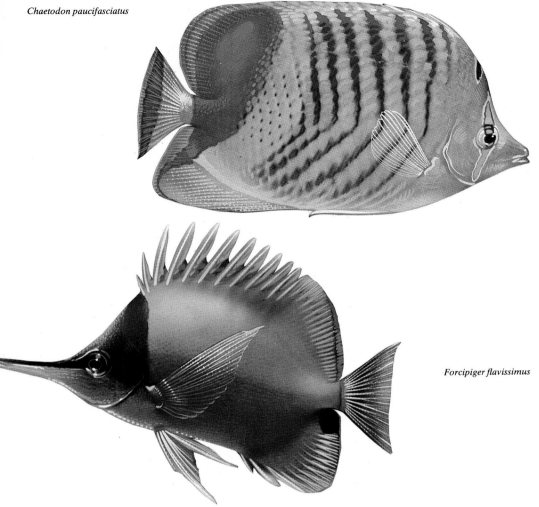

Forcipiger flavissimus

Chaetodon paucifasciatus – red back butterflyfish (Red Sea chevron butterflyfish)

Size – To 14 cm (5.5 in)
Range – Red Sea and Gulf of Aden.
Feeding – In nature: omnivorous. In aquarium: feed the usual varied diet.
Aquarium care – Provide coral or rubble cover in an aquarium of 250 liters (60 gal.) or larger kept at 24–28° C (75–80° F).

This species may be difficult to obtain in tropical fish stores. In nature, it may be encountered in both coral-reef and rubble areas down to 30 m (100 ft). Two close relatives, Merton's butterflyfish (*C. mertensii*), with orange markings, and the Indian Ocean chevron butterflyfish (*C. madagascariensis*) occur in the Indo-Pacific. All are hardy aquarium species.

Forcipiger flavissimus – long-nosed butterflyfish

Size – To 15 cm (6 in)
Range – Widespread in Indian and Pacific Oceans.
Feeding – In nature: omnivorous; feeds extensively on crevice-dwelling invertebrates. In aquarium: will thrive on a variety of foods including chopped fish, shrimp, squid, brine shrimp, and flake food.
Aquarium care – Does well in medium, 300-liter (80-gal.) or larger aquaria at temperatures from 21 to 28° C (70–82° F).

This attractive species is relatively easy to keep as long as it is not harassed by tankmates. It feeds on crevice-dwelling organisms on coral reefs, amongst rubble and on rock walls, at depths ranging from 1 to 30 m (3–100 ft) or more. A close relative, *F. longirostris*, has a longer snout but is generally rare in the tropical fish industry.

Chaetodontidae

Chaetodon auriga

Chaetodon ephippium

Chaetodon argentatus

Chaetodon aculeatus

Chaetodon argentatus – Asian butterflyfish (three-band butterflyfish, silver and black butterflyfish)

Size – To 20 cm (8 in)
Range – Southern Japan to Philippines.
Feeding – In nature: omnivorous. In aquarium: will accept a wide variety; feed occasional live food.
Aquarium care – Does well in captivity. Provide at least a 200-liter (50-gal.) aquarium. Should thrive from 20 to 28° C (68–82° F).

This omnivorous species occurs at 5–20 m (16–66 ft). It is found on rocky reefs in the colder portions of its range and on coral reefs in the warmer regions.

Chaetodon auriga – threadfin butterflyfish

Size – To 23 cm (9 in)
Range – Indo-Pacific from Hawaii to the Red Sea.
Feeding – In nature: omnivorous, including coral, crustaceans, worms. In aquarium: will accept a wide variety of fresh, frozen or dry foods.
Aquarium care – Small specimens will adapt to a tank of 150 liters (40 gal.) or more kept between 23 and 28° C (73–82° F).

This is a popular species with the home aquarist and will survive several years if a suitable habitat and varied diet are provided.

Chaetodon aculeatus – Caribbean longsnout butterflyfish (Poey's butterflyfish, Ross butterflyfish)

Size – To 10 cm (4 in)
Range – Gulf of Mexico, Florida and north Caribbean Sea.
Feeding – In nature: feeds on crevice-dwelling invertebrates amongst corals and rocks. In aquarium: will accept a variety of foods.
Aquarium care – A hardy species that can be kept in aquaria of 200 liters (50 gal.) or larger. Does well between 20 and 27° C (68–80° F).

This is a relatively deep-water species that usually occurs at 20–50 m (66–260 ft), often near drop-offs. Adults occur usually either solitary or in pairs.

Chaetodon ephippium – saddle-back butterflyfish

Size – To 20 cm (8 in)
Range – Widespread in the Pacific Ocean from southern Japan to Australia and Thailand, and west to Hawaii.
Feeding – In nature: omnivorous including coral polyps. In aquarium: should be fed on a wide variety of foods.
Aquarium care – Delicate, recommended for the more advanced aquarist. Requires a medium- or large-sized aquarium, 300 liters (80 gal.) or more, and prefers temperatures from 24 to 28° C (75–82° F).

Angelfishes

Angelfishes are almost as popular with hobby aquarists as butterflyfishes; but adults of the larger species should only be kept in large aquaria of 2,000 liters (about 500 gal.) or more. They are distinguished from butterflyfishes by the presence of a strong preopercular spine. Juveniles often have a different color pattern than adults, especially in *Pomacanthus* and *Holacanthus*. Approximately 75 species occur in tropical seas, most in the Indo-Pacific along the western Pacific margin. They are typically shallow-water species that occur between the surface and 15 m (about 50 ft) in association with coral and rocky reefs, but some species occur in deeper water, down to 60 m (about 200 ft). Angelfish may be divided into three main types of feeders: sponge, algae or plankton feeders. Their normal diet is usually supplemented with benthic and encrusting organisms such as bryozoans, tunicates and polychaetes. Sponge feeders are best avoided as aquarium fishes. Little is known about angelfish reproduction. Spawning usually occurs above the bottom. The eggs are buoyant and float to the surface, where they hatch in 18–30 hours. In at least some species a male will have a harem of several females. The principal modern sources of information on angelfishes are Steene (1977) and Allen (1979).

Holacanthus clarionensis – clarion angelfish

Size – To 25 cm (10 in)
Range – Eastern Pacific including Revillagigedo Islands and the southern tip of Baja California, Mexico; Guadalupe Islands, Mexico.
Feeding – In nature: omnivorous, browses on a variety of plants and invertebrates. In aquarium: feeds readily on plant and animal material.
Aquarium care – Keep adults in large aquarium of 400 liters (100 gal.) or larger at 20–28° C (68–82° F).

This colorful species is very abundant at the Revillagigedo Islands, 400 km (250 miles) south of Cabo San Lucas, Mexico, where huge feeding aggregations form at dusk. It is then

particularly easy to capture them with a hand net. Adults occur from just below the surface down to at least 70 m (230 ft). Juveniles are colored much like those of the king angelfish (*H. passer*) and are usually in shallow water. Adults of the same size may be very antagonistic toward each other.

Pomacanthidae

Holacanthus passer

Holacanthus ciliaris

Holacanthus ciliaris – queen angelfish

Size – To 45 cm (18 in)
Range – Tropical western Atlantic from Brazil to Florida.
Feeding – In nature: sponges and other sessile invertebrates plus some algae. In aquarium: will accept a variety of fresh or frozen seafood, flake food, etc.
Aquarium care – A hardy aquarium species. Adults require large aquaria of 500 liters (125 gal.) or larger, kept at temperatures from 20 to 28° C (68–77° F).

This species is well known to aquarists in both Europe and America along with its close relative, the blue angelfish (*H. bermudensis*). The queen angel is easily distinguished by its black forehead spot covered with blue spots. A hybrid of the two species occurs where the two species overlap and is sometimes called "Townsend's angel." Queen angels usually occur alone or in pairs on coral reefs and are found from the surface to at least 70 m (230 ft). Juvenile queen angelfish sometimes act as cleaner fish and remove ectoparasites from other fishes. Another species of *Holacanthus* (*H. tricolor*), the rock beauty, occurs in the western Atlantic but tends to do poorly in captivity and is not usually recommended to the aquarist.

Holacanthus passer – king angelfish (Passer's angelfish)

Size – To 30 cm (12 in)
Range – Eastern Pacific from the Gulf of California to the Galápagos Islands.
Feeding – In nature: omnivorous, including sponge and plant material. In aquarium: feeds readily on fresh or frozen seafoods, vegetables.
Aquarium care – Juveniles may be kept in small aquaria but at least 150 liters (40 gal.) is recommended. Adults need large aquaria and individuals should vary in size from each other by at least 3 cm (1 in) to lessen fighting. Does well at cooler temperatures of 20–24° C (68–76° F).

Occurs from surface to at least 80 m (260 ft). Easily captured with scuba at night.

Pomacanthus zonipectus

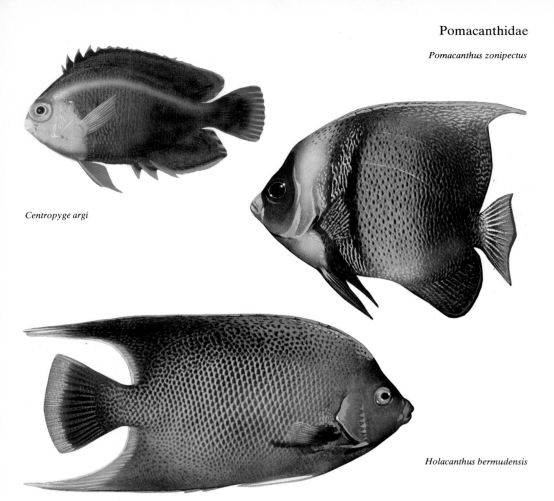

Centropyge argi

Holacanthus bermudensis

Pomacanthus zonipectus – Cortez angelfish

Size – To 45 cm (18 in)
Range – Eastern Pacific from Sea of Cortez to Peru.
Feeding – In nature: grazes on benthic invertebrates. In aquarium: feeds readily on a variety of seafoods.
Aquarium care – Adults require a very large aquarium of at least 2,000 liters (500 gal.) at 20–24° C (68–76° F). Juveniles may be kept in aquaria of 500 liters (125 gal.) or larger.

Holacanthus bermudensis – blue angelfish

Size – To 45 cm (18 in)
Range – Western Atlantic, Bermuda and Gulf of Mexico; rare in the Bahamas.
Feeding – In nature: sponges, tunicates and other invertebrates. In aquarium: usually feeds readily and will thrive on a varied seafood diet supplemented with flake food.
Aquarium care – As for the queen angelfish.

Centropyge argi – cherub pygmy angelfish

Size – To 6.5 cm (2.5 in)
Range – Bermuda, West Indies and southern Gulf of Mexico.
Feeding – In nature: primarily algae. In aquarium: include flake foods rich in plant material, vegetables.
Aquarium care – A good aquarium fish. Can be kept in aquaria of 100 liters (25 gal.) and larger at temperatures from 20 to 24° C (68–76° F).

This attractive species is relatively rare in shallow water and most often seen in rubble areas at 30–70 m (100–230 ft).

Pomacanthidae

Pomacanthus arcuatus – gray angelfish

Size – To 50 cm (20 in)
Range – Tropical western Atlantic from Brazil to Florida with accidentals to New England.
Feeding – In nature: omnivorous with sponges dominant. In aquarium: feed a varied diet including fish and squid supplemented with flake foods.
Aquarium care – Adults require large aquaria of at least 2,000 liters (500 gal.). Keep at temperatures of 20–28° C (68–82° F).

This species is common in coral-reef areas, usually alone or in pairs. It is easily approached and occurs at depths down to 30 m (100 ft). Juveniles are very similar to those of its close relative, the French angelfish, both of which may live several years in captivity.

Pomacanthus arcuatus juvenile

Pomacanthus paru

Pomacanthus imperator

Pomacanthus imperator – emperor angelfish

Size – To 31 cm (12 in)
Range – Indo-Pacific from Africa to the Pitcairn Islands and rarely Hawaii.
Feeding – In nature: sponges, tunicates and other invertebrates. In aquarium: usually feeds readily and thrives on a variety of diets.
Aquarium care – Requires a large aquarium of 500 liters (125 gal.) or more and warm temperatures of 24–28° C (76–82° F).

The emperor angelfish is a popular aquarium fish because of its attractive color pattern and hardiness. It is usually found singly or in pairs on outer coral reefs at depths ranging from 1 to 25 m (3–82 ft). However, unless collected in pairs it is usually aggressive to members of its own species, and toward other large species of angelfishes. If kept with other angelfish be sure that they differ in size by 2–3 cm (1 in) or more to help minimize fighting.

Pomacanthus paru – French angelfish

Size – To 38 cm (15 in)
Range – Tropical Atlantic; Brazil to Florida, also West Africa.
Feeding – In nature: omnivorous including sponges and algae. In aquarium: feed a varied diet.
Aquarium care – As for the gray angelfish.

Very similar to the gray angelfish but differs in coloration of the caudal fin. Some individuals act as cleaner fish and remove ectoparasites from other fishes.

136

Pomacanthus maculosus – yellow-banded angelfish

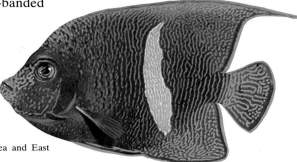

Size – To 30 cm (12 in)
Range – Indian Ocean including the Red Sea and East Africa.
Feeding – In nature: primarily sponges and tunicates. In aquarium: feed a varied diet.
Aquarium care – A large aquarium of 500 liters (125 gal.) or more is recommended, kept at 24–28° C (76–82° F).

Pomacanthus maculosus

Euxiphipops navarchus – blue-girdled angelfish

Size – To 25 cm (10 in)
Range – Indo-Australian Archipelago including the Philippines.
Feeding – In nature: omnivorous. In aquarium: usually accepts a wide variety of foods including flake foods.
Aquarium care – Suitable in a community tank with peaceful species. Provide plenty of dimly lit hiding places. Keep at 22–28° C (72–82° F).

Juveniles of 8 cm (3 in) or so are usually available to the home aquarist. Keep one or two in a large community tank. They are often shy at first and shun bright open areas but once adapted they are highly prized. This species is found in protected lagoons and drop-off areas that are rich in coral. They usually occur singly.

Apolemichthys arcuatus – bandit angelfish

Size – To 18 cm (7 in)
Range – Hawaii.
Feeding – In nature: sponges. In aquarium: feed a varied diet including chopped shrimp and squid, brine shrimp and flake food which includes plant material.
Aquarium care – Keep in a medium aquarium of 300 liters (80 gal.) or larger at 24–28° C (75–82° F) and provide holes and caves for cover.

This species is included for the aquarist looking for the rare and unusual, but it is a difficult species to keep. Experimentation is required to determine the best combination of space, cover, lighting, diet and tank-mates. In nature this species is usually found from 12 to 50 m (40–160 ft) or more on rubble bottoms. It is usually very easy to capture with a hand net.

Euxiphipops navarchus

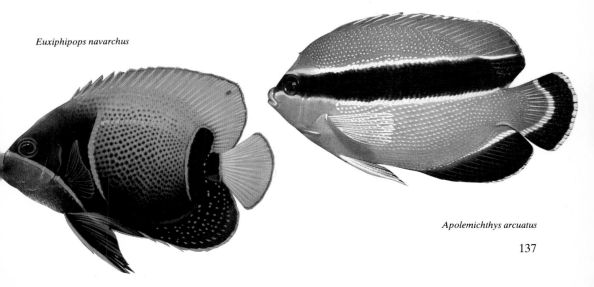

Apolemichthys arcuatus

Centropyge loriculus

Centropyge potteri

Centropyge flavissimus

Centropyge bispinosus

Centropyge loriculus – flame angelfish

Size – To 12 cm (5 in)
Range – Primarily central tropical Pacific including Johnson Island but also found in New Guinea and Palau.
Feeding – In nature: omnivorous. In aquarium: normal varied diet.
Aquarium care – A hardy species and excellent aquarium fish. Small specimens can be kept in an aquarium as small as 75 liters (20 gal.) but larger aquaria are preferred. Temperature range: 24–28° C (75–82° F).

Usually found on outer-reef slopes, at 5–25 m (15–80 ft). The name *C. flammeus*, sometimes used in the literature, is invalid.

Centropyge potteri – Potter's angelfish (Potter's pygmy angelfish)

Size – To 10 cm (4 in)
Range – Hawaii.
Feeding – In nature: algae and invertebrates. In aquarium: will accept a variety of live, fresh, frozen and dried foods; include plant matter.
Aquarium care – Usually adapts well but should be given plenty of hiding places. Requires 200 liters (50 gal.) or a larger aquarium at 20–25° C (68–77° F).

This species is easy to capture in Hawaii with a barrier net. It can be aggressive in the aquarium and should be observed carefully and removed if it causes problems.

Centropyge flavissimus – lemonpeel angelfish

Size – To 10 cm (4 in)
Range – Indo-Pacific from the Great Barrier Reef to Hawaii and the Marquesas Islands.
Feeding – In nature: algae. In aquarium: algae and other plant matter (vegetables, flake food) plus chopped shrimp, squid and live brine shrimp.
Aquarium care – Although this is primarily an algae-eater in nature, it should receive a varied diet in the aquarium to insure good nutrition. Requires at least a 200-liter (50-gal.) aquarium at 24–28° C (75–82° F) with abundant and varied cover.

This species is common in the central Pacific in shallow water, 3 m (10 ft) and down to 20 m (66 ft). Its close relative, the rare herald's angelfish (*C. heraldi*), lacks the blue ring around the eye.

Centropyge bispinosus – two-spined pygmy angelfish

Size – To 8 cm (3 in)
Range – Indo-Pacific from East Africa, west to Gilbert Islands, north to Japan and south to Lord Howe Island.
Feeding – In nature: algae. In aquarium: as for the lemonpeel angelfish.
Aquarium care – Keep in a 200-liter (50-gal.) aquarium or larger at 24–28° C (75–82° F) and provide many hiding places.

The two-spined pygmy angelfish usually stays close to cover on coral or rubble bottoms, where it occurs from 5 to 50 m (15–60 ft).

Chaetodontoplus mesoleucas –
vermiculated angelfish

Size – 17 cm (7 in)
Range – Indo-west Pacific from southern Japan to Indonesia and Japan.
Feeding – In nature: primarily sponges and tunicates. In aquarium: feed a varied diet including chopped seafood, live brine shrimp, vegetable matter, flake food.
Aquarium care – Recommended for the experienced aquarist only as dietary requirements are not well understood. Requires an aquarium of 300 liters (80 gal.) or more at 24–28° C (75–82° F).

This angelfish, although shaped like a butterflyfish, possesses a well-developed preopercular (cheek) spine. It is best known from the Philippines, Indonesia and New Guinea. Usually found alone on coral reefs between 2 and 20 m (6–66 ft), this species is generally easy to approach and capture.

Pygoplites diacanthus – regal angelfish

Size – To 25 cm (10 in)
Range – Indo-Pacific from East Africa and the Red Sea to the Marquesas Islands.
Feeding – In nature: primarily sponges and tunicates. In aquarium: a varied diet is essential; include chopped shrimp, squid, live brine shrimp and flake food and vegetables; a food block may be helpful.
Aquarium care – A difficult species to maintain and recommended for only experienced aquarists. Keep adults in large aquaria of 500 liters (125 gal.) or larger at 24–28° C (76–82° F). It is essential to provide plenty of caves, crevices and holes for cover.

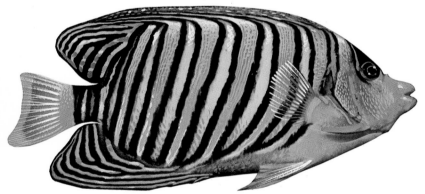

This species is common on the Great Barrier Reef but is usually collected for export in the Philippines and Sri Lanka. It usually occurs in rich coral areas from shallow water to 25 m (80 ft).

Damselfishes

Damselfishes are laterally compressed marine fishes which possess both spiny and soft fin-rays and have ctenoid scales. They belong to the order Perciformes. A single nostril is present on each side of the head and the tail is usually forked, although rounded in some clownfishes and truncated in *Dascyllus*. A few species live in temperate waters and some reach 30 cm (12 in) or more. The majority of the 200 and more known species occur in areas of reef-building corals, in the tropical western Pacific. Damselfishes spawn in nests prepared and guarded by the male. The nests are usually simple, often nothing more than a cleaned area on the side of a large boulder where the male entices the female to lay her eggs, which he then fertilizes. A single male may spawn with several females in succession. Many species of damselfishes are highly pugnacious in captivity, which makes them unsuitable for most aquarists. However, some species, including *Chromis*, *Dascyllus* and various clownfish species, are much less aggressive and make excellent aquarium specimens either in a community or single-species tank. Feeding is rarely a problem as most species feed readily on a wide variety of foods ranging from meat and seafood to prepared foods.

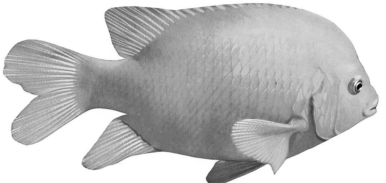

Hypsypops rubicundus adult

Hypsypops rubicundus – Garibaldi (adult)

Size – To 35 cm (14 in)
Range – Monterey Bay to Magdalena Bay, Baja California, Mexico.
Feeding – In nature: omnivorous but usually eats large quantities of sponges. In aquarium: a diet of chopped fish or squid is adequate but they will accept and thrive on almost any aquarium food.
Aquarium care – Adults are large, highly territorial and, in community aquaria, will constantly nibble on sedentary species. A single adult requires an aquarium of 750 liters (200 gal.) or more. When several are kept, a crevice or other hiding areas should be provided for each. Keep at between 13 and 24° C (55–75° F).

Garibaldi are most common between the intertidal zone and 18 m (60 ft). The males establish a nest by removing all but one or two species of red algae which form a carpet-like surface for spawning. The males guard their nest area aggressively except against receptive females, which are enticed to spawn and lay their eggs on the bed of algae. Both the males and females are polygamous.

Sub-adult Garibaldi

Size – To approx. 10 cm (4 in)
Range – As adults.
Feeding – As given above.
Aquarium care – As for adults.

Sub-adult Garibaldi are a subdued orange with blue markings. Until they become bright orange and lose their blue markings they are relatively ignored by the aggressive adults.

Juvenile Garibaldi

Juvenile Garibaldi are very colorful and usually appear in shallow water amongst iridescent red algae in July and August. Though colorful they are relatively inconspicuous in their habitat. They can occasionally be found in intertidal pools in the late summer and autumn.

Abudefduf troschelli – Panamic sergeant major (pintano)

Size – To 23 cm (9 in)
Range – Gulf of California to Peru; Galápagos Islands.
Feeding – In nature: plankton and benthic invertebrates. In aquarium: will thrive on a wide variety of foods: chopped fish, meat, etc.
Aquarium care – A hardy species but tends to nip aggressively at tank-mates. Keep small specimens in an aquarium of 75 liters (20 gal.) or more at 20–28° C (68–82° F).

This species and its well-known relative from the Atlantic (*A. saxatilis*) are abundant, hardy fishes in shallow water. Breeding males become dark and bluish and establish a nest on the cleaned face of a boulder where they fertilize the eggs laid by the female. In captivity their natural aggressiveness can create problems, but may be lessened by crowding them, to inhibit their ability to establish territories. Close relatives include *Nexillaris concolor* (= *A. declivifrons*) in the eastern Pacific, *A. abdominalis* in Hawaii, and *A. bengalensis* in the Indo-Pacific.

Microspathodon dorsalis – giant damselfish (midnight damselfish)

Size – To 30 cm (12 in)
Range – Gulf of California to Columbia; Galápagos Islands.
Feeding – In nature: primarily herbivorous. In aquarium: will accept chopped shrimp, fish, etc.: should receive plant material supplement.
Aquarium care – An aggressive species. Adults require a large aquarium of 1,200 liters (300 gal.) or more, kept at temperatures of 20–28° C (68–82° F). Boulder cover should be provided.

This shallow-water species is usually found among large boulders inshore. A close relative, *M. bairdi*, is occasionally found in the lower Gulf of California and is abundant in the Revillagigedo and Galápagos Islands.

Juvenile giant damselfish

Aquarium care – They may nip or bite tank-mates but can usually be kept successfully with active species such as angelfishes and butterflyfishes.

Juvenile giant damselfish have conspicuous light blue spots along the back. This distinguishes them from other similar species in the region.

Chromis cyanea – blue chromis

Size – To 13 cm (5 in)
Range – Bermuda, Florida, Caribbean.
Feeding and aquarium care – As for the blue-green chromis, but will do well in cooler water of 21–26° C (70–79° F).

Usually occurs alone or in small groups on shallow reefs, rarely more than 1 m (3 ft) above the bottom.

Chromis cyanea

Microspathodon dorsalis juvenile

Pomacentridae

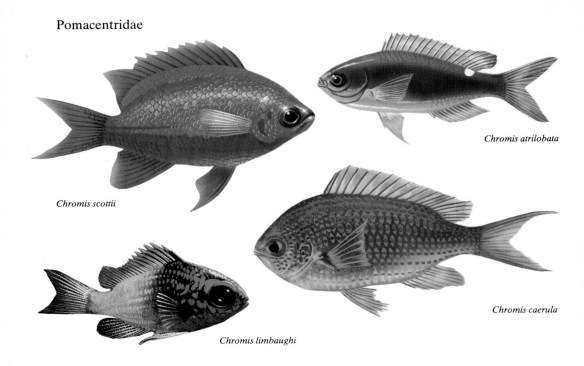

Chromis scottii

Chromis atrilobata

Chromis caerula

Chromis limbaughi

Chromis atrilobata – scissortail chromis (scissortail damselfish; casteñeta)

Size – To 7.5 cm (3 in)
Range – Gulf of California to Peru; Galápagos Islands.
Feeding – In nature: zooplankton. In aquarium: chopped shellfish, squid and fish; brine shrimp.
Aquarium care – A good aquarium species. This is a schooling species in nature and does best if several are kept together. Provide cover in a medium- or large-sized aquarium kept at 20–24° C (68–75° F).

This species occurs in large aggregations above rocky reefs where it feeds on zooplankton. When not actively feeding and at night it retreats to caves and crevices. Most common at 3–25 m (10–80 ft). A peaceful species, it does well with others of its kind or in a community tank. This applies to many *Chromis* species.

Chromis caerula – blue-green chromis (blue-green puller)

Size – To 10 cm (4 in)
Range – Indo-Pacific: East Africa to Tuamotu Islands.
Feeding – In nature: zooplankton. In aquarium: a variety of foods including chopped fish, squid, shrimp and brine shrimp.
Aquarium care – A schooling species. Hardy, active and usually not aggressive in the aquarium. Keep at 22–28° C (72–82° F).

Extremely abundant in coral atolls, where it swarms above the reef.

Chromis scottii – purple chromis

Size – To 10 cm (4 in)
Range – Tropical west Atlantic.
Feeding – In nature: bottom-swarming plankton. In aquarium: will thrive on a variety of foods. Does well on chopped shrimp and squid with occasional live brine shrimp.
Aquarium care – A good aquarium fish. Juveniles are more brightly colored, tend to school and are less likely to fight than adults. Small specimens can be kept in an aquarium of 150 liters (40 gal.) at temperatures from 21 to 26° C (70–79° F).

This bottom-living species is usually found below 25 m (90 ft), although the juveniles may occur in water as shallow as 6 m (20 ft) in the summer.

Chromis limbaughi – Connie's chromis (Cortez blue and yellow chromis)

Size – To 9 cm (3.5 in)
Range – Central and southern Gulf of California.
Feeding – In nature: primarily bottom-swarming plankton. In aquarium: does well on a variety of foods, such as chopped shrimp, squid and fish, supplemented with live or frozen brine shrimp, prepared aquarium foods.
Aquarium care – This bottom-living chromis is usually a peaceful aquarium fish and does well in medium or large aquaria, kept at between 20 and 23° C (68–73° F).

Colorful in the wild, they unfortunately tend to fade rather quickly in the aquarium. This is a bottom-dwelling species usually found in rocky areas below 15 m (50 ft). It is abundant around the islands in the La Paz region.

142

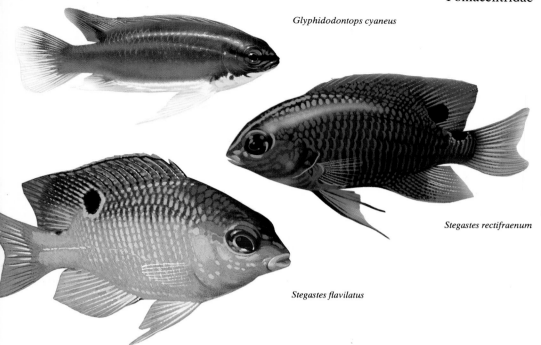

Glyphidodontops cyaneus

Stegastes rectifraenum

Stegastes flavilatus

Chrysiptera cyaneus – blue devil

Size – To about 8 cm (3 in)
Range – Indo-Australian Archipelago to Samoa.
Feeding – In nature: omnivorous; feeds on attached algae and plankton, especially crustaceans and tunicates. In aquarium: live brine shrimp and chopped seafoods supplemented with prepared foods that contain plant matter.
Aquarium care – One of the less aggressive damselfishes. The blue devil can be kept in a community tank but also makes attractive a single-species tank. Provide abundant coral for cover. Keep several together in a tank of 100 liters (25 gal.) or more. Keep at 22–28° C (72–82° F).

This is one of the most delightful damselfishes for the aquarist. It is colorful and active, yet less aggressive than most members of the family. Mature males are bicolored with yellow ventral surfaces and tails. Females lack the yellow tail and have a black spot at the base of the second dorsal fin. However, the color and pattern vary considerably with geographic location. For example, males from Palau have bright orange rather than yellow markings. This species is common on reef flats where it may form swarms at the edge of the drop-off while feeding on plankton or disperses on the reef flat to feed on bottom-swarming organisms and algae. It can be captured with a barrier net or trapped in a large jar by using fish for bait.

Stegastes rectifraenum – Cortez damselfish

Size – To 13 cm (5 in)
Range – Gulf of California and outer coast of Baja California to Magdalena Bay.
Feeding – In nature: primarily herbivorous. In aquarium: will thrive on a variety of diets.
Aquarium care – Adults are drab and aggressive and not usually kept in aquaria. They require abundant cover (holes, caves, and crevices) in a large aquarium, 400 liters (100 gal.) or greater. They are hardy and will tolerate water temperatures that range above and below 20–28° C (68–82° F). It is usually advisable to keep only one fish or a mated pair.

Stegastes flavilatus – Beaubrummel damselfish

Size – To 10 cm (4 in)
Range – Gulf of California to Ecuador.
Feeding – As for the Cortez damselfish.
Aquarium care – As for Cortez damselfish. Juveniles are aggressive but can be kept in community tanks with larger active fish. Be sure to provide adequate space and cover.

Adults of this species are distinguished from the Cortez damselfish by yellowish tinged margins of the dorsal, anal and caudal fins. The juvenile is very distinctive, with the lower half of its body bright yellow. The ecology and behavior is much like that of the Cortez damselfish.

143

ANEMONEFISHES

Anemonefishes are often called clownfishes because of their bright color and conspicuous markings. They are particularly interesting because of their symbiotic relationship with normally piscivorous (fish-eating) sea anemones. Of the 26 recognized species, 25 are in the genus *Amphiprion* and one is in the genus *Premnas* (Allen, 1975). All of them are from the Indo-West Pacific. For a comprehensive review consult Allen (1972). Anemonefishes are small to medium damselfishes that feed on zooplankton close by a host anemone during the day and retreat amongst the anemone's tentacles at night or when frightened. Most species also include algae in their diet. They avoid being stung and killed by the anemone apparently because their mucus becomes "conditioned" and inhibits the discharge of the anemone's toxic nematocysts. An anemone is usually host to a pair of adults and may also harbor one or more juveniles. Host anemones include species of the genera *Cryptodendrum, Parasicyonus, Physobrachia*, but especially *Radianthus* and *Stoichactis*. Spawning usually occurs throughout the year and takes place on a rock surface near the anemone. The female lays 300–700 eggs which are guarded by both parents, with the male taking the primary responsibility. The eggs hatch in six to ten days and the fry are pelagic for the early part of their lives.

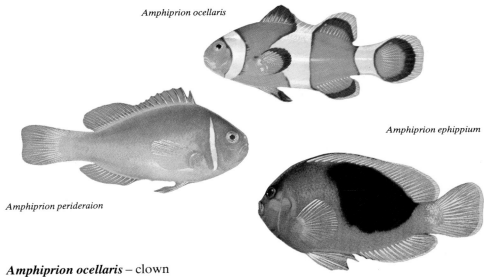

Amphiprion ocellaris

Amphiprion ephippium

Amphiprion perideraion

Amphiprion ocellaris – clown anemonefish

Size – To 7.5 cm (3 in)
Range – Indo-Pacific including from Ryukyu to Australia; Philippines, New Guinea.

Commonly available but often misidentified as *A. percula*.

Amphiprion perideraion – false skunk anemonefish

Size – To 7.5 cm (3 in)
Range – Indo-Pacific including the South China Sea, Micronesia, and Melanesia.

A delicate but peaceful species. Easy to capture.

Amphiprion ephippium – red saddleback (tomato clown, fire clown)

Size – To 10 cm (4 in)
Range – Andaman Sea, Sumatra, Java.
Feeding – In aquarium: feed a varied diet of chopped shrimp, fish, clams, supplemented with live brine shrimp and algae, or flake food rich in plant material.
Aquarium care – A good choice for the beginner. Juveniles may be kept in aquaria as small as 60 liters (15 gal.) but adults should have at least 200-liter (50-gal.) aquaria. Anemonefishes do not require a host anemone in captivity, but spawning may be facilitated if one is present. Temperatures of 28–29°C (82–85°F) are often recommended. However, at Scripps Aquarium *A. chrysopterus* and *A. frenatus* have been successfully maintained at 23–25°C (74–77°F) and spawn twice a month.

DAMSELFISHES

The genus *Dascyllus* contains seven species of small to medium damselfishes, several of which are popular aquarium species. These are peaceful fishes, that are usually compatible in community tanks, but should be given ample space and hiding places amongst rocks and coral. All are from the Indo-Pacific and include *D. albisella* from Hawaii. *Dascyllus* form aggregations above coral reefs where they feed on zooplankton. They retreat into the reef when threatened. They also include algae in their diet. Some *Dascyllus*, especially as juveniles, have a symbiotic relationship with anemones similar to that of anemonefishes, but they are less dependent on the anemones for survival. Reproductive behavior is also similar to that of anemonefishes. Spawning occurs on rock surfaces and on dead coral branches. The eggs are guarded by the male until they hatch, usually a period of about three days. The larvae spend a brief period in the surface plankton before settling on the reef. Juveniles may be kept in aquaria as small as 60 liters (15 gal.), although larger aquaria are preferable. Optimal temperatures are probably 24–26°C (75–79°F), but temperatures as low as 21°C (70°F) are usually well tolerated. Feed the usual varied diet and include plant material.

Dascyllus aruanus – humbug

Size – To 6 cm (2.5 in)
Range – Widespread in the tropical Indo-Pacific. Usually found around coral heads in lagoons and coastal areas from the surface to depths of 12 m (40 ft).

Distinguished by its three black bars with none on the tail.

Dascyllus aruanus

Dascyllus melanurus

Dascyllus trimaculatus

Dascyllus trimaculatus – threespot damselfish

Size – To 15 cm (6 in)
Range – Widespread in the tropical Indo-Pacific from the surface to depths of 55 m (180 ft)

Occurs in small to large aggregations in lagoons and along the outer reef.

Dascyllus melanurus – black-tail dascyllus

Size – To 6.5 cm (2.5 in)
Range – Primarily in the tropical west Pacific regions.

Distinguished by its four black bars, including one on the tail.

Hawkfishes

This small family of fishes includes approximately 35 species in 10 genera, the majority of which live in the Indo-Pacific. Most are small, rather sedentary predators, which perch like hawks on rocks or coral, while waiting for small prey to pass by, which they seize and swallow whole. The family is characterized by cirri on the nostril margin and on the membranes between the fin spines. Their pectoral fins are usually adapted for perching by means of enlarged lower pectoral fin-rays, which are unbranched and often separate from each other or finger-like. Many species rest on branches of coral or gorgonians and are often cryptically colored. They are usually expert at escaping collectors and are sometimes captured by removing whole coral heads or sea fans, a destructive practice which should be avoided. Coral-dwelling species are most easily collected at night with a suitable anesthetic, a practice which does not harm the habitat if done carefully. Most species of hawkfishes make excellent aquarium fishes as long as they are not kept with species small enough to be swallowed.

Oxycirrhites typus – longnose hawkfish

Size – To 12.5 cm (5 in)
Range – Tropical Indo-Pacific and eastern Pacific, including the Red Sea, Philippines, Hawaii and the Gulf of California.
Feeding – In nature: little is known, probably bottom-swarming plankton, perhaps also crevice organisms and coelenterate polyps. In aquarium: thrives on live brine shrimp which should be supplemented with any other aquarium foods that it will accept.
Aquarium care – Though uncommon, this is an excellent aquarium species that does well in aquaria of 150 liters (40 gal.) or more kept at room temperature, 20° C (68° F). It will probably thrive at temperatures between 19 and 27° C (66–81° F).

This is a deep-water species of hawkfish, usually found at depths greater than 30 m (100 ft) perched on black coral or sea fans. Its bright red markings become neutral and inconspicuous in the hawkfishes' normal habitat, which lies beyond the depth where visible red light penetrates. Often considered rare, it is probably only poorly known because of its deep-water habitat and cryptic nature. In the Gulf of California this species is usually found below 30 m (100 ft) in yellow sea fans, where it is very difficult to observe without an artificial light source. Its long snout and small mouth are well adapted for feeding on crevice organisms and bottom-swarming plankton. The longnose hawkfish lays demersal eggs (Lobel, 1975) and is a good candidate for rearing in captivity.

Cirrhitichthys oxycephalus – coral hawkfish (red-spotted hawkfish, halcón de coral)

Size – To 9.5 cm (3 in)
Range – Tropical Indo-west and eastern Pacific, including the Gulf of California.
Feeding – In nature: bottom-swarming plankton and small fishes. In aquarium: feeds readily on a variety of foods, including chopped seafood, brine shrimp, etc.
Aquarium care – A hardy aquarium species that does well

in community tanks. Provide coral or small crevices for cover and keep at 20–27° C (68–81° F) in tanks of 80 liters (20 gal.) or larger.

This species is common on coral heads in shallow water. Its range extends into cooler, subtropical water regions where coral is small and into the Central Gulf of California where coral is absent. In these areas it is found living in crevices or amongst small rocks.

ORDER PERCIFORMES – FAMILY POLYNEMIDAE

Threadfins

This family is characterized by its subterminal mouth and long unattached pectoral fin-rays. It includes seven genera and about 35 species, some of which may reach almost 2 m (7 ft) in length. The free fin-rays are thought to contain tactile and chemoreceptors which are used to locate food in soft bottoms. Threadfins (or tasselfishes) occur worldwide in tropical and subtropical marine and brackish waters. Only the juveniles of the smaller species are suitable aquarium fishes.

Polydactylus oligodon – smallscale threadfin

Size – To 22 cm (8.5 in)
Range – Florida to Brazil.
Feeding – In nature: shrimp, crabs and infauna. In aquarium: chopped seafood.

Aquarium care – Provide a large aquarium with a sandy bottom for juveniles. For adults use an aquarium of 2,000 liters (500 gal.) or larger.

These fish usually occur in sandy areas, where they often follow breaking waves right into the beach in search of food as it becomes exposed by wave action.

147

Wrasses

Wrasses are among the most conspicuous and abundant of reef fishes. Over 400 species are known worldwide. Most are tropical although some species occur in temperate waters. All are marine. Wrasses exhibit a tremendous diversity varying from slender cigar-shaped to robust and deep-bodied, and range in size from 5 to 100 cm (2–84 in) in length. They are characterized by a peculiar jerky swimming motion which occurs because their major propulsion is provided by the pectoral fins instead of the caudal fin. In rapid flight, however, the caudal fin is also used for added speed. The lips are thick and protrusible with the teeth mostly separate. Rounded canine teeth, which may be tusk-like, are obvious in the front of the mouth. Wrasses are diurnal. Some burrow into the sand at night for protection; others hide in crevices. Most species browse on benthic organisms, but plankton-feeders, scavengers, predators and cleaner fishes also occur in this family. Many species exhibit more than one color phase, including juvenile, adult male and adult female patterns. Sex reversal is common with the sex-reversed phase (usually a male) very distinctive in coloration. Sex-reversed individuals play a major role in the reproduction of many species and often initiate group spawning, but they may also spawn with individually selected mates. Many variations in sexual physiology and behavior occur. Although many species of wrasses are good aquarium fishes, caution must be used in their selection as some species are highly pugnacious. They should be kept in aquaria provided with deep sand cover, well aerated with a subsand or reverse flow filter. Rocks should be used to provide holes and crevices for those species which require them for hiding at night or cover in the day.

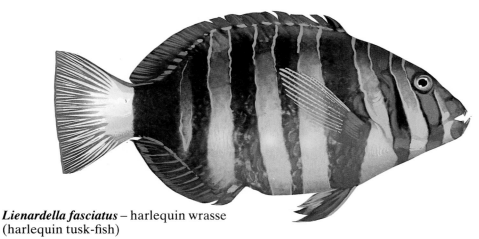

Lienardella fasciatus – harlequin wrasse
(harlequin tusk-fish)

Size – To 25 cm (10 in)
Range – Tropical western Pacific including the Ryukyu Islands, Taiwan, Great Barrier Reef, and New Hebrides.
Feeding – In nature: small invertebrates and fish. In aquarium: will accept a variety of chopped fish, squid, shellfish.
Aquarium care – Recommended only for the advanced aquarist. Provide well-aerated sand for burrowing. Keep at 23–26° C (73–79° F). Adults will require a large aquarium of 2,000 liters (500 gal.) or more.

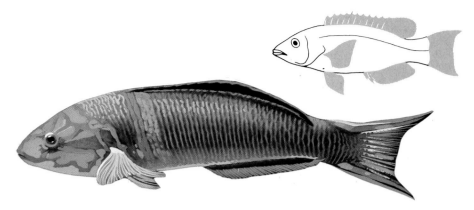

Thalassoma pavo – ornate wrasse

Size – To 20 cm (8 in)
Range – Warm eastern Atlantic Ocean and the Mediterranean Sea.
Feeding – In nature: primarily carnivorous. In aquarium: feeds readily on standard aquarium foods including chopped fish and other seafood.
Aquarium care – Generally does well in community tanks. Requires a sand bottom suitable for burrowing at night. May become aggressive in captivity after it reaches its maximum size. Keep at 18–27° C (64–75° F).

Several close relatives are also good aquarium fishes including the *T. lutescens* which is widespread in the tropical Indo-Pacific, extending to the Gulf of California and Panama. A few species of *Thalassoma*, however, such as the *T. viridens*, can be very aggressive and are best avoided.

Thalassoma lucasanum – secondary stage

Thalassoma lucasanum – rainbow

Thalassoma lucasanum – Cortez rainbow wrasse (arco iris)

Size – To 10 cm (4 in)
Range – Gulf of California to Panama; Galápagos Islands.
Feeding – In nature: small benthic invertebrates and bottom-swarming plankton; also acts as a cleaner fish and scavenger. In aquarium: chopped shrimp and other seafoods.
Aquarium care – An excellent aquarium fish that does well in community tanks. Small individuals can be kept in 75-liter (20-gal.) aquaria at temperatures from 20 to 28° C (68–82° F) with aerated sand bottoms and rocks or coral for cover.

Swarms of rainbow wrasses occur on shallow reefs. They come readily to broken urchins, which can be used to help net or trap them. The blue-headed phase is a secondary or sex-reversal male while the normal ("rainbow") color phase includes juveniles, males and females.

Labridae

Gomphosus varius female

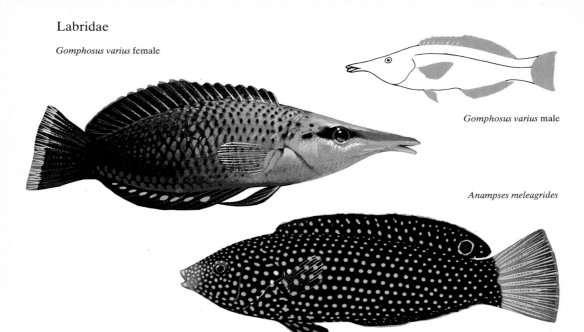

Gomphosus varius male

Anampses meleagrides

Gomphosus varius – bird wrasse

Size – To 25 cm (10 in)
Range – Tropical Indo-Pacific, including Hawaii.
Feeding – In nature: primarily a crevice feeder. In aquarium: chopped seafood supplemented with some form of plant material.
Aquarium care – Keep in a tank of 200 liters (50 gal.) or larger with a well-aerated sand bottom.

A popular and hardy aquarium species that does well in community tanks. Males are green to blue-green; females brown.

Anampses meleagrides – guinea-hen wrasse (spotted wrasse)

Size – To 30 cm (12 in)
Range – Tropical Indo-Pacific; not found in Hawaii or eastern Pacific.
Feeding and aquarium care – As for the ornate wrasse.

Hemipteronotus pavoninus – Cortez razorfish (Pacific razorfish)

Size – To 25 cm (10 in)
Range – Tropical Pacific and Indian oceans.
Feeding – In nature: small invertebrates and fishes, including garden eels. In aquarium: chopped seafood.
Aquarium care – Requires a tank bottom covered with at least 7 cm (3 in) or more of well-aerated sand. Adults should have an aquarium of 1,200 liters (300 gal.) or larger.

The razorfish is common in sandy areas near reefs. When threatened and at night it burrows into the sand. It can be taken by hook and line with small hooks, or trapped. This is an aggressive species which can greatly disrupt community tanks.

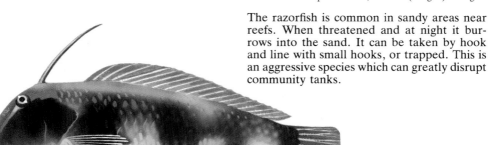

Hemipteronotus pavoninus

Coris gaimardi – clown wrasse

Size – To 20 cm (8 in)
Range – Tropical Indo-Pacific; not found in Hawaii.
Feeding – In nature: small benthic animals. In aquarium:
brine shrimp, chopped seafood, flake foods, krill, etc.
Aquarium care – A peaceful aquarium species; the brightly
colored juveniles are usually preferred. As with other
species, well-aerated sand should be provided. Keep at 22–
27° C (72–81° F).

Coris gaimardi

Labroides dimidiatus – cleaner wrasse

Size – To 7 cm (3 in)
Range – Widespread tropical Indo-Pacific.
Feeding – In nature: a cleaner wrasse, but also feeds on
small free-living invertebrates. In aquarium: live brine
shrimp, other planktonic organisms, chopped shrimp, flake
food.
Aquarium care – An attractive and useful addition to most
community tanks. Does well at 22–28° C (72–82° F).

Labroides dimidiatus

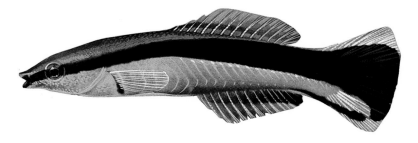

ORDER PERCIFORMES – FAMILY OPISTOGNATHIDAE

Jawfishes

Jawfishes have large mouths and big eyes; they live in burrows they construct themselves. The
body is more or less cylindrical in shape, tapering uniformly toward the tail. The large mouth with
its conspicuous upper jaw is subterminal in position; both jaws contain moderate-sized canine
teeth. The dorsal and anal fins are long and continuous with no notch; the pelvic fins are placed
anterior to the pectoral fins; the tail is usually rounded. Scales are cycloid and absent from the
head; the lateral line is high on the body and extends only about halfway to the tail. Jawfishes are
usually found below 4 m (13 ft) in mixed bottoms of sand or sediment mixed with stones, shells,
etc. Their burrows, which open into a chamber, are meticulously constructed from shells and
stone which are manipulated with the jaws. Foreign objects dropped into their burrows are

unceremoniously carried to the entrance and spat out. At night a shell or stone is used as a trap door to obscure the entrance. Jawfishes feed on crustaceans and sometimes on fishes that pass by the burrow. During courtship males hover above their burrows and carry out a display to attract females. After spawning the female returns to her own burrow, while the male incubates the eggs in his mouth until they hatch. About 30 species are known, primarily tropical. They appear to be absent from the western Pacific.

Opistognathus rhomaleus

Piebald jawfish

Opistognathus rhomaleus – giant Cortez jawfish

Size – To 60 cm (24 in)
Range – Magdalena Bay and the Gulf of California and the Revillagigedo Islands.
Feeding – In nature: crustaceans and fishes. In aquarium: chopped and whole seafood.
Aquarium care – Only for the aquarist who has the largest of aquariums. Should have a tank of 1,000 liters (250 gal.) or more with 30 cm (12 in) of bottom material for burrow construction. Keep at 18–25° C (64–77° F).

This large species is fairly often caught by anglers and shrimp trawlers and occasionally by scuba divers. It is an interesting aquarium fish but less appealing than the previous species to most people.

Opistognathus n. sp. – piebald jawfish

Size – To about 15 cm (6 in)
Range – Gulf of California and southward.
Feeding – In nature: unknown; probably bottom-swarming crustaceans and possibly small fishes. In aquarium: adapts readily to feed on chopped fish, squid, clam and shrimp.
Aquarium care – Suitable for single-species or community tanks which must be tightly covered to prevent escape. Provide substrate as previously described. Keep at 20–24° C (68–75° F).

This and the previous species are being described by Dr. R. H. Rosenblatt of Scripps Institution of Oceanography, and Dr. E. Brothers. It is usually encountered in the same habitat as the blue-spotted jawfish but is much less abundant. Unlike its blue-spotted relative, this is a peaceful species in the aquarium. It is very easy to capture with scuba using hook and line.

Opistognathus aurifrons

Blue-spotted jawfish

Opistognathus aurifrons – yellowhead jawfish

Size – To 10 cm (4 in)
Range – Florida and the West Indies.
Feeding – In nature: carnivorous, small crustaceans and fishes. In aquarium: initiate feeding with live brine shrimp then supplement with chopped shrimp, squid and clams, and krill or other small whole crustaceans.
Aquarium care – A good aquarium species. Keep in single-species tanks or community tanks. Provide a bottom of sand mixed with mouth-sized building materials and a few larger rocks. Mixed material from coral beaches works well. Keep at 22–27° C (73–81° F).

The yellowhead jawfish is an attractive and interesting aquarium species that usually does well in captivity if provided with suitable substrate. It may have problems with goiter. Scuba divers can capture this species by dropping a small fish hook down its burrow and snagging the fish as he attempts to expel the hook. It has been bred in captivity.

Opistognathus n. sp. – blue-spotted jawfish

Size – To 10 cm (4 in)
Range – Gulf of California and southward.
Feeding – In nature: primarily crustaceans. In aquarium: live adult brine shrimp and other small live crustaceans, chopped shrimp, squid and clams.
Aquarium care – A very aggressive species toward its own kind; otherwise peaceful. Usually only one or a pair can be kept together. Provide a deep, tightly covered aquarium of 150 liters (40 gal.) or more with several inches of bottom material over a subsand filter. Include small stones and shells for burrow building. Keep at 20–24° C (68–75° F).

This species usually occurs in large colonies near rocky areas at depths ranging from 4 to 20 m (13–65 ft). It can be captured by scuba divers by dropping a small hook into its burrow. After capture it is advisable to transport each specimen in a small tube or pipe with the ends covered by netting. The tube can be used as a temporary burrow when the fish is introduced into the aquarium.

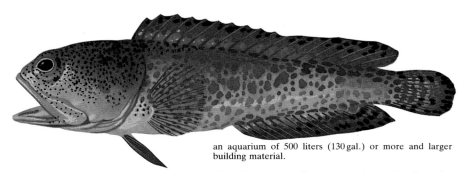

Opistognathus punctatus – fine-spotted jawfish

Size – To 40 cm (16 in)
Range – Scammon's Lagoon, Baja California, Mexico to Panama.
Feeding – In nature: small fishes and crustaceans. In aquarium: chopped seafood.
Aquarium care – As for previous species but adults require

an aquarium of 500 liters (130 gal.) or more and larger building material.

This is an excellent aquarium fish for the aquarist who has the facilities to handle it. It is a prodigious digger and can move huge quantities of materials in a single day, which it is inclined to do if it finds its burrow unsatisfactory. It is easy to catch with scuba and a hook and line and can be taken from the surface while angling over suitable habitat.

153

Parrotfishes

Since parrotfishes are such a conspicuous element of tropical reefs, aquarists are often interested in keeping them. However, because of their large size and specialized diet, they are difficult to maintain even by large public aquaria. For those who wish to try, juveniles are recommended as they usually adapt more readily to captivity. Parrotfishes are robust and generally large, ranging from 45 to 200 cm (18–72 in). They are moderately compressed, moderately deep to deep-bodied. Many species develop a large forehead hump. The scales are cycloid and very large. The dorsal and anal fins are long, the dorsal fin is continuous. The mouth is terminal; the jaw teeth are fused to form a strong parrot-like beak; strong pharyngeal teeth are present, well adapted for grinding coral and coralline algae, etc. About 70 species are known worldwide, all marine.

Scarus ghobban – bluechin parrotfish

Size – To 80 cm (30 in)
Range – Tropical Indian and Pacific Oceans.
Feeding – In nature: browses on algae, coral and other attached organisms. In aquarium: feed a varied diet including plant material. Some aquarists have had success feeding vegetable matter embedded in plaster of Paris (sometimes cast as coral heads).
Aquarium care – Regardless of the species of parrotfish chosen, try to obtain juveniles. Provide a large aquarium with a deep sand bottom and some rocks.

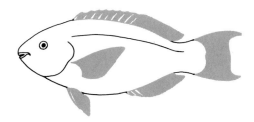

Parrotfishes are common in shallow tropical waters where they are active by day and hide in caves and crevices at night; some species secrete a cocoon of mucus, which may suppress their odor and help them avoid detection. Polychromatism is common; females and males may have completely different coloration and the juvenile phase may differ as well. In *Scarus ghobban* males and females differ while juveniles of both sexes have the same coloration as females. Parrotfishes are easiest to collect at night with scuba but a stout net is required to restrain them. They will readily rupture conventional hand nets.

Triplefin Blennies

Triplefins are small fishes characterized by having their dorsal fins divided into three parts; the first two supported by spines, the third by soft rays. Their bodies are slender and cylindrical, with the eyes placed near the top of the head; the mouth is subterminal. The tail is fan-like, truncate but slightly rounded; the pelvic (ventral) fins are jugular in position and attached anterior to the pectoral fins; the anal fin is long. The scales are ctenoid. Triplefins are common in shallow water where they may be seen flitting about on rocky faces. They are cryptic overall but usually can display conspicuous markings for communication. All are marine, tropical, and found in the Atlantic, Pacific and Indian Oceans. Approximately 95 species are known in 15 genera.

Enneanectes pectoralis – redeye triplefin

Size – To 4 cm (1.5 in)
Range – Florida and the West Indies to Venezuela.
Feeding – In nature: primarily small crustaceans. In aquarium: live brine shrimp nauplii and adults; other live zooplankton and worms, frozen krill; use prepared foods as a supplement.
Aquarium care – Not well known to the home aquarist. Do best in single-species tanks where several of each sex can be kept together. Territorial. Provide a rocky habitat. If available, use rocks with attached worm tubes or holes. Keep at 22–24° C (72–75° F).

The redeye triplefin exhibits sexual dimorphism. Mature males have more red on the head and body than females. This species occurs from near the surface to depths of 10 m (33 ft) or more.

Tripterygion nasus – Mediterranean triplefin

Size – To 7 cm (3 in)
Range – Mediterranean and Adriatic Seas.
Feeding – In nature: primarily bottom-swarming crustaceans. In aquarium: live brine shrimp and other planktonic organisms, small worms; prepared foods.
Aquarium care – Does best in a single-species tank, but can be kept in a community tank with peaceful species. Provide large rocks as a substrate. Keep at 22–25° C (72–77° F).

Males are very colorful when in spawning condition; females are a drab brown. These fish live on the surface of rocks from the intertidal zone to a depth of 25 m (80 ft).

Lizard triplefin – new genus and species

Size – To 7.5 cm (3 in)
Range – Gulf of California.
Feeding – In nature: copepods and other small bottom-swarming organisms. In aquarium: live brine shrimp nauplii and live adult brine shrimp, other small living crustaceans.
Aquarium care – Suitable for single-species tanks, or community tanks containing peaceful species. Provide large rocks for perching and narrow crevices for cover. Keep at 20–24° C (68–75° F).

This species is being described by Dr. R. H. Rosenblatt of Scripps Institution of Oceanography. It is endemic to the Gulf of California, where it is locally very abundant. Its breeding behavior has been observed in nature (Thomson *et al.* 1979) but it has not been bred in captivity. Breeding males become dark and flash their light-colored tails to attract females.

Enneanectes pectoralis

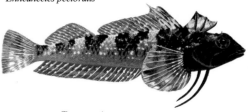

Trypterygion nasus

Lizard triplefin

155

Pikeblennies

Chaenopsis alepidota – orangethroat pikeblenny

Size – To 15 cm (6 in)
Range – Gulf of California and the Pacific coast from Southern California to Capo San Lucas.
Feeding – In nature: carnivorous; primarily small crustaceans; also small worms and fishes. In aquarium: live brine shrimp, worms, chopped seafood; prepared foods.
Aquarium care – Does well in single-species tanks or community tanks with small or peaceful species. Provide rocks with attached worm-tubes or use artificial tubes, such as drinking straws, for cover. Several can be kept in a 200-liter (50-gal.) tank; but males are territorial.

The orangethroat pikeblenny lives in worm-tubes usually near reefs on sand and cobble bottoms. It occurs from near the surface to depths of at least 20 m (65 ft). Skin or scuba divers can easily collect this species by gathering rocks and shells which have worm-tubes containing fish attached, or by digging up tubes of parchment worms which contain fish.

Emblemaria hypacanthus – banner blenny (signal blenny)

Size – To 5 cm (2 in)
Range – Sea of Cortez.
Feeding – In nature: bottom-swarming crustaceans. In aquarium: adult and newly hatched brine shrimp (*Artemia*), other live planktonic organisms, small worms. Supplement with prepared foods.
Aquarium care – Territorial. Best kept in single-species tanks. Try one male with two or three females in a 75-liter (20-gal.) aquarium. Furnish the tank with rocks containing gastropod tubes or holes. Keep at 20–23° C (68–73° F).

Male banner blennies are highly territorial tube-dwellers. They advertise their presence by flaring their enlarged sail-like dorsal fins as they pose at the entrance to their tubes. Females, which lack the enlarged fin, may either be in the open or in tubes. The male displays to attract the female by rapidly moving in and out of his tube and flashing or waving his dorsal fin. If the female is receptive she will enter his tube to mate and lay eggs. After mating the female departs and the eggs are guarded by the male until they hatch.

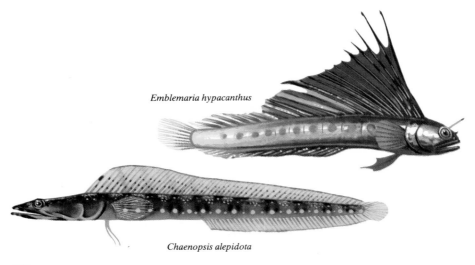

Emblemaria hypacanthus

Chaenopsis alepidota

Clinids

Clinids are similar and closely related to combtooth blennies. They differ in usually having conspicuous scales and in having patches of conical jaw teeth instead of rows of bristle-like "combteeth." They are moderately elongate and compressed fishes, typically with a pointed snout, and with cirri on the head especially above the eyes or on the nape. Their dorsal fins are usually continuous and have more spines than rays. The first few spines may be produced and partially or completely separated by a notch from the remainder of the fin. The pelvic (ventral) fins are placed anterior to the pectoral fins. Most clinids are cryptically colored, secretive, solitary fishes that occur along rocky shores at depths ranging from the surface to a depth of 30 m (100 ft). Many are found in water less than 10 m (30 ft), but a few species occur as deep as 40 m (130 ft). Those whose feeding habits are known are carnivorous. Clinids that live in vegetation frequently match it perfectly, and some even mimic it. The giant kelpfish, *Heterostichus rostratus*, has been observed positioned with its snout against a kelp stem and its body undulating back and forth like a kelp blade, until an unsuspecting prey fish swims by, at which time the kelpfish darts out suddenly to capture it. Some clinids are polychromatic and occur in several color phases ranging from red, to brown, to green, being identical in color to vegetation in its habitat. Sexual dichromatism may also be present, with males and females having different patterns of dark markings. Clinids are found worldwide in tropical and temperate seas. About 175 species are recognized, distributed in 40 genera. They are usually of limited interest to aquarists since most species tend to be secretive in the aquarium and some species are territorial and aggressive as well. In addition to the species discussed below, some species of *Malacotenus* may be of interest to the aquarist.

Gibbonsia elegans – spotted kelpfish

Size – To 16 cm (6 in)
Range – Central California to Magdalena Bay, Mexico.
Feeding – In nature: carnivorous. In aquarium: chopped seafood.
Aquarium care – Suitable in the home aquarium at cool room temperatures of about 23° C (73° F). Provide rocks or vegetation (artificial or real) for cover. Do not keep with aggressive species.

This is a warm-temperate water species similar in some respects to its relative in the Gulf of California, *Labrisomus xanti*. It is commonly encountered in tidepools where it hides in vegetation, which it matches almost

perfectly. It can be collected fairly easily with a hand net after bailing out tidepools. The female lays her eggs in vegetation where the male guards them until they hatch. Several closely related species also occur in the same general geographic region.

157

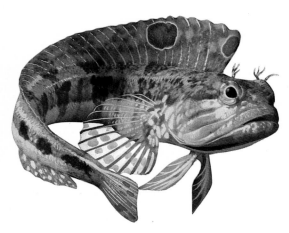

Neoclinus blanchardi – sarcastic fringehead

Size – To 30 cm (12 in)
Range – San Francisco to Magdalena Bay, Mexico.
Feeding – In nature: carnivorous. In aquarium: chopped seafood, whole shrimp.
Aquarium care – Will do well in a large home aquarium at cool room temperatures. Keep at 13–20° C (53–68° F) in a tank provided with a tube or burrow. Suitable in a community tank but only with large fishes.

The sarcastic fringehead is a hole-dwelling species that is most commonly encountered on canyon walls and steep faces. It defends its territory with an impressive flaring of its huge jaws and will even attack divers (although it is not capable of causing significant injury). Once located, this species is easy to collect with the aid of a fish anesthetic. This is an interesting and amusing species for the temperate-zone aquarist.

ORDER PERCIFORMES – FAMILY LABRISOMIDAE

Blennies

Labrisomus xanti – largemouth blenny

Size – To 18 cm (7 in)
Range – Gulf of California to Jalisco, Mexico.
Feeding – In nature: carnivorous; primarily benthic crustaceans. In aquarium: chopped seafood.
Aquarium care – Easy to maintain. Territorial but suitable in community tanks. Provide crevices for cover. A small pair can be kept in a community tank of 75 liters (20 gal.). Keep at 20–23° C (68–73° F).

cover. Both species are relatively easy to capture with a hand net and are normally compatible in the aquarium. Male largemouth blennies have a larger head than females and develop red coloration around the head when sexually active, usually in the spring.

This large clinid is sedentary, except when feeding or defending its territory. It is a shallow-water, crevice-dwelling, diurnal predator often found in close association with the Sonora blenny *Malacoctenus gigas*. The latter relies on vegetation instead of crevices for

Combtooth Blennies

Blennies are small scaleless fishes with blunt heads that occur in shallow water amongst rocks or coral, some in areas of strong wave action. Many are aggressive species, and blennies as a group are avoided by most aquarists. Typically they have oblong compressed bodies with smooth skin, although vestigial scales are present on some species. Cirri are commonly present on the head. The eyes are usually placed near the top of the head. The mouth is usually subterminal in position with close-set, often sharp comb-like teeth in the jaws. The dorsal fin is continuous but may have a noticeable notch. One of the distinguishing characters of the family is the placement of the pelvic (ventral) fins anterior to the pectoral fins. Blennies may be herbivorous or carnivorous. Most are cryptic and territorial. Typically they lay demersal eggs in shells or other shelters where the male guards them until they hatch. Sexual dimorphism occurs in some species, with the males developing more colorful markings and sometimes having more distinctive fins. Mimicry is not uncommon. For example, some species mimic cleaner fishes but, instead of removing parasites from host fishes, these blennies attack them and tear off scales or pieces of skin and flesh. Over 270 species in 46 genera occur in tropical and temperate waters worldwide. Only a few species are known in the western Atlantic. Blennies are hardy in captivity. Some tame readily and make interesting pets. Other species can be highly aggressive in aquaria, and their territorial requirements must be met if they are to be kept successfully with other fishes.

Exallias brevis – short-bodied blenny

Size – To 15 cm (6 in)
Range – Tropical Indo-Pacific from Sri Lanka to central Polynesia and Hawaii.
Feeding – In nature: omnivorous browser. In aquarium: live brine shrimp, krill and chopped seafood; supplement with prepared foods containing plant matter.
Aquarium care – Seldom maintained. If kept in a community tank, watch for fin-nipping of its tank-mates. Provide hiding places. Keep at 22–28° C (72–82° F).

This is a rather secretive species that is usually found from the outer edge of the reef down to depths of at least 10 m (35 ft). Many other blennies are available and make interesting aquarium specimens. However, if you find damaged fins on your angelfish, butterflyfish and other tank-mates, a blenny may be guilty!

Blenniidae

Hypsoblennius gentilis

Meiacanthus atrodorsalis

Ophioblennius steindachneri

Hypsoblennius gentilis – bay blenny

Size – To 15 cm (6 in)
Range – Central California to Magdalena Bay, Mexico, and middle to upper regions of the Gulf of California.
Feeding – In nature: benthic invertebrates and algae. In aquarium: chopped seafood; supplement with krill, live brine shrimp and prepared foods if desired; feeds readily.
Aquarium care – Becomes very tame in the aquarium but can be aggressive toward sedentary species. Tolerates a wide temperature range and can be kept at various room temperatures with no heater. Provide rocks and shells for cover.

The bay blenny is a hardy fish that tames quickly in captivity. It is common in tidepools in the upper Gulf of California and in bays and estuaries along the outer coast of Baja California and California. The rockpool blenny (*H. gilberti*) replaces the bay blenny in tidepools along the open coast; while the mussel blenny (*H. jenkinsi*) is primarily a hole-dweller and inhabitant of mussel beds. It is frequently found on pilings. These latter species do not tame as readily as *H. gentilis*.

Meiacanthus atrodorsalis – poison-fang blenny

Size – To 7 cm (3 in)
Range – Tropical western Pacific from the Moluccas to Samoa.
Feeding – In nature: carnivorous; planktonic crustaceans and benthic invertebrates. In aquarium: live brine shrimp, krill, chopped clams, squid and shrimp; prepared foods.
Aquarium care – Suitable in the community tank. Provide a 75-liter (20-gal.) or larger aquarium with rocky crevices for cover, but leave a large swimming space. Keep at 22–28° C (72–82° F).

Ophioblennius steindachneri – Panama-fanged blenny

Size – To 18 cm (7 in)
Range – Gulf of California to Peru.
Feeding – In nature: omnivorous; algae and sessile invertebrates. In aquarium: feeds readily on chopped seafood.
Aquarium care – Territorial; best kept in a single-species tank, provided with crevices and rocky ledges. Keep at 20–23° C (68–73° F).

This blenny has large fang-like canine teeth in the rear of the mouth, which it uses for protection, and sharp anterior grazing teeth that can inflict severe injury to other fishes in the aquarium. It is expert at disabling a larger fish by biting off its fins. The Panama-fanged blenny is most common on steep rocky coasts in shallow-water areas exposed to surge. The juvenile is black and white with red markings, and is sometimes mistaken for a separate species.

The poison-fang blenny has grooved canine teeth, with venom sacs at the base. This appears to be effective protection against open-water predators which seem to learn to avoid it. This species is found in lagoons and on seaward reefs from depths of 1–30 m (3–100 ft) or more. It is difficult to capture and only rarely available to the aquarist.

Aspidontus taeniatus – sabertooth blenny (cleaner mimic)

Size – To 13 cm (5 in)
Range – Tropical Indo-Pacific from the Red Sea to the Tuamotu Islands.
Feeding – In nature: scales, fins and skin of larger fishes; also worms and other invertebrates. In aquarium: small worms, chopped fish and other seafoods.
Aquarium care – Probably suitable in a community tank, but keep well fed and be prepared to remove it if it attacks other fishes. Provide tubes or holes for shelter. Keep at 22–28° C (72–82° F).

This species is primarily of interest to the aquarist looking for the unusual or wishing to study behavior. It is a remarkable mimic of the cleaner wrasse *Labroides dimidiatus*. This allows it to approach unsuspecting fishes, from which it rips scales or pieces of skin instead of removing parasites. Adult fishes often learn to recognize the sabertooth and avoid being victimized but juveniles are often successfully attacked.

ORDER PERCIFORMES – FAMILY STICHAEIDAE

Pricklebacks

Pricklebacks are small fishes with long slender compressed bodies. The mouth is terminal and equipped with small conical teeth. The dorsal and anal fins are long, and may or may not be attached to the tail fin; the dorsal fin is prickly to touch. Pelvic fins may be present or absent; if present they are anterior to the pectoral fins. Scales if present are small and cycloid. With the exception of the ribbon prickleback (*Phytichthys chirus*), brown, gray, and black colors predominate. Some species are elaborately decorated with cirri, especially on the head, particularly the decorated warbonnet (*Chirolophis decoratus*). Pricklebacks are bottom fish and occupy a variety of habitats from the rocky intertidal zone to muddy and sandy bottoms over 300 m (975 ft) in depth. Shallow-water species lay clusters of eggs in nests under rocks. The eggs are guarded by either of the parents, which fans them continuously to ensure adequate oxygen for the developing embryo and to keep the eggs free of sediment. Little is known of the reproductive habits of deep-water species. About 57 species of pricklebacks occur, primarily in the cold waters of the North Pacific Ocean, with a few in the North Atlantic. Some intertidal species can adapt to temperatures in the neighborhood of about 20° C (68° F).

Anoplarchus purpurescens – cockscomb prickleback

Size – To 20 cm (8 in)
Range – Aleutian Islands to California.
Feeding – In nature: omnivorous; primarily algae, worms and amphipods, also small molluscs and other crustaceans. In aquarium: chopped shrimp, squid or fish supplemented with prepared foods containing plant material.

Aquarium care – A hardy, peaceful species. Provide a sand bottom with rocks for cover. Keep at 10–18° C (50–65° F); may acclimate to 20° C (68° F) or more.

A peaceful species that will reproduce in captivity. Pairs seek nesting areas in the intertidal zone where the female lays clusters of about 3,000 eggs in column-like masses wedged under rocks. She guards them until they hatch (about three weeks).

Gunnels

Gunnels are small eel-like fishes with long slender bodies. The mouth is terminal; the teeth are small and conical. The dorsal and anal fins are long and confluent with the tail fin; the pelvic fins are small or absent; if present, they are placed ahead of the pectoral fins. Scales are small, cycloid and inconspicuous. Coloration is predominantly green, yellow, or red. Polychromatism may occur and result in several color phases within the same species. Gunnels are bottom fishes found in rocky or soft-bottomed areas where vegetation occurs. They feed upon small crustaceans and other small invertebrates that live amongst the vegetation. Reproduction occurs in winter or early spring. Clusters of eggs are laid in nests under rocks and tended by one or both parents until they hatch, in about 30 days at 10°C (50°F). About 15 species occur, most in the cold-temperate waters of the North Pacific, a few in the North Atlantic.

Apodichthys flavidus – penpoint gunnel

Size – To 46 cm (18 in)
Range – Kodiak, Alaska to Santa Barbara, California.
Feeding – In nature: feeds primarily on small crustaceans; also other small invertebrates. In aquarium: chopped shrimp and other chopped seafood supplemented with brine shrimp and other living invertebrates.

Aquarium care – This is a cold-water species and does best at temperatures below 15°C (59°F), but it may adapt to cool-room temperatures. Provide flat rocks for cover and a sand or gravel bottom. A subsand filter is satisfactory but a screen should be placed over the first centimeter (0.5 in) of sand to keep the fish from uncovering the filter plate. The aquarium should be a low-profile type of at least 75 liters (20 gal.).

The penpoint gunnel is a bottom-living species that forages for food amongst eel grass and algae in the intertidal and upper subtidal zones. It occurs in a variety of color phases, and is usually found in matching vegetation when feeding. When nesting or not feeding it hides under rocks. Normally it can be collected in the intertidal zone during the lowest tides. Spawning occurs in winter. The eggs are laid in a ball-like cluster and are tended by one or both parents until they hatch, usually about 30 days. In captivity it has been spawned and reared beyond metamorphosis of the larvae.

Graveldivers

To say that this is a small family is really an understatement, since it contains only one known species. The graveldiver is a small worm-like fish found only along the northeast Pacific coast. This unusual fish is found in a most unlikely habitat, amongst the gravel of cobble beaches on partially protected coasts. This is an environment in which anything but a highly specialized fish would be ground to death by the rolling gravel. The graveldiver is of interest only to the aquarist looking for the highly unusual.

Scytalina cerdale – graveldiver

Size – To 15 cm (6 in)
Range – Southeast Alaska to central California.
Feeding – In nature: interstitial organisms. In aquarium: brine shrimp nauplii and adults, worms, chopped shrimp and small bite-size crustaceans.

Aquarium care – Keep in a chilled aquarium of 50 liters (10 gal.). Use a subsand filter with a planter screen over 1–2 cm (0.5–1 in) of sand to prevent burrowing. Cover the screen with several centimeters of large gravel. Preferred temperature 5–10° C (41–50° F).

ORDER PERCIFORMES – FAMILY GOBIIDAE

Gobies

Gobies form the largest family of marine fishes, with more than 800 species. Most gobies can be distinguished by their pelvic fins which are fused to form a sucking disk. A few gobies lack fused pelvics but are believed to have evolved from ancestors which did possess them. Gobies are small, less than 10 cm (4 in) long, usually elongate, slightly compressed, and stiff-appearing with a broad caudal peduncle. Their heads are usually blunt, with a large oblique mouth and small teeth set in the jaw. The eyes are usually placed high on the head. Two dorsal fins are present. The caudal fin is normally rounded, but is sometimes pointed, or emarginate. Scales may be cycloid, ctenoid, or absent. The lateral line is absent; the swim bladder is usually absent. Gobies are carnivorous bottom fishes that usually live in direct contact with the substrate. Typically they are observed perched on their pelvic fins near a burrow or other shelter. A few species swim or hover just above the bottom. Some gobies live symbiotically with other animals. Most gobies are found in pairs. Their eggs are usually laid in a shelter and guarded by the male. Gobies occur worldwide, mostly in tropical seas but they are able to exploit nearly all aquatic environments, including fresh water. Many species are good aquarium fishes. A number of species have reproduced in captivity.

Lythrypnus dalli – blue-banded goby (Catalina goby)

Size – To 6 cm (2.5 in)
Range – Central California to the Gulf of California; Guadalupe Island.
Feeding – In nature: carnivorous; primarily small crustaceans including amphipods and copepods. In aquarium: live and frozen brine shrimp, chopped seafoods; prepared foods.

The blue-banded goby is often abundant on rocky surfaces which contain holes, cracks or crevices as well as in burrows in clay-canyon walls. Depths may range from the intertidal zone to 75 m (250 ft). It is a short-lived species that spawns in the spring or summer of its first year and rarely lives more than two years.

Aquarium care – Provide a rocky habitat with numerous holes and crevices. Keep at 15–22° C (59–72° F) in a single-species tank or a community tank with other small, peaceful species. Several can be kept in a tank as small as 40 liters (10 gal.).

Spawning occurs in a sheltered area selected by the male, which tends the eggs until they hatch. This species will spawn in captivity. It is relatively easy to collect with a slurp gun.

163

Gobiidae

Gobiosoma digueti

Coryphopterus personatus

Gobiosoma digueti – banded cleaner goby (gobio barbero)

Size – To 3 cm (1.25 in)
Range – Gulf of California to Colombia.
Feeding – In nature: acts as a cleaner fish; also browses on surface-dwelling invertebrates. In aquarium: brine shrimp nauplii; surface-dwelling copepods, small worms; prepared foods.
Aquarium care – This is a very small species which needs to be provided with secure refuges in cracks and burrows. Can be kept in a community tank. Keep at 20–23° C (68–73° F).

This goby has been observed cleaning large predatory species such as groupers and morays. It is apparently protected in part by a noxious mucus.

Gobiosoma puncticulatus – redhead goby

Size – To 5 cm (2 in)
Range – Gulf of California to Ecuador.
Feeding – In nature: carnivorous; sometimes a cleaner fish. In aquarium: brine shrimp nauplii, small worms, small crustaceans; supplement with prepared foods.
Aquarium care – Can be kept in a community tank if provided with suitable refuges, cracks, holes and crevices. Keep at 20–23° C (68–73° F).

Coryphopterus personatus – masked goby

Size – To 4 cm (1.5 in)
Range – Bermuda to the Virgin Islands.
Feeding – In nature: primarily plankton. In aquarium: brine shrimp nauplii, live plankton (if possible), prepared foods.
Aquarium care – Keep in a single-species tank. Provide caves with crevices for shelter. Keep at 22–28° C (72–82° F).

This is one of the most abundant species in the tropical western Atlantic. Unlike most gobies which rest on the substrate, the masked goby is a free-swimming species which usually occurs in aggregations near coral. It may also be found hovering in caves. Occurs at depths from 3 to 40 m (10–130 ft) and more.

Gobiosoma puncticulatus

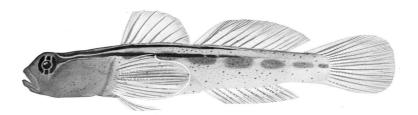

This is a territorial species that often lives commensally with club-spined urchins. Territorial disputes between redhead gobies often involve jaw-wrestling, which can lead to serious injuries or death in the aquarium.

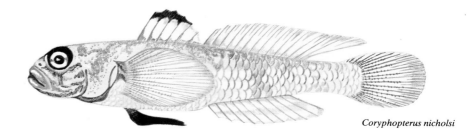

Coryphopterus nicholsi

Gobiosoma oceanops – neon goby

Size – To 6 cm (2.4 in)
Range – Florida and Yucatan.
Feeding – In nature: a cleaner fish; also browses on small benthic crustaceans. In aquarium: feeds readily on typical aquarium foods.
Aquarium care – An excellent aquarium species that is hardy and active yet peaceful. Suitable in a community tank except with hamlets, which will eat the gobies. Provide rock and coral cover. Keep at 22–28° C (72–82° F).

This is one of several species of gobies that act as cleaner fishes. Its color and markings are very similar to the cleaner wrasse *Labroides dimidiatus* of the Indo-Pacific. The neon goby is found from depths of less than 1 m (3 ft) to 40 m (130 ft), usually on coral heads but also in caves or crevices. Spawning takes place in a burrow which is guarded by the male until the eggs hatch, usually eight to twelve days. It has been bred in captivity.

Coryphopterus nicholsi – blackeye goby (bluespot goby)

Size – To 15 cm (6 in)
Range – Northern British Columbia to Magdalena Bay, Baja California, Mexico.
Feeding – In nature: carnivorous, primarily bottom-swarming crustaceans. In aquarium: does well on chopped seafoods such as clams, squid, etc.
Aquarium care – Hardy and easy to maintain. Provide a sand bottom with a few rocks for burrowing under. Suitable in single-species or community tanks. Keep at 15–22° C (59–72° F).

The blackeye goby occurs under a wide range of conditions in brackish to saline waters, from the intertidal zone to depths of 100 m (330 ft) or more, in bays and estuaries or along the open coast and at temperatures from 0 to 24° C (32–75° F).

Gobiosoma oceanops

Gobiosoma multifasciatum

Gobiosoma multifasciatum – greenband goby

Size – To 5 cm (2 in)
Range – Bahamas to the Lesser Antilles.
Feeding – In nature: carnivorous; small invertebrates. In aquarium: brine shrimp nauplii, small worms, prepared foods.
Aquarium care – Provide rocky surfaces with abundant crevices. Suitable in a community tank. Keep at 22–28° C (72–82° F).

This is a shallow-water species usually found in rocky areas hiding under sea urchins. It occurs from just below the surface to about 3 m (10 ft). In captivity it is shy, at least initially.

165

Gobiidae

Eleotrides strigatus

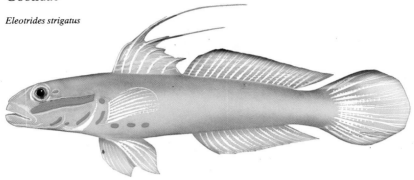

Eleotrides strigatus – golden-headed sleeper (blue-streak goby)

Size – To 15 cm (6 in).
Range – Tropical Indo-Pacific from East Africa to Tahiti; absent from Hawaii.
Feeding – In nature: carnivorous; benthic invertebrates, fish eggs, small fishes. In aquarium: feed a varied diet of live brine shrimp and other planktonic crustaceans if available, plus such foods as frozen krill, small worms, chopped shrimp, squid, and clams; supplement with prepared foods if desired.
Aquarium care – Provide a bottom of mixed sand and rubble with a few rocks so that the fish can construct a burrow. If a subsand filter is used, cover it with a layer of sand which is protected with a plastic screen to prevent the filter from being uncovered. Keep at 22–28°C (72–82°F).

This attractive species requires special attention to ensure that it adapts well to captivity. In nature it is a burrowing species usually found in sandy areas among coral or reef flats and in atoll lagoons. It should be allowed to establish a burrow before other fishes are introduced into the aquarium. Otherwise it can be introduced in a tube buried vertically in sand with its open end covered with netting. After two or three days the netting can be removed and, hopefully, the fish will use the tube as its burrow until it establishes its own.

Nemateleotris magnifica – firefish (magnificent hover-goby)

Size – To 6 cm (2.5 in)
Range – Tropical Indo-Pacific from East Africa to Pitcairn Islands and north to Hawaii.
Feeding – In nature: primarily bottom-swarming plankton, especially copepods. In aquarium: live and frozen brine shrimp, other live planktons, small worms, frozen krill.
Aquarium care – Provide an aquarium with a substrate of 10 cm (4 in) or more, suitable for the construction of burrows. A mixture of sand, gravel, coral rubble, and a few small stones usually works well. Introduce other species only after the gobies are established. Keep at 22–28°C (72–82°F).

Firefish are usually found hovering over sand patches on the seaward slopes of coral reefs at depths ranging from 1 to 60 m (3–200 ft). They live in burrows which may be 30 cm (12 in) or more deep and are difficult to collect. One useful strategy is to wait until the goby has left its burrow, then cover it with a piece of plexiglass. When the goby tries to re-enter, it can then be netted (sometimes!).

Nemateleotris magnifica

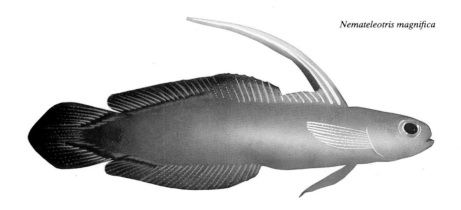

Gobiodon citrinus

Gobiodon citrinus – coral goby

Size – To 6 cm (2.4 in)
Range – Tropical Indo-Pacific from East Africa to Fiji.
Feeding – In nature: carnivorous; worms and other inverte-brates, fish eggs. In aquarium: brine shrimp nauplii, small worms, prepared foods, frozen krill, fish eggs.
Aquarium care – Provide branched and "leafy" coral for cover. May be suitable in community tanks but does best in single-species tanks. Keep at 22–28° C (72–82° F).

The coral goby inhabits the branches of corals. It lays its eggs in the angles at the base of coral branches. This species is highly vari-able in color, ranging from drab green to bright yellow or orange.

Ioglossus

Ioglossus n. sp. – aqua verde flasher (Cortez hover-goby)

Size – To 9 cm (3.5 in)
Range – Gulf of California from Bahía San Augustín, Sonora to Aqua Verde Bay, Baja California.
Feeding – In nature: unknown. Probably bottom-swarming crustaceans. In aquarium: adult and newly hatched live brine shrimp; supplement with small worms, plankton, frozen krill, etc.
Aquarium care – Keep in a single-species tank. Provide a substrate suitable for burrowing. Keep at 20–23° C (68–73° F).

This species has rarely been captured and has not yet been maintained alive. It was first taken at Aqua Verde Bay, Baja California, in 1965 and has since been found at a few other locations. It inhabits mixed sediment and shell bottoms near rocky reefs and poses an inter-esting challenge to the collector aquarist.

Periophthalmus spp. – mudskipper

Size – To 15–30 cm (6–12 in)
Range – Africa and Indo-west Pacific Ocean.
Feeding – In nature: carnivorous; small crustaceans and insects. In aquarium: small live crabs and other crusta-ceans, insects, worms, krill and chopped seafood.
Aquarium care – The aquarium, which must have a secure tightly fitting lid, should be only partially filled and provided with an exposed sand or mud bank at one end and one or more exposed rocks. Mangroves may be used to add authenticity. Keep at 26–30° C (79–85° F).

Because of their aggressiveness, mudskippers are usually kept in single-species tanks. In nature they spend much time out of water, choosing to remain and hunt rather than retreat with the falling tide. Since they rely on accessory air-breathing organs when out of water, they need to be in a tightly covered aquarium in a highly humid atmosphere.

Periophthalmus

167

Surgeonfishes

Surgeonfishes are small to moderate in size, deep-bodied and highly compressed. Typically they have a sharp retractile spine on each side of the caudal peduncle. Some, such as the unicornfish (*Naso* spp.), have two or three separate spines. The area surrounding the spines is often brightly colored. Moorish idols, now normally included in this family, lack the spines. The mouth is terminal, small, and contains small jaw teeth. The dorsal fin is long and continuous; the caudal fin may be truncate, forked or emarginate with long trailing edges. The skin is leather-like and covered with small prickly scales; the lateral line is complete. Most surgeonfishes are diurnal, herbivorous, and graze in shallow water on algae attached to rocks and coral. Some are omnivorous; a few feed on zooplankton. The caudal spines are used in intraspecific territorial and dominance disputes and apparently as a defense against predators. Spawning usually occurs in shallow reefs and may involve pairs or groups. The eggs may be pelagic or demersal and are adhesive. Surgeonfishes occur worldwide in tropical waters. About 75 species are known in nine genera. Many are popular aquarium fishes.

Zebrasoma flavescens – yellow tang

Size – To 20 cm (8 in)
Range – Tropical west and central Pacific Ocean from southern Japan to Hawaii.
Feeding – In nature: primarily filamentous algae. In aquarium: chopped seafood and brine shrimp supplemented with plant matter and prepared foods high in plant matter. If feasible, provide marine algae occasionally.
Aquarium care – Territorial, tends to fight with its own kind. Try keeping one or two in a community tank. Keep at 21–24° C (70–75° F).

The yellow tang occurs at depths from 1 to 30 m (3–100 ft). Shallow-water specimens feed extensively on green algae; deep-water specimens may be omnivorous. This species is easy to capture with a barrier net where coral growth is not too heavy. It also enters traps readily. Yellow tangs are healthiest in large sunlit tanks with a self-sustaining algae growth.

Acanthurus triostegus – convict tang

Size – To 15 cm (6 in)
Range – Circumtropical except the west Atlantic.
Feeding – In nature: primarily filamentous algae. In aquarium: chopped seafood supplemented with plant matter, such as broccoli, peas, spinach, etc. Also prepared foods which contain plant matter.
Aquarium care – Suitable in both single-species and community tanks. Keep several together at 22–28° C (72–82° F) in as large a tank as possible, preferably over 400 liters (100 gal.).

Convict tangs form schools, sometimes huge, as they roam in search of algae. They are abundant on outer-reef flats and on seamounts and are found at depths ranging from the surface to 30 m (100 ft) or more. Juveniles are easily collected in tidepools. Adults can be chased into a barrier net or hand-netted at dusk as they aggregate for their final feeding of the day. This species usually establishes a pecking order in the aquarium, which typically results in the most subordinate fish starving.

Acanthurus triostegus

Prionurus punctatus – yellowtail surgeonfish (cochinito)

Size – To 60 cm (2 ft)

Range – Gulf of California to El Salvador including the Revillagigedo Islands.

Feeding – In nature: herbivorous. In aquarium: accepts a wide variety of foods including fish, squid and clams, etc. Supplement with plant matter if desired.

Aquarium care – Extremely hardy. Only juveniles are suitable for the conventional home aquarium but they grow slowly in captivity and are an excellent addition to the community tank. Keep at 20–23° C (68–73° F).

Adult and juvenile yellowtail surgeonfish form aggregations at depths from less than 3 m to 12 m (10–40 ft) and occasionally to 30 m (100 ft) or more. They can be captured by chasing them into a barrier net or diving by night with scuba and a hand net. Small juveniles are yellow and very similar to the yellow tang (*Zebrasoma flavescens*). They are much less abundant than adults.

Naso unicornis – unicornfish

Size – To 50 cm (20 in)

Range – Tropical Indo-Pacific from East Africa to the Tuamotu Archipelago and Hawaii.

Feeding – In nature: herbivorous, commonly includes *Sargassum* in its diet. In aquarium: chopped seafoods supplemented with prepared foods high in plant material plus *Sargassum* or other algae.

Aquarium care – Usually a single specimen is kept in a large community aquarium that has been provided with coral and rocks. Keep at 22–28°C (72–82° F).

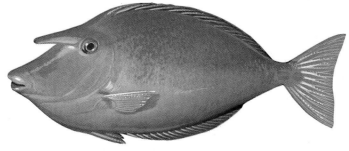

This species is of particular interest because of the horn on its forehead. In nature it occurs singly or in small aggregations in reef channels where it can be captured by hook and line using *Sargassum* as bait, or driven into a barrier net.

Naso lituratus – orangespine unicornfish

Size – To 40 cm (15 in)

Range – Tropical Indo-Pacific from East Africa to the Tuamotu Archipelago and Hawaii.

Feeding – In nature: primarily herbivorous. In aquarium: usually feeds readily on chopped seafood and worms; supplement with plant matter and prepared foods high in plant matter.

Aquarium care – A good aquarium species. Keep several of different sizes in a single-species or community tank. Provide coral and rocks for cover. Keep at 22–28° C (72–82° F).

This species occurs on both exposed and protected reefs, usually around coral heads, at depths ranging from 1 to 40 m (3–130 ft). It can be captured by barrier net.

Acanthurus lineatus – clown surgeonfish

Size – To 28 cm (11 in)

Range – Tropical Indo-Pacific from East Africa to the Tuamotu Archipelago.

Feeding – In nature: primarily herbivorous; filamentous green algae. In aquarium: prepared foods rich in plant matter, supplemented with chopped seafoods, live brine shrimp and if possible green algae.

Aquarium care – Small specimens are suitable for the home aquarium; however, they tend to be quarrelsome with each other. Keep only one specimen in a community tank and provide ample hiding spaces. The aquarium should be at least 75 liters (20 gal.). Keep at 22–28° C (72–82° F).

This species is most abundant in the shallow waters of outer reef flats and reef faces down to 6 m (20 ft). It can be trapped or captured with a barrier net.

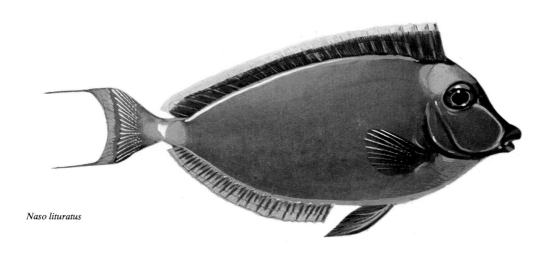

Naso lituratus

Acanthurus lineatus

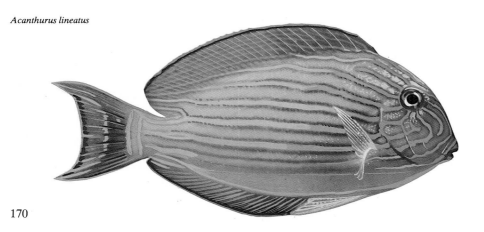

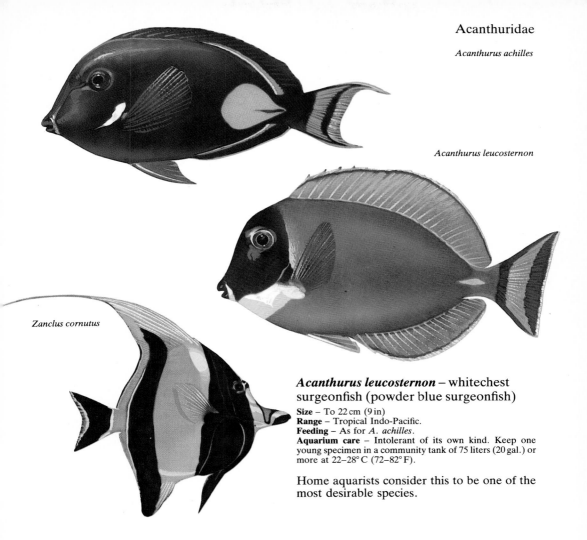

Acanthurus achilles

Acanthurus leucosternon

Zanclus cornutus

Acanthurus leucosternon – whitechest surgeonfish (powder blue surgeonfish)

Size – To 22 cm (9 in)
Range – Tropical Indo-Pacific.
Feeding – As for *A. achilles*.
Aquarium care – Intolerant of its own kind. Keep one young specimen in a community tank of 75 liters (20 gal.) or more at 22–28° C (72–82° F).

Home aquarists consider this to be one of the most desirable species.

Zanclus cornutus (= Z. canescens) – Moorish idol

Size – To 23 cm (9 in)
Range – Tropical Indo-Pacific from East Africa to Panama including Hawaii and the Gulf of California.
Feeding – In nature: omnivorous including sponges, coralline algae and crevice-dwelling invertebrates. In aquarium: sometimes difficult to feed. Try chopped shrimp, squid and clams along with live brine shrimp, krill, small worms and plant matter. Usually accepts broccoli.
Aquarium care – Several can be kept together in a community tank except with fin-nipping species. They do best in a large aquarium with ample swimming space and "bolt-holes" (shelters which have at least two entrances). Keep at 20–28° C (68–82° F).

This is a popular species but it can be finicky in captivity. It does best with plenty of space and cover. Easily collected at night with scuba and a hand net.

Acanthurus achilles – Achilles tang

Size – To 25 cm (10 in)
Range – Tropical western and central Pacific from Melanesia to Hawaii.
Feeding – In nature: primarily herbivorous. In aquarium: chopped seafood such as clams, squid, fish, etc. supplemented with plant matter and prepared foods containing plant matter.
Aquarium care – Suitable in community tanks. Young specimens do best. Keep one in a community tank of 75 liters (20 gal.) or more at 21–24° C (70–75° F).

This is an inshore species usually found near coral reefs, often in surge channels. It can be trapped or captured with a barrier net.

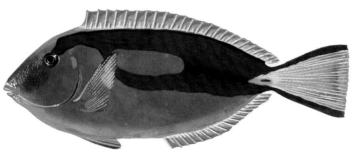

Feeding – In nature: primarily herbivorous. In aquarium: chopped clams and squid, supplemented with algae and plant matter or prepared foods rich in plant matter.
Aquarium care – It is usually best to keep a single specimen in a community tank. Provide a large swimming area and some cover amongst rocks and coral.

Paracanthurus heptatus – flame-tail surgeonfish (flag-tail surgeonfish)

Size – To 25 cm (10 in)
Range – Tropical Indo-Pacific from East Africa to the Line Islands.

This species is widespread but nowhere abundant. In some areas, such as Guam, it has become quite rare because of overcollecting.

ORDER PERCIFORMES – FAMILY SIGANIDAE

Rabbitfishes

Like the surgeonfishes, rabbitfishes possess protective spines, but in this case it is the spines of the dorsal and anal fins which are venomous and can cause a painful sting. Rabbitfishes are compressed, deep-bodied fishes with small to moderate mouths and teeth adapted for grazing on vegetation. They vary from brightly colored and conspicuous, especially as juveniles, to drab and cryptic. Many species occur in schools on reef flats or in lagoons. Some species as adults are found on reef slopes to depths of 30 m (100 ft) or more. This is a small family which includes only two genera and about 10 species, distributed in the tropical marine waters of the Indo-Pacific region and eastern Mediterranean Sea. Only one species is normally of interest to aquarists.

Lo vulpinus – fox-face (fox-fish)

Size – To 25 cm (10 in)
Range – Tropical Pacific from the East Indies to the Marshall Islands.
Feeding – In nature: primarily herbivorous. In aquarium: accepts most aquarium foods; be sure to include plant matter.
Aquarium care – Aggressive toward its own species but peaceful with other species. Keep one or a pair in a large community tank with an ample area of open sand. Keep at 22–28° C (72–82° F).

This species is common in shallow weedy areas but is also found on wrecks and reefs. Caution: its dorsal spines are venomous and can cause painful injuries during handling.

Dragonets and Mandarin Fishes

Dragonets and mandarin fishes are small bottom-dwelling fishes with flattened heads and large filamentous fins. The head is usually broad and flattened, with large eyes which are superior in position. The mouth is small and terminal with weak teeth; the gill openings are reduced. Two dorsal fins are present. The caudal fin may be truncated, rounded or lanceolate, with pronounced rays. Dragonets and mandarin fishes occur from intertidal areas and shallow reefs to deeper waters. Many species hide in the sand during the day. Sexual dimorphism is common, with the males having larger fins. Fertilization is internal. The eggs are pelagic. These fishes are found worldwide in tropical seas. About 40 species are known in eight genera. Several species are attractive aquarium fishes, but tend to be delicate.

Synchiropus picturatus – spotted mandarin fish (psychodelic fish)

Size – To 10 cm (4 in)
Range – Tropical west Pacific.
Feeding – In nature: carnivorous. In aquarium: small worms, Tubifex, etc. and crustaceans including live brine shrimp; prepared foods.

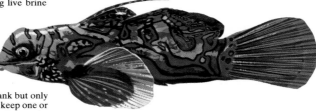

Aquarium care – Can be kept in a community tank but only with peaceful species. Aquarists often prefer to keep one or a pair in a single-species tank. Provide a sand bottom and a few shallow crevices for cover. Keep at 22–28° C (72–82° F).

This species is usually found in quiet, shallow waters. In Palau it is common at the base of sea walls in the inner lagoons where it can be collected with a hand net or fish anesthetics.

Triggerfishes

Triggerfishes are characterized by a trigger mechanism which locks their stout dorsal and anal fin spines in an erect position, allowing the fish to wedge itself tightly in a crevice to escape capture. They are deep-bodied compressed fishes, wedge-shaped anteriorly, with a small terminal mouth and protruding incisors. The eyes are small. The body is covered with rough, squarish scales and leathery skin. Two dorsal fins are present. The second is placed well back on the body, symmetrically opposed to the anal fin. The tail may be truncate, emarginate or sometimes rounded. Triggerfishes are primarily shallow-water inshore species, common on coral and rocky reefs. They are usually solitary, but some species may form aggregations, sometimes in surface waters. They are well adapted to feeding on a variety of hard-shelled animals, including urchins, crabs and corals. Most species will readily take bait. At night they wedge themselves in crevices for protection, at which time they can be easily collected by divers by depressing the second dorsal spine to release the trigger and allow removal of the fish from the crevice. When cruising on the reefs, triggerfishes use the dorsal and anal fins for locomotion. When pursued they use the caudal fin for additional propulsion. Many triggerfishes are good to eat but some species, especially when large, are known to cause ciguatera poisoning. Approximately 120 species are

173

known from the tropical Atlantic, Pacific and Indian Oceans. A few venture into temperate waters. Triggerfishes are often colorful and many are popular aquarium fishes. They are hardy, but some species are aggressive and difficult tank-mates.

Balistoides conspicillum

Balistoides conspicillum (= B. niger) – clown triggerfish

Size – To 50 cm (20 in)
Range – Tropical Indo-Pacific from East Africa to Samoa.
Feeding – In nature: carnivorous; able to capitalize on hard-shelled invertebrates. In aquarium: chopped seafood, whole crabs and other aquarium foods.
Aquarium care – Small specimens are suitable in the community tank, but may become aggressive as they grow and have to be removed. Provide crevices for cover. Keep at 22–28° C (72–82° F).

This is a highly prized aquarium species, but it tends to dominate its tank-mates. The clown triggerfish is usually found on outer-reef slopes and drop-offs. It is also relatively common on shipwrecks. Depths normally range from 3 to 40 m (10–130 ft). The significance of its pattern is unknown but it has been observed to roll over and flash its belly spots when pursued, perhaps a maneuver to confuse predators visually.

Balistapus undulatus – undulated triggerfish (orange-lined triggerfish)

Size – To 30 cm (12 in)
Range – Tropical Indo-Pacific except Hawaii (and North America).
Feeding – In nature: carnivorous; includes coral in its diet. In aquarium: chopped seafood, such as shrimp, clams, squid, and fish; should also be provided with a plaster of Paris food block.
Aquarium care – Aggressive, may have to be separated from tank-mates. Keep at 22–28° C (72–82° F).

Try small specimens in community tanks, but be prepared to remove them if they are too combative. Common on the outer reef slopes to 40 m (130 ft).

Balistapus undulatus

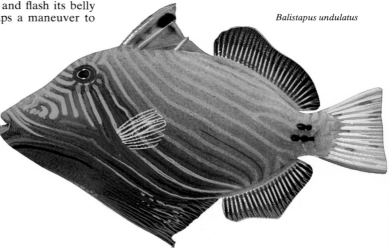

Balistes vetula

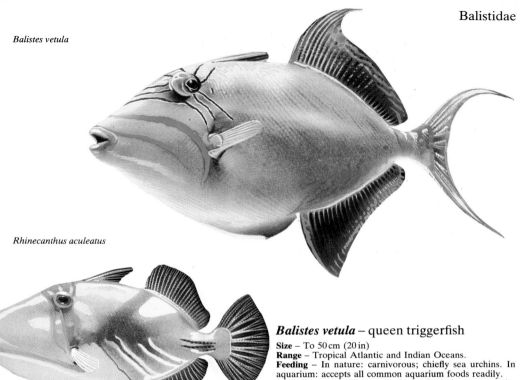

Rhinecanthus aculeatus

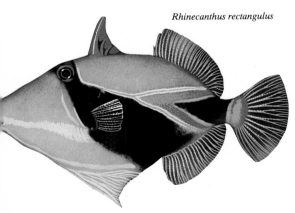

Rhinecanthus aculeatus – Picasso fish (humu-humu-nuku-nuku-a-puaa)

Size – To 30 cm (12 in)
Range – Tropical Indo-Pacific from East Africa to Polynesia including Hawaii.
Feeding – In nature: carnivorous; feeds on crustaceans and other invertebrates. In aquarium: chopped fish, squid and clams; other foods if desired.
Aquarium care – Small specimens are suitable in community tanks. Provide crevices. Keep at 22–28°C (72–82°F).

This is a well-known aquarium species. Usually only a single specimen is kept in a community tank. It is common in shallow protected areas and can be collected from crevices.

Rhinecanthus rectangulus

Balistes vetula – queen triggerfish

Size – To 50 cm (20 in)
Range – Tropical Atlantic and Indian Oceans.
Feeding – In nature: carnivorous; chiefly sea urchins. In aquarium: accepts all common aquarium foods readily.
Aquarium care – Keep a single specimen in a community tank. Provide crevices for cover at night. Keep at 22–24°C (70–75°F).

One of the most attractive and frequently seen triggerfish in aquaria. It is peaceful with other species although combative with its own kind. As they mature, sexual dimorphism develops; males become more brightly colored and develop longer trailing edges on their dorsal, anal, and caudal fins. They apparently have not reproduced successfully in captivity.

Rhinecanthus rectangulus – humu humu (humu-humu-nuku-nuku-a-apua)

Size – To 23 cm (9 in)
Range – Tropical Indo-Pacific from East Africa to Polynesia including Hawaii.
Feeding – In nature: omnivorous; includes crustaceans, urchins and algae in its diet. In aquarium: chopped seafoods; supplement with plant matter if desired.
Aquarium care – This species is usually more combative than the Picasso fish. Although a single specimen can usually be kept in a community tank, it should be watched and removed if it causes problems. Keep at 22–28°C (72–82°F).

Adults tend to be found on the outer reef in areas of surge. Juveniles may be found in tidepools and can sometimes be collected by picking up rocks with holes that contain hiding fish.

Balistidae

Sufflamen verres – orangemice triggerfish

Size – To 38 cm (15 in)
Range – Baja California to Ecuador.
Feeding – In nature: carnivorous; includes crustaceans, urchins, molluscs and worms in its diet. In aquarium: chopped seafoods; does well on a fish and squid diet.
Aquarium care – Suitable in community tanks. Keep at 20–24° C (68–75° F).

This is a hardy species that adapts easily and is long-lived in captivity. Juvenile specimens are well suited to the home aquarium but are not abundant in nature. Active by day, this species usually occurs singly and seeks crevices for protection at night. It can be captured by day or night by releasing the first dorsal spine by hand and removing the fish from a crevice.

Xanthichthys mento – pink-tailed triggerfish

Size – To 30 cm (12 in)
Range – Tropical Pacific.
Feeding – In nature: omnivorous. In aquarium: feeds readily on almost anything it is offered.
Aquarium care – Hardy and active; usually visible. Suitable in large community tanks with large fishes. Keep at 20–30° C (68–86° F).

The pink-tailed triggerfish is most common on the outer slopes of coral reefs and off the steep faces of seamounts where it is often pelagic. Although adapted to preying on hard-shelled invertebrates, it will scavenge anything organic including ship-board waste. It can be easily captured by hook and line. A close relative, the sargassum triggerfish (*X. ringens*), occurs in the Atlantic Ocean and is an excellent aquarium species.

Sufflamen verres

Melichthys nigel

Xanthichthys mento

Melichthys niger – black triggerfish (black durgon)

Size – To 36 cm (14 in)
Range – Tropical Indian, Pacific and Atlantic Oceans.
Feeding – In nature: omnivorous; capable of feeding on hard-shelled animals such as crabs and urchins. In aquarium: chopped fish, squid and clams supplemented with crabs and plant matter.
Aquarium care – Small specimens are excellent fishes for the home community tank. They are hardy and active, yet peaceful. Keep at 22–28° C (72–82° F).

Although dark green or black in general appearance, the light blue lines along the base of the dorsal and anal fins give this species a distinctive appearance. It is usually found on the outer slope of coral reefs. Like other triggerfishes it can be captured in crevices by depressing the second spine of the dorsal fin to "unlock" it.

Oxymonacanthus longirostris – long-nosed filefish

Size – To 10 cm (4 in)
Range – Tropical Indo-Pacific from the Red Sea to Samoa.
Feeding – In nature: primarily coral polyps. In aquarium: try a mixed diet of chopped seafoods, brine shrimp, small worms and frozen krill along with prepared foods.
Aquarium care – Keep several together in a single-species tank. Provide coral for cover. Keep at 22–28° C (72–82°F).

Feeding is a problem since in nature this species feeds on coral polyps; experiment to find a diet that is both nutritious and acceptable. After this species has acclimated and is feeding, you may wish to try introducing it into a community tank; but be sure it gets enough to eat. The filefish is usually found in shallow water among coral branches where it is difficult to collect.

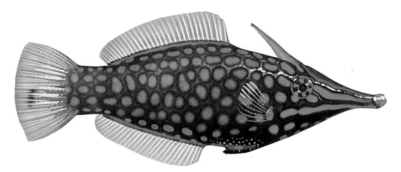

Oxymonacanthus longirostris

ORDER TETRAODONTIFORMES – FAMILY TETRAODONTIDAE

Puffers

Puffers are soft-bodied fishes which can gulp water to enlarge themselves and thus discourage predators. They have strong jaws with the teeth fused to form four beak-like incisors, two in each jaw. The dorsal and anal fins have soft-rays only and along with the anal fin provide the main propulsion. Although slow-swimming, they are maneuverable and can swim backward with ease. The scales may be modified as prickles or absent. The viscera of some species (e.g. "the fugus") contains a deadly toxin. Puffers are found worldwide in tropical and temperate seas in a wide variety of habitats. Approximately 10 species are known, distributed in 10 genera. Most species have been successfully kept in community tanks.

Canthigaster punctatissima

Canthigaster punctatissima – sharpnose puffer

Size – To 9 cm (3.5 in)
Range – Gulf of California to Panama.
Feeding – In nature: unknown. In aquarium: does well on a diet of chopped seafood plus live brine shrimp.
Aquarium care – Suitable in community tanks; but it can be combative with its own species. Keep at 20–24° C (68–75° F). Regular partial water changes are recommended.

This species is very common in the Gulf of California along the southern Baja California peninsula. It is a poor swimmer that usually stays close to cover and is easily caught with a hand net. This species also exudes a toxic mucus when handled or frightened but it can be kept successfully in a large community tank of 400 liters (50 gal.) or more. Several close relatives, including the saddled sharpnose puffer (*C. valentini*) of the Indo-west Pacific, may be available to the hobbyist.

Arothron meleagris – spotted puffer (guinea fowl puffer)

Size – To 30 cm (12 in)
Range – Tropical Pacific.
Feeding – In nature: carnivorous; feeds on a variety of invertebrates ranging from coral to tunicates. In aquarium: chopped seafood.
Aquarium care – Produces a toxic mucus but can be kept successfully in large aquaria. Keep at 22–28° C (68–82° F). Regular partial water changes are recommended, especially when this species is first introduced.

Similar precaution to the previous species is recommended. This species has a conspicuous golden phase, the ecological significance of which is not understood. Easy to collect.

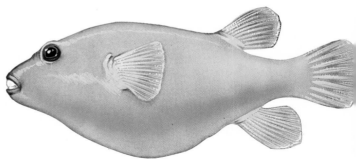

Arothron meleagris – golden phase

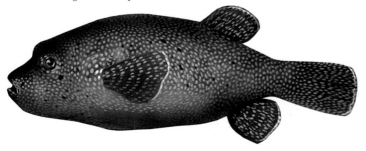

Arothron meleagris – normal phase

Boxfishes, Cowfishes and Trunkfishes

Boxfishes are small, slow-swimming, box-shaped fishes which have their bodies enclosed in bony plates. The skin contains a toxic substance which is released when the fish is stressed. In a closed space this can be fatal to itself or other fishes. They tend to be avoided by predatory fishes even though they are often found in the open and conspicuous. When shipping these species, each fish should be enclosed in a separate container and when introducing them into an aquarium precautions must be taken to avoid poisoning tank-mates. Sexual dimorphism occurs in some species with the male being more colorful and less robust than the female. Boxfishes are found worldwide in tropical seas. About 25 species are known in 12 genera.

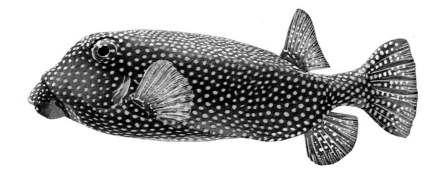

Ostracion meleagris

Lactoria fornasina – five-horned cowfish

Size – To 15 cm (6 in)
Range – Tropical Indo-Pacific from East Africa to Hawaii.
Feeding – In nature: primarily sand-dwelling invertebrates. In aquarium: chopped seafoods, worms, krill.
Aquarium care – Beware: this species exudes toxic mucus when excited. Keep in a single-species tank or introduce it into a community tank by itself and wait two weeks before adding other fishes. Keep at 22–28° C (72–82° F). Regular, partial water changes are recommended.

These fishes are recommended primarily for the advanced aquarist. They require special handling because of the toxins they exude from the skin which can kill both themselves and their tank-mates. When shipping, pack only one per bag.

Ostracion meleagris – Pacific boxfish (white-spotted boxfish)

Size – To 15 cm (6 in)
Range – Tropical Indian and Pacific Oceans.
Feeding – In nature: primarily benthic invertebrates and algae. In aquarium: chopped fish, squid, clams and shrimp; prepared foods.
Aquarium care – Suitable only in a large tank to which it should be acclimated before other fish are added. Keep at 22–28° C (72–82° F). Regular partial water changes are recommended.

Like other boxfishes and cowfishes, this species exudes toxic substances when disturbed. However, with suitable precautions it can be successfully maintained.

Lactoria fornasina

Porcupinefishes (Spiny Puffers)

Porcupinefishes have much in common with the smooth puffers but have their scales modified as spines and contain only a single fused canine tooth in the front of each jaw. They are found worldwide in tropical seas or sometimes in temperate waters. Only about 15 species are known, distributed in five genera. Small specimens make interesting additions to community tanks.

Diodon holocanthus

Diodon holocanthus – porcupinefish (balloon fish, pez erizo)

Size – To 45 cm (18 in)
Range – Circumtropical.
Feeding – In nature: invertebrates. In aquarium: chopped seafood.
Aquarium care – Small specimens are suitable in community tanks. Keep at 20–28° C (68–82° F).

Spiny puffers are not normally of interest to aquarists because of their large size. This species is widely available and easily captured.

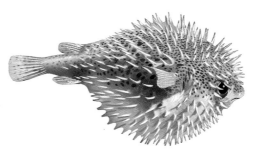

Diodon hystrix

Righteye Flounders

Adult flatfishes have highly compressed bodies, but lie on one side. Young flatfishes are normal in shape. As they develop torsion occurs, and both eyes migrate to one side of the head. The fish then lie on the eyeless side. Pleuronectidae are predominantly right-sided, although, as is also the case with the lefteye flounders, both right-sided and left-sided may occur within the same species. Righteye flounders are found primarily in cooler waters ranging from polar through the temperature regions and over a wide depth range. Some occur in brackish water, a few in fresh water. About 100 species are known, distributed in 41 genera.

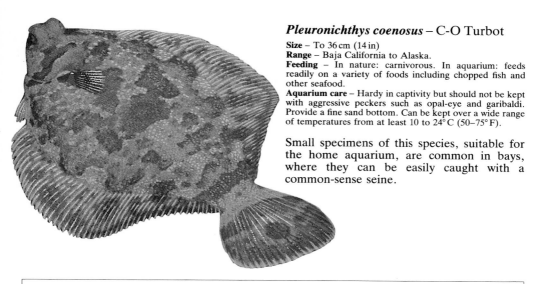

Pleuronichthys coenosus – C-O Turbot

Size – To 36 cm (14 in)
Range – Baja California to Alaska.
Feeding – In nature: carnivorous. In aquarium: feeds readily on a variety of foods including chopped fish and other seafood.
Aquarium care – Hardy in captivity but should not be kept with aggressive peckers such as opal-eye and garibaldi. Provide a fine sand bottom. Can be kept over a wide range of temperatures from at least 10 to 24° C (50–75° F).

Small specimens of this species, suitable for the home aquarium, are common in bays, where they can be easily caught with a common-sense seine.

ORDER PLEURONECTIFORMES – FAMILY BOTHIDAE

Lefteye Flounders

Members of this family are predominantly left-sided; that is, the eyes are on the left side of the head, which faces upward. They are common on soft bottoms over a wide depth range, and occur primarily in tropical and temperate seas. Most are carnivorous and feed on small fishes and crustaceans. Over 200 species are known in 36 genera.

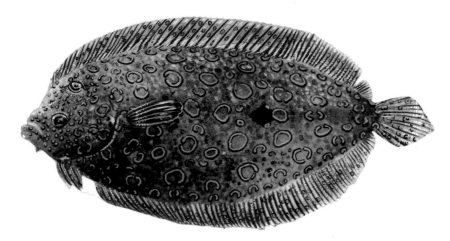

Bothus mancus – Pacific peacock flounder

Size – To 40 cm (16 in)
Range – Tropical Indo-Pacific from East Africa to Pitcairn Island and north to Hawaii.
Feeding – In nature: carnivorous; feeds on benthic crustaceans and fishes. In aquarium: chopped clams, squid and fish.
Aquarium care – Small specimens are suitable for the home aquarium and can be kept in community tanks provided with large areas of sand. Keep at 22–28° C (72–82° F).

Flatfish are an often forgotten addition to the community tank. They are widespread on sandy areas of the reef flat and lagoon where a keen observer can collect them with a hand net.

181

INVERTEBRATES

Donald Wilkie – H. Douglas Kemper Jr.

For convenience we usually speak of animals as vertebrates (with backbones) and invertebrates (without backbones). The vertebrates – fishes, amphibians, reptiles, birds and mammals – are contained in a single phylum, Phylum Chordata. Invertebrates, on the other hand, are a much larger group dispersed in over 30 phyla, represented by hundreds of thousands of species making up over 95% of all living animals now known to science. In the home aquarium, many predatory invertebrates are readily maintained on live whole or chopped seafoods similar to their natural prey. The algae-feeders generally do well if provided with suitable, natural or prepared plant food. The plankton-feeders can be supplied with "clam milk" consisting of finely minced or liquefied clams, worms, fish and other seafoods mixed with a small amount of aquarium water; this should be administered upon or near the animal through an eyedropper or with planktonic organisms including brine shrimp. It may be a good idea to turn off pumps and filters for a short time to eliminate currents during the feeding process. Generally, all marine invertebrates require the same excellent water quality and other conditions as for any fish aquarium.

Sea Anemones

About 1,000 species of anemones live from tidepools to the dark depths, and from the poles to the tropics in all oceans of the world. Resemblance to a group of natural flowers suggested the name but, of course, anemones are not plants. They are animals in the same phylum as jellyfishes and corals. Many anemones have striking patterns and vivid colors. Some of the large tropical forms are partners with certain fishes, shrimps and other symbionts, and may be quite important to the aquarium. All, from the smallest of about 5 cm (2 in) in diameter to the giants of over 1 m (36 in) across, make interesting and attractive subjects for the marine aquarist. Some, such as the plumose anemone *Metridium*, are plankton-feeders. But most are predators, paralyzing fishes and other prey with multitudes of tiny poisonous darts, nematocysts, which line the tentacles. Contact with the tentacles of some species can prove quite painful.

Stoichactis spp. – giant anemone

Size – To 1.5 m (60 in) in diameter
Range – Tropical coral reefs worldwide.
Feeding – In nature: preys on fishes and other reef forms. In aquarium: whole live or chopped seafoods placed on tentacles.

Truly a giant of a sea anemone, these animals are quite hardy in a well-maintained marine aquarium.

Acropora cervicornis – staghorn coral

Size – To 300 cm (120 in) high
Range – Florida Keys, Bahamas and West Indies to Brazil.
Feeding – In nature: plankton. In aquarium: newly hatched brine shrimp.

Staghorn coral is difficult to maintain alive. Its skeleton may be used for esthetics and cover. Similar coral is widespread in the tropical Indo-Pacific.

Anthopleura xanthogrammica – giant green anemone

Size – To 20 cm (8 in) in diameter
Range – North Pacific from Alaska to Panama.
Feeding – In nature: fishes and other small marine organisms. In aquarium: whole or cut pieces of seafood placed on tentacles.

Specimens of this large anemone, and its smaller relative *A. elegantissima* from the cold North Pacific, should be kept at around 10°C (50°F) in a refrigerated marine aquarium. Those collected in warmer regions can be kept at ambient ocean temperatures.

Tealia lofotensis – strawberry anemone

Size – To 10 cm (4 in) in diameter
Range – Washington State to San Diego.
Feeding – In nature: all manner of marine organisms. In aquarium: pieces of seafood.

Occurs from the low intertidal zone to 15 m (50 ft) deep and survives well in aquaria. Does best at temperatures below 15°C (59°F).

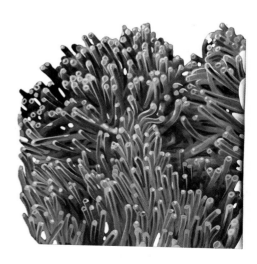

Corynactis californica – pink colonial anemone

Size – To 2.5 cm (1 in) in diameter
Range – Central California to Mexico.
Feeding – In nature: plankton. In aquarium: live adult and newly hatched brine shrimp and other small crustaceans including finely chopped seafoods.

This bright attractive colonial anemone adds color to the temperate-zone aquarium. It does well at cool room temperatures of 20°C (68°F) or less. Occurs from the low intertidal zone to 30 m (100 ft) or deeper. Common on floats, wharves and sea structures as well as rocky faces and reefs. May be found with sea fans and other attached invertebrates.

Radianthus spp. – clownfish anemone

Size – To more than 25 cm (10 in) in diameter
Range – Tropical Indo-Pacific coral reefs.
Feeding – In nature: fishes and other reef forms. In aquarium: whole or chopped seafoods placed on tentacles.

Many of the large anemones are symbiotic with other animals, but *Radianthus* is the typical "clownfish" anemone.

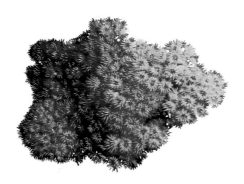

Balanophyllia elegans – orange cup coral

Size – To 12 cm (5 in) high
Range – British Columbia, Canada to Mexico.
Feeding – In nature: plankton. In aquarium: does well on newly hatched and adult brine shrimp; also other live plankton.

Keep in a cool aquarium at 10–20° C (50–68° F) with subdued lighting.

Cerianthus spp. – tube anemone

Size – Large species may have tube lengths exceeding 60 cm (24 in) and tentacle spreads of 15 cm (6 in)
Range – About 50 species are found in both warm and cold seas worldwide.
Feeding – In nature: prey on various marine forms. In aquarium: small whole or cut pieces of seafood placed on tentacles.

Cerianthus usually requires a deep substrate of 15 cm (6 in) or more for burrowing. Proper temperature depends on the species and its natural habitat.

PHYLUM ANNELIDA

Worms

Of the 30 or so animal phyla, about 13 are groups of "worms" – flatworms, ribbon worms, round worms, horsehair worms, arrow worms, acorn worms, beard worms, segmented worms and others. All are represented in the marine environment. Some are parasitic, but many others are free-living. The most familiar are the annelids or segmented worms which include the earthworms on land, and the polychaetes of the sea. A few colorful tropical flatworms are available occasionally to the aquarist but more often it is the fan and featherduster worms that find their way into the marine aquarium. These worms are represented by two major groups, serpulids which secrete hard calcareous tubes, and sabellids with more flexible, membranous tubes. Each retracts rapidly into the tube at the first hint of danger.

CLASS POLYCHAETA
Spirobranchus giganteus – spiral-gilled or Christmas tree worm

Size – Gills to 2 cm (1 in)
Range – Tropical coral reefs.
Feeding – In nature: plankton. In aquarium: newly hatched brine shrimp and "clam milk."

This sabellid usually burrows in coral. As with all tube worms, your specimen will have to get accustomed to slow movements of an eye-dropper to receive sufficient nutrients.

Molluscs

Mollusc means "soft-bodied," but most molluscs secrete a tough external shell for protection. There are over 120,000 species in the phylum including a diverse variety of chitons, snails, slugs, tusk shells, clams, oysters, mussels, octopods, cuttlefish and squids. Some are difficult to maintain in the aquarium as it may be impossible to supply their specialized diets, or because of the ease with which others prey upon and eliminate them. Many molluscs, however, make interesting and challenging additions to your captive marine environment, even if you must set up one or more special aquaria.

CLASS GASTROPODA

The class Gastropoda includes the aquatic and terrestrial snails, slugs and nudibranchs. It is the largest group of molluscs, with over 100,000 species characterized by a single shell, usually spiral in shape, and a larger muscular foot for locomotion. When danger threatens, most snails retract into their shells. Many species have an operculum, a hard shell-like plate, which effectively seals the opening. Other protection is required by the shell-less land slugs and marine nudibranchs. The slugs secrete a distasteful slime. The colorful nudibranchs may also be distasteful to some predators, but many that feed on anemones and other coelenteretes retain the poisonous nematocysts of their prey intact, and transport it to their own skins for protection.

Cypraea spp. – cowries

Size – The largest species reach 13 cm (5 in) in length
Range – Warm and tropical seas worldwide.
Feeding – In nature: forage on algae and detritus. In aquarium: graze on algae, detritus and may scavenge to some degree.

Most cowries live on sand and coral bottoms around reefs. The shells are prized by collectors, but in life they may be camouflaged by the large mantle.

Murex spp. – murex

Size – Some species grow to 13 cm (5 in)
Range – Temperate and tropical seas worldwide.
Feeding – In nature: predatory on other molluscs, fishes and other small marine creatures. In aquarium: live or cut seafoods.

Murex shells are heavily ornamented and sought by collectors. They require good water quality, but the temperature depends on the species and its natural habitat.

Cyphoma gibbosum – flamingo tongue snail

Size – To 3 cm (1.25 in)
Range – North Carolina to the West Indies.
Feeding – In nature: sea fans and other soft coral polyps. In aquarium: try a wide variety of chopped seafoods plus assorted marine organisms.

The smallish flamingo tongues are related to the cowries. They are quite colorful but are difficult to maintain due to their specialized food requirements.

Cones

Cones are warm-water and coral-reef animals with beautifully marked, colorful shells. They are highly prized by collectors. Most snails eat by means of the radula, a rasping row of teeth, used to scrape algae, or bite through the flesh of prey. In the cones the radula is modified into a single barbed tooth connected to a venom gland and used as a dart to paralyze prey. The auger shells *Terebra* are similarly equipped, and while they are not known to be dangerous to man, some cones can be fatal. Members of both groups should be considered extremely hazardous and are not recommended for the home aquarium.

Conus californicus – California cone snail

Size – To 5 cm (2 in)
Range – Warmer seas worldwide. Central California to Baja California, Mexico.
Feeding – In nature: predatory on fishes, worms, other molluscs and small marine animals. In aquarium: live fishes, worms and other marine animals depending on species.

Although most species of cones are not recommended for the home aquarium, the California cone is not known to have caused serious injury to humans.

Nudibranchs

Also known as "sea slugs," these animals are snails without shells. Many are gorgeous creatures with bright colors and striking patterns. Most are species-specific as to their food and feed exclusively on certain soft corals and similar organisms which are difficult to supply in the home aquarium. While there are a number of tropical and warm-water species of nudibranchs, the group is more diverse and abundant in colder waters, particularly northeast Pacific areas such as Puget Sound. The sea hares, which are not nudibranchs but are close relatives, are herbivorous and might be more easily maintained in the larger home aquarium.

Hermissenda crassicornis – nudibranch

Size – To 5 cm (2 in)
Range – North Pacific; Puget Sound.
Feeding – In nature: hydroids, ascidians, eggs and other molluscs; may also scavenge. In aquarium: small whole, or pieces of seafoods.

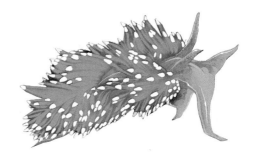

Most nudibranchs are difficult to supply with their specific foods in captivity, but *Hermissenda* is less fussy and fares well in the cold-water aquarium around 10° C (50° F). Those captured in shallow water south of Point Conception, California, will tolerate warmer water.

Octopuses

"Devilfish" was the name used historically for the monster of all sea monsters, the octopus. The octopus may look like a fearful creature, but in reality it is a shy and retiring sort. A number of species live in all oceans of the world. The largest, *O. dolfleini* of the North Pacific, can have an arm span of over 7 m (20 ft) and weigh more than 50 kg (100 lb), but the majority span less than 30 cm (12 in). Octopods are members of the class Cephalopoda, which means "head-foot." Their relatives include the cuttlefish, nautiluses and squids, all of which have arms or tentacles lined with sucker-like disks with which they capture or hold their prey. Many, if not most, cephalopods have venom glands associated with their parrot-like beaks and can inflict a dangerous bite. Some squids bite fiercely when handled, but octopods seem quite gentle and usually refuse to bite. There is an exception; the smallish blue-ringed octopus (*Hapalochlaena maculosa*) of the tropical Pacific is not bashful in biting and its venom has proved fatal to man. This species should not be kept in the home aquarium. Squids and cuttlefish prove difficult to maintain in the aquarium, but many of the small octopods do quite well if provided with adequate shelter and a secure, tight-fitting lid. Since octopods are among the most intelligent of creatures, the lid is of great importance as these escape artists can slither through the tiniest of openings. Any space large enough to accommodate the small hard beak may mean that the creature will end up desiccated on the carpet.

Octopus bimaculatus – two-spotted octopus

Size – To 75 cm (30 in) in length
Range – Southern California to Baja California, Mexico.
Feeding – In nature: crabs, shrimp, fishes and molluscs. In aquarium: same as in nature, prefers live foods.

The spots on the body of this species are large with dark centers and usually bordered by a dark ring. Subtropical water temperatures are suitable.

Crustaceans

Over 30,000 species of crustaceans are found in the largest phylum of animals, the Arthropoda, which has 1,000,000 species of insects, spiders, mites, millipedes, centipedes and others among its members. The marine crabs, shrimps, hermit crabs and barnacles make up the crustaceans of most interest to the aquarist. The barnacles and some of the smaller shrimps and crabs are plankton-feeders, and some can be maintained on "clam milk" in the aquarium. The larger crabs and hermits are, however, voracious predators and scavengers. Given the same good water quality and other conditions required by the properly maintained marine aquarium, these species usually thrive. Crustaceans have hard exoskeletons, which they must shed periodically in order to grow. It is not uncommon to find whole skeletons in the aquarium after shedding. It takes a little time, usually a few days, for the new exoskeleton to harden. During this time the animal is quite vulnerable to predators such as fishes and other crustaceans. Be sure there are plenty of hiding places for your specimen, or gently place it in a safe container or other aquarium until the crucial period passes. In addition to the aforementioned animals, the subphylum Crustacea also contains the lobsters. Tropical species, usually available to the hobbyist, are not closely related to the

Atlantic "clawed" lobster *Homarus*, but the genera *Panulirus* and *Jassus* include interesting representatives of the group.

Pagurus acadianus – acadian hermit crab

Size – To 3 cm (1.25 in)
Range – Florida to Texas including the Bahamas and West Indies.
Feeding – In nature: scavenges, or preys on fishes, worms and other sea life. In aquarium: pieces of seafood.

Hermit crabs are generally easily maintained, but are voracious predators. They must be provided with a selection of new, larger shell "homes" as they grow.

Hymenocera picta – painted prawn

Size – To 6 cm (2.5 in)
Range – Tropical Indo-Pacific.
Feeding – In nature: feeds exclusively on seastars. In aquarium: seastars, and various seafoods.
Aquarium care – Provide rocky crevices and coral for cover. Keep at 24–28° C (75–82° F). Suitable in community tanks with small-mouthed peaceful species.

Lysmata wurdemanni – cleaner shrimp

Size – To 7 cm (3 in)
Range – Chesapeake Bay to Brazil.
Feeding – Ectoparasites, organic detritus, small attached organisms.

Besides the banded coral shrimp, many other species of cleaner shrimps are available to the marine aquarist. Grabham's cleaning shrimp (*Lysmata grabhami*) from the West Indies is particularly attractive. On the west coast the striped tidepool shrimp *Hippolysmata californica* is a common cleaner of the moray and suitable for the home aquarium.

Squilla empusa – mantis shrimp

Size – To 25 cm (10 in)
Range – Atlantic coast of the United States to Brazil.
Feeding – In nature: digs burrows to await its prey of small fishes and other forms. In aquarium: live or dead, whole or cut seafood.

Smaller reef forms are available to the aquarist, but regardless of size be careful of the powerful, rapacious claw, which can inflict a painful injury.

Crustacea

Stenopus hispidus – banded coral shrimp

Size – To 8 cm (3 in) in length
Range – Widely distributed in warmer seas.
Feeding – In nature: a cleaning shrimp; picks ectoparasites from fishes. In aquarium: finely chopped seafoods.

This shrimp establishes a cleaning station on the reef and in the aquarium, and picks parasites from the regular fish visitors.

Petrolisthes spp. – porcelain crab

Size – Usually to 2.5 cm (1 in)
Range – Widely distributed in coral seas with some species in temperate waters.
Feeding – In nature: plankton and small organisms. In aquarium: finely chopped or minced seafoods.

Porcelain crabs live in both cold and warm seas. This genus is often associated with coral-reef anemones.

PHYLUM ECHINODERMATA

Echinoderms

Echinoderm means "spiny-skinned." The phylum includes seastars, brittle stars, sea urchins, sea cucumbers, the sea lilies and leather stars. Sea lilies and leather stars are usually of little interest to the aquarist, as members of this class (Crinoidea) are fragile and difficult to maintain. The seastars, on the other hand, are symbols of the sea. Many of the approximately 2,000 species live in shallow coastal waters worldwide. The typical star has five arms, but some species have as many as 30, usually in multiples of five. Some seastars are voracious predators and, even though they have little commercial value themselves, can be of economic importance by causing the depletion of commercial clam and oyster beds. Other commonly seen echinoderms are the sea cucumbers. There are about 500 species worldwide. Most live in coastal waters on mud and sand bottoms, or in rock and coral crevices. Some species have the disconcerting habit of ejecting their entire digestive tract when stressed; a predator is left with the insides while the cucumber is off to regenerate anew. Sea urchins are the third commonly seen echinoderm. The typical urchin is covered with formidable spines. Of the approximately 750 species, most are inshore forms. In the mouth opening can be seen an apparatus called "Aristotle's lantern" containing five sharp teeth which are used to chew and scrape algae and other edible materials as the urchin creeps along.

CLASS ECHINOIDEA

Sea urchins and sand dollars are in the class Echinoidea. Most urchins are omnivorous grazers and scavengers, scraping algae and debris from the aquarium substrate, glass and decorations. If kept away from predatory seastars and large fishes, they are generally long-lived in the aquarium. One should be careful of urchin spines. They can be quite sharp and some contain a toxin which is painful. Also be cautious of the pedicillariae, which are small grasping claws found on urchins and some seastars. These pincers help keep the dorsal surface free of debris, and serve in defense. In some species, like *Toxopneustes*, the pedicillariae are highly venomous and can be dangerous, perhaps even deadly.

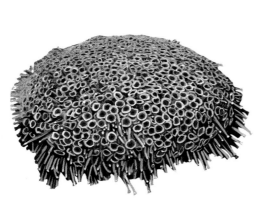

Toxopneustes spp. – sea urchin

Size – To 13 cm (5 in) in diameter
Range – Temperate and tropical oceans.
Feeding – In nature: omnivorous; feeds on algae and scavenges. In aquarium: algae and pieces of seafood.

This urchin group has venomous pedicillariae and some species are decidedly dangerous. They are not recommended for the home aquarium.

Eucidaris tribuloides – slate pencil urchin

Size – To 6 cm (2.5 in) in diameter
Range – South Carolina to Brazil.
Feeding – In nature: omnivorous, browses on plant and animal material. In aquarium: grazes on algae, and may scavenge on pieces of seafood.

This is one of several interesting genera and species of tropical reef urchins available to the marine aquarist.

Arbacia punctulata – purple sea urchin

Size – To 5 cm (2 in) in diameter
Range – Mediterranean and tropical eastern Atlantic.
Feeding – In nature: primarily herbivorous. In aquarium: herbivorous, feeds on algae; may scavenge.

Species of this genus have been used extensively in scientific laboratories for development and genetic research.

Echinoidea

Diadema antillarum – long-spined or hatpin urchin

Size – Spines may be 30 cm (12 in) in length
Range – West Indies and Florida Keys.
Feeding – In nature: primarily algae-grazer. In aquarium: algae, chopped seafoods.

Danger! The spines of this urchin are extremely sharp and brittle. They contain venom which, while not deadly, can produce a painful, irritating wound.

CLASS ASTEROIDEA

Seastars

Seastars range in size from less than 1 cm to over 100 cm (0.5–36 in) in diameter. They can be of various vivid colors – orange, pink, red, gray, green, brown, purple and blue. Molluscs seem to be their favorite foods, but some prey on other seastars, urchins, fish, shrimp and crabs. Seastars are famous for being able to regenerate all or parts of their bodies. Most species can regenerate only from the central disk, but *Linckia*, a tropical and subtropical genus, can regenerate entirely from just a piece of an arm. Members of this genus, in fact, may intentionally separate an arm as a form of asexual reproduction.

Linckia spp. – purple linckia seastar

Size – To 20 cm (8 in)
Range – Widespread in tropical seas.
Feeding – In nature: omnivorous. In aquarium: pieces of seafood.

Most purple linckias are hardy and do well at temperatures around 24° C (75° F). They are easy to keep in the aquarium.

Asterias forbesi – common Atlantic seastar

Size – To 13 cm (5 in)
Range – Gulf of Maine to Texas.
Feeding – In nature: primarily clams, mussels and oysters. In aquarium: prefers clams, mussels or oysters.

These are the familiar seastars of wharves and pilings along the Atlantic coast of North America and are a serious threat to commercial shellfish beds.

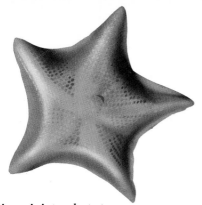

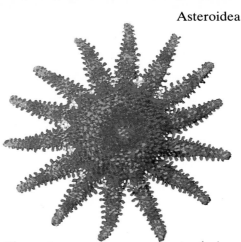

Patira miniata – bat star

Size – To 10 cm (4 in) in diameter
Range – Alaska to Baja California and Revillagigedo Islands, Mexico.
Feeding – In nature: omnivorous, seaweeds, sponges, urchins, eggs. In aquarium: algae, pieces of seafood. It will also press against the substrate or aquarium glass to digest diatoms and other matter.

This is one of the hardiest of all seastars in captivity and does well at room temperature. A relative, *Asterina gibbosa*, is found throughout the Mediterranean and on the Atlantic coast of Africa, to the Azores.

Chossaster papposus – rose seastar (spiny seastar)

Size – To 18 cm (7 in)
Range – Arctic Ocean to Gulf of Maine; Alaska to Washington.
Feeding – In nature: preys on other starfishes.

This is among the most beautiful of the seastars. Unfortunately it requires cool water of 13° C (55° F) or less to thrive.

CLASS HOLOTHUROIDEA

Sea Cucumbers

About 500 species of sea cucumbers, class Holothuroidea, live in oceans worldwide. At first glance it is difficult to tell heads from tails, but on closer examination the feeding or oral tentacles indicate the anterior end. Most cucumbers creep along in mud or sand, "mopping-up" diatoms and detritus from the sea floor. Others wave multi-branched oral tentacles in the currents to trap plankton. Some species are quite small, but many grow to over 30 cm (12 in) in length, and a few such as *Actinopyga* and *Stichopus* can be 100 cm (40 in) long and up to 20 cm (8 in) in diameter. Besides being able to eject their insides, some sea cucumbers are protected from predators by a poison called holothurin. Extracts of this substance prove fatal when injected into laboratory mice, and it is potent enough to kill fishes in the confines of the home aquarium. This toxin seems innocuous to man under normal circumstances. Natives of the South Seas use pieces of sea cucumbers to poison tidepool fishes which are then gathered for food. In many parts of the world sea cucumbers themselves are eaten. If you or your specimen supplier are not sure of the toxic properties of a sea cucumber, avoid it in your community tank or set up a separate aquarium and test its toxicity with some dispensable fishes.

Cucumaria miniata – red sea cucumber

Size – To 25 cm (10 in) long
Range – Northeast Pacific; from Alaska to central California.
Feeding – In nature: plankton. In aquarium: "clam milk," brine shrimp, chopped seafoods.

When an oral tentacle is saturated with food it is pulled into the mouth and cleaned off. Cold water around 10° C (50° F) is required for this species.

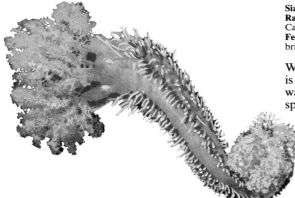

Fresh-water Plants

Donald Wilkie – H. Douglas Kemper Jr.

While fresh-water plants may help water conditions by removing nitrogenous wastes, carbon dioxide and sulfur, and by adding oxygen, they are not essential to the basic biological function of the aquarium. Their most important role is in providing shelter, spawning media, and food for your fishes; helping to prevent "green water" by competing with algae, and last but not least, providing a more natural and pleasing environment for both you and your fishes. A few fresh-water plants, such as hornwort, bladderworts, duckweeds, water lilies and some others, are strictly aquatic. Most are "amphibious" and can grow either completely submerged, partially inundated, or in wet, swampy soil. In the aquarium, as in nature, environmental conditions – temperature, light, water hardness, pH, water level and soil – affect plants and their growth. As with all life forms, abrupt environmental changes should be avoided when dealing with aquarium plants. However, while certain "ideal" conditions such as soil are given here for selected species, these plants could adapt to a broad range of conditions. Your aquarium's biological filter system is probably the single most important life-support element for your fishes. The addition of planting soil may interfere with it functioning. For this reason it is not usually recommended, nor is it usually necessary, to add "soil" for your aquarium plants. The quartz and granite gravels, 2–5 mm (0.06–0.12 in) grain size, typically available as biological filter media for the undergravel filter, are normally suitable as an aquatic plant substrate. The various types of fluorescent and other artificial lights available to fit your aquarium give you an excellent choice of practical and healthful illumination for your specimens.

FAMILY ARACEAE
Cryptocoryne spp.
This is probably the most important aquarium plant genus. Dozens of species are available. They should be planted in bunches, not singly. They prefer coarse, loamy sand, soft water and temperatures in the 20–28°C (68–82°F) range. This family is originally from the Old World tropics. Subdued sunlight or artificial light is satisfactory. Reproduces by rhizomes or runners.

FAMILY HYDROCHARITACEAE
Elodea (= anacharis) canadensis – pondweed
Pondweed is often abundant in North American temperate ponds. It is propagated by cuttings and extremely easy to grow in bright room light at room temperatures. In North America it is commonly used in goldfish tanks.

FAMILY LEMNACEAE
Lemma spp. – duckweed
These small-leaved floating plants propagate readily and provide an excellent surface screen. Duckweeds thrive over a wide range of temperatures. Several species occur.

FAMILY ALIOMATACEAE
Echinodorus spp.
In nature these are tropical American marsh plants and tend to grow above water level. Originally from tropical South America, members of this group are commonly called Amazon sword plants. They prefer coarse sand with peat and loam, along with medium to hard water. Artificial illumination and temperatures of 20–24° C (68–75° F) are suitable. Propagates by runners and seeds.

FAMILY CABOMBACEAE
Cabomba spp.
This group is native to warm temperate and tropical America. It generally prefers very soft water, coarse sandy loam, and temperatures in the 18–28° C (64–82° F) range. It requires intense light for best growth. Can be propagated by cuttings.

FAMILY APONOGETONACEAE
Aponogeton spp.
This genus contains several species of attractive, hardy plants originally from tropical Asia, Australia and Madagascar. They prefer soft water in the 20–28° C (68–82° F) range, and grow ideally in sandy loam and peat. They should be planted about 1 cm (0.5 in) under the gravel substrate. Subdued sunlight or artificial light is satisfactory. Reproduction is by seeding.

Marine Plants

Most aquarists do not include marine plants in their tanks as the majority of marine plants have requirements that are difficult or impossible to meet in the home aquarium. However, a number of marine plants can be sustained. Most of them are green algae (Chlorophyta). The most commonly used are species of *Caulerpa*, especially the sea-pen alga (*Caulerpa prolifera*). Other species commonly used include Irish moss (*Chondrus crispus*), Neptune's shaving brush, Merman's shaving brush (*Pencillus* sp.), sea lettuce (*Ulva* spp.) and dead-man's fingers (*Codium fragile*). In addition filamentous green alga (*Enteromorpha* spp.) may grow on the walls or decorations voluntarily. Care must be taken to remove rich growths if they begin to die, otherwise they will foul the tank. *Enteromorpha* is a good source of food for herbivorous fishes and can be grown outdoors in culture tanks on rocks or other substrate to be moved to the community aquarium for feeding. The marine plants mentioned all require strong light, 1–2 watts per 4 liters (1 gal.). Many aquarists use a combination of Gro-Lux and daylight fluorescent lights to provide the needed spectra. Nutrients must be supplied. Some of them will come from waste products of the fishes; but trace elements should be replaced by frequent small water changes or by adding prepared solutions to the tank.

Caulerpa prolifera – sea-pen alga

Size – Usually to 30 cm (12 in)
Range – North Carolina to Brazil.

This is a widespread hardy species found from just below the lower tide level in lagoons to depths of 100 m (330 ft) or more along the coast. It is probably the best species for those inexperienced in keeping marine plants.

DISEASES OF FISHES

"An ounce of prevention is worth a pound of cure." When it comes to fishes, nothing could be truer! Most serious disease outbreaks can be avoided with sound aquarium management; but if problems occur, it is important to detect them early and initiate the proper treatment immediately. The serious aquarist should learn to diagnose common diseases himself, since it is often not practical to obtain professional assistance. In this section, the most common diseases of fresh-water and marine fishes will be discussed. Many others do occur, but they are encountered less frequently or primarily in specialized situations, such as in hatcheries.

A wide variety of chemicals has been used to treat fish diseases, often on the basis of trial and error rather than controlled experimentation. Frequently the chemical used is a toxin to which the pathogen is more susceptible than the host fish. Since the toxicity varies with the species of fish involved, considerable care and judgment must be exercised in selecting dosages. The treatment and dosages suggested here have been used successfully at Scripps Aquarium or are commonly reported to be successful elsewhere. Success in treating diseases varies, depending upon a number of factors including severity of the disease, efficacy of the medication, developed resistance and virulence of the pathogens, natural and acquired immunity of the fish and aquarium conditions. The aquarist may find that medication which appears to be effective on one occasion is ineffective on another and that an alternative treatment is necessary. For that reason, several treatments have been included for many diseases. (During treatments it is desirable to discontinue charcoal or carbon filtration; otherwise the medication may be removed from solution by adsorption, rendering the treatment ineffective.) A comprehensive catalogue of drugs and chemicals used for the treatment of fish disease may be found in the handbook prepared by Herwig (1979). For additional information, consult Amlacher (1970), Reichenbach-Klinke (1973), Kingsford (1975) and Post (1983).

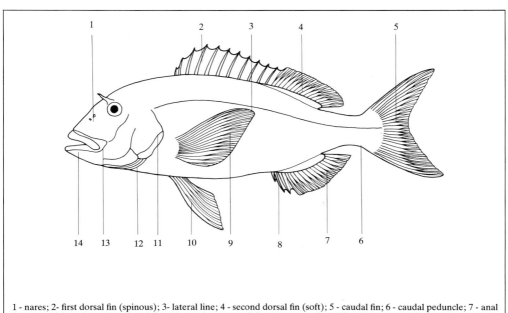

1 - nares; 2- first dorsal fin (spinous); 3- lateral line; 4 - second dorsal fin (soft); 5 - caudal fin; 6 - caudal peduncle; 7 - anal fin; 8 - anal fin spines; 9 - pectoral fin; 10 - pelvic or ventral fin; 11 - operculum; 12 - gill aperture; 13 - jaw; 14 - mouth.

DISEASES OF FRESH-WATER FISHES

Fungal diseases

SYMPTOMS – Fine hair-like tufts appear on the body and fins, especially in the area of wounds. The fins may be hemorrhagic and eroded.

CAUSE – Fungi, frequently of the genus *Saprolegnia* and related genera. These organisms are widespread in the natural environment and usually become pathogenic as a secondary problem following an injury due to fighting or the loss of body slime after being netted. Infections sometimes follow the lowering of the aquarium temperature. Poor tank husbandry is often a major contributing factor. Uneaten food in the aquarium provides a substrate for a bloom of fungus, which can readily invade fishes.

TREATMENT – 1) Thoroughly vacuum the aquarium to remove any organic waste. Shut off the charcoal or carbon filtration. Add 0.15 ppm of malachite green to the aquarium and repeat every three days until the infection subsides. 2) In stubborn cases where the fish can be handled without additional trauma, a one-hour bath may be used: add 0.5 ml of formalin (37–40%) per 1 of bathwater plus 1 ppm malachite green. Immerse the fish for one hour then remove to an infection-free aquarium. Note: Malachite green is reported to be carcinogenic. Avoid contact with the powder and concentrated solutions.
Other treatments include: 1) Sodium chloride (or uniodized table salt) baths. Add 15–30 g. per liter and immerse the fish for 30 minutes. Repeat the following day and subsequent days if necessary. Thoroughly vacuum the aquarium to remove any organic waste. 2) A 5–90-minute bath of potassium permanganate at a dosage of 5–10 ppm; the time and dose depending upon the hardiness of the fish. 3) Proprietary treatment may be helpful.
Other fungal diseases include gill fungi, frequently caused by *Branchiomyces*. This is extremely difficult to cure and sadly the best course of action is usually to destroy the fish, sterilize the aquarium and its associated equipment and begin again.

BACTERIAL DISEASES

1. Cottonmouth disease

SYMPTOMS – Fungus-like tufts appear around the mouth and do not respond to treatments normally used for fungus.

CAUSE – Although *Saprolegnia* can occur in the mouth area, this disease is caused by filamentous bacteria (*Flexibacteria* and others).

TREATMENT – Antibiotics can be added directly to the aquarium. The following are frequently used: 1) Chloramphenicol (Chloromycetin ®) as a long-term bath, at a dose of 10 ppm. Repeat at two to five-day intervals. Caution: chloramphenicol may inhibit filter bacteria and therefore result in an increase in ammonia. This can be controlled by partial water changes. 2) Furanace ® (nifurpirinol) can also be used as a long-term bath; a dosage of 0.1 to 0.3 ppm is usually effective.

2. Furunculosis (Goldfish ulcer disease)

SYMPTOMS – Fish may have one or more ulcers, usually in the form of a hole with inflamed margins in the skin and muscle. Reddish sticky pus may be present. Common in goldfish, carp and other cyprinids.

CAUSE – Bacteria, usually *Aeromonas salmoncida*.

TREATMENT – The disease is difficult to control and often recurs after treatment. A variety of antibiotics have been used effectively as a long-term bath. Effectiveness can vary, depending upon the resistance of the particular strain of bacteria.

Drug	*Dose*
Neomycin	60 ppm
Chloramphenicol	10 ppm

Furanace ® (nifurpirinol)	0.3 ppm
Gentamycin sulfate	5 ppm
Oxytetracycline	50 ppm

Kingsford (1975) recommends the use of neomycin in combination with chloramphenicol.

3. Tail rot or fin rot

SYMPTOMS – Eroded fins, usually with adjacent hemorrhagic areas.

CAUSE – The pathogen is usually a bacterium, but fungi and protozoans may also be involved. The rotting often follows an injury, such as nipping by other fishes, and is aggravated by poor tank husbandry.

TREATMENT – Proprietary treatments are available. If a bacterium is suspected, neomycin, chloramphenicol, oxytetracycline, or nifurpirinol may be effective, as described under furunculosis and cottonmouth disease. If a protozoan is implicated, a potassium permanganate bath may be helpful at a dose of 10–20 ppm for one hour; or 3–5 ppm as a long-term bath. These dosages may be toxic for some species.

4. Tuberculosis

SYMPTOMS – This disease is difficult to diagnose without a pathological examination. It is most frequently seen in tetras and other characins, cyprinids and anabantids, but can probably occur in all aquarium species. Symptoms may include fin rot, ulcers, loss of pigment, loss of weight, loss of appetite, popeye and nodules in the internal organs.

CAUSE – The bacteria *Mycobacterium* spp.

TREATMENT – Usually the best course of action is to destroy the fish and sterilize the tank with all associated equipment. Antibiotic therapy is rarely successful and should be tried only if sensitivity tests indicate that a suitable antibiotic is available.

PROTOZOAN DISEASES

---

1. "Ich," white spot disease (Ichthyophthiriusiasis)

SYMPTOMS – The skin is usually speckled with small white spots. Respiration becomes rapid. If not treated promptly, the entire tank of fish may be lost.

CAUSE – A ciliated protozoan, *Ichthyophthirius*. This disease is widespread in aquarium fishes, which may survive for long periods without symptoms, only to break out when the fish are stressed, perhaps by a rapid temperature change or the addition of new fish.

SUGGESTED TREATMENTS – Proprietary cures are available at pet stores. Alternatively you may wish to use one of the following treatments: 1) Malachite green 0.15–0.2 ppm. This is usually the preferred treatment. 2) Raise aquarium water temperature to 30°C (86°F) or more (but only with fishes which will tolerate high temperatures). Maintain for 10 days. 3) As above, but add 5–10 ppm of acriflavine (trypaflavine). Note: will kill plants. 4) Methylene blue. Mix a stock solution of 5 g of methylene blue in 100 ml of water. Add 6 ml of stock solution per 100 liters of aquarium water (dosage equals 3 ppm). Maintain for 10 days at 27°C (82°F). Note: Do not use with plants. Fishes can be treated in a separate tank. During the 10 days the infected tank is empty, the parasite will die for lack of a host. 5) Acriflavine (trypaflavine) 5–10 ppm at normal aquarium temperature. 6) Quinacrine hydrochloride (atabrine hydrochloride) 5 ppm for 10 days in a darkened tank; then use carbon filtration to remove residual dosage. A number of other external protozoans are associated with freshwater fishes and may be harmless under normal circumstances, but become pathogenic under conditions of crowding or stress. These include *Trichodina*, *Costia* and *Cyclochaeta*. Most will respond to the same treatments as *Ichthyophthirius*.

2. Flukes (Trematodes)

Two groups of flukes commonly infect fish: the monogenetic trematodes, which occur on the skin and gills; and the digenetic trematodes, which are primarily internal. The monogenes can cause severe problems in aquaria because they are transmitted directly from fish to fish, while the digenes require intermediate hosts and rarely multiply in aquaria. Monogenetic trematodes that cause problems in aquaria usually have hooks as well as suckers. Perhaps as many as 6,000 species have been described. Most are host-specific, that is (in nature), occur only on one species of fish. In the aquarium, however, flukes from one species of fish may multiply rapidly and attack all fish in the tank.

External flukes

SYMPTOMS – The fish "flash" or scratch against the bottom sand. The eyes become cloudy, and upon close examination the flukes may be seen with the naked eye or a hand lens. Diagnosis can be confirmed with a mucus smear and a dissecting microscope.

TREATMENT – 1) Short-term bath. Add 1–3 ml of 37% formaldehyde solution (formalin) per 4 liters. Leave the fish for 30 to 60 minutes. (Caution: Remove the fish sooner if it appears to become distressed by the treatment.) Repeat the treatment one or two days later. If possible, sterilize the aquarium. Otherwise, be prepared to deal with further outbreaks. 2) Long-term bath. The fish may be removed to a treatment tank or left in the home tank. Add 2–4 ppm of methylene blue dye. Continue the treatment for three to seven days, then remove the fish and change the water. 3) Long-term bath. As above, but use 10 ppm of acriflavine (trypaflavine). 4) Long-term bath. Treat in the aquarium or a treatment tank with Dylox (Dipterex, Masoten, Neguvon, Trichlorofon) at a dosage of 0.25 ppm to 0.5 ppm. Repeat the treatment once or twice a week for four weeks. Dylox is easily removed with carbon filtration. Caution: Dylox is a powdered insecticide. Avoid both skin contact and breathing the dust. Wear gloves and a dust mask when preparing your solution. (A new solution should be mixed every few days in order to maintain its effectiveness.)

Note: In our experience Dylox is the most effective long-term bath, while formalin is the preferred short-term bath.

Gill flukes

SYMPTOMS – Rapid respiration, inflamed gills, and scratching against the bottom. A diagnosis can be confirmed with a mucus smear taken from the gills. The sample can be taken without damage to the gills by using a toothpick or other small, smooth strip of wood.

TREATMENT – As above for external flukes.

VIRAL DISEASES

A number of important viral diseases occur in hatchery fishes. These are difficult to diagnose and treat and are rarely of concern to aquarists. One viral disease aquarists may encounter in both fresh-water and marine fishes is lymphocystis. This manifests itself as globular wart-like cysts on the exterior of the body, especially the fins. It proceeds slowly and is usually apparent when the fish is acquired. It is seldom fatal, but to date appears incurable except that when it occurs on fins, the affected area may be excised. The severed portion of the fin will regenerate.

DISEASES OF MARINE FISHES

Fungal diseases

Fungal diseases, except for *Ichthyophonus*, are rare in marine aquarium fishes. When they do occur, it is often in brackish water or in poorly maintained aquaria. *Ichthyophonus* attacks the heart, viscera and lateral muscles and is generally unresponsive to treatment.

TREATMENT – Treat external infections with potassium permanganate or malachite green, as for fresh-water fishes. Copper sulfate treatments may also be effective (see under marine white spot disease).

BACTERIAL DISEASES

1. Fin rot

SYMPTOMS – As for fresh-water fishes.

TREATMENT – As for fresh-water fishes. In addition, copper sulfate treatment may be beneficial.

2. Vibriosis (Vibrio disease)

SYMPTOMS – Small red spots, usually on the anterior ventral surfaces. Ulcers, loss of skin and cloudy eyes may follow.

TREATMENT – Antibiotics may be effective against some strains. Neomycin, chloramphenicol, furanace and furacin have all been reported to be helpful on occasion. Dosages: Neomycin – 50 ppm; chloramphenicol – 10 ppm; furacin – 30 ppm; furanace – 0.1–0.3 ppm.

PROTOZOANS

The two most serious diseases that usually occur in marine aquarium fishes are caused by protozoans.

Marine white spot disease (Cryptocaryoniasis)

SYMPTOMS – Numerous white spots on the body, cloudy eyes, increased respiration rate and increased mucus production. The diagnosis can be confirmed by a mucus or gill smear examined under a low-power compound microscope.

CAUSE – *Cryptocaryon irritans*, a ciliated protozoan which flourishes in the mucus on the body and gills and attacks epidermal and dermal tissue. This disease usually spreads to all of the fishes in the tank, except for those few species such as moray eels that appear to be immune.

TREATMENT – This disease can be rapidly fatal unless treated promptly. The infectious stage, known as the trophont, is protected by the envelope of mucus on the fish and is largely unaffected by most treatments. After a brief time, the parasite leaves the fish's body and forms cysts on the substrate. Following a period of multiplication within the cysts, hundreds of free-swimming individuals known as tomites are released in the aquarium water. It is only the two free-swimming stages that are normally susceptible to chemical treatments. A major difficulty in getting rid of the disease is that the cysts are highly resistant to treatment and can remain dormant in the aquarium for undetermined periods of time. For this reason, public aquaria routinely maintain a prophylactic dose of copper sulfate in their marine aquaria.

COPPER TREATMENT – Proprietary solutions containing copper are available at pet stores and are usually effective. Caution: copper is highly toxic to invertebrates and, at high dosages, to fishes. To maintain properly an effective and safe treatment level, daily analysis of the aquarium water is advised. Economical and easy-to-use test kits are obtainable at aquarium shops and laboratory supply firms. Usually a dose of 0.2–0.4 ppm of copper as Cu^{++} is effective; but 0.4 is toxic to some species of fishes. This level should be maintained for at least 10 days, preferably longer.

COPPER TREATMENT SCHEDULE –

Mix a 10% stock solution of copper sulfate and distilled water: Add 100 g of copper sulfate plus 10 g of citric acid per liter of water. In the absence of a copper analysis, the following schedule should result in a suitable dosage:
Day 1 – add 1 ml of stock solution per 75 liters of aquarium water
Day 2 – add 0.7 ml per 75 liters
Day 4 – add 0.25 ml per 75 liters
Day 6 and alternate days – continue to add a dosage of 0.25 ml per 75 liters for the duration of the treatment.

SULFATHIOZOLE SODIUM TREATMENT – Sulfathiozole sodium sometimes appears to be effective at a dosage of 75 ppm. Repeat the dose every five days for 10–20 days. This treatment is not toxic to invertebrates.

Brooklynella disease (Brooklynellaiasis)

SYMPTOMS – This protozoan disease is known from a number of marine aquarium species, and is usually associated with fishes that have been traumatized. The fish are characterized by discolored lesions in the skin, increased mucus production and respiratory distress. The causative organism is a heart-shaped ciliated protozoan 55–85 microns long that feeds on the epithelial cells of the skin and gills.

TREATMENT – 1) Formalin bath: 250 ppm for 50 min; repeat in 2–3 days. 2) Fresh-water dip: 1–2 min.; repeat in 2–3 days. 3) Malachite green: 0.13 to 0.15 ppm as a long-term bath or added directly to the aquarium. Repeat in 3 days.

Velvet disease (Oodiniumiasis)

SYMPTOMS – Similar to marine white spot disease, but the spots are small and dust-like. The gills become heavily infected and respiration is rapid.

CAUSE – A flagellated protozoan, *Amyloodinium* (= *Oodinium*) *ocellatum*. The disease may be confirmed by examination of a wet mount of gill tissue. However, the organism is small (perhaps only 10 microns when first attached and growing to 100 microns in the gills) and difficult to identify without practice.

TREATMENT – As for marine white spot disease.

Flukes

Marine fish have the same problems with flukes as fresh-water fish.

TREATMENT – 1) Formaldehyde solution (formalin) in a short-term bath of 30 min–2 hrs at a rate of 1–2 ml per 4 liters. 2) Dylox (Dipterex etc.). This can be used as a long-term bath in the aquarium or treatment tank. Use a dose of 0.25 ppm–0.5 ppm. Repeat every three to five days if necessary. Caution: Dylox is dangerous to handle. 3) Fresh-water dip. A short-term bath of 30–60 seconds is often effective, but the fish must be removed to an uninfected tank after treatment. Treatment should be repeated the next day. Caution: This treatment requires holding the fish in a net, which is in itself stressful. Also, some marine fishes do not tolerate the fresh-water dips well.

OTHER PROBLEMS

Lateral line disease (Hole-in-the-head disease).

SYMPTOMS – Erosion of the lateral line canal on the side of the body and the head.

CAUSE – This disease is not well understood, but a number of disease organisms have been implicated including fungi, protozoa, and bacteria. Nutrition (lack of plant matter) may also be a factor.

TREATMENT – Without identification of the causative organism and sensitivity test, the aquarist must resort to broad-spectrum or shotgun treatments. The following are reported to be beneficial: 1) Acriflavine: 10 mg per liter long-term bath. 2) Flagyl (metronidazole): 5 ppm for three days, followed by partial water change and carbon filtration to remove any residual drug. 3) Neomycin: 50 ppm. 4) Chloramphenical: 10 ppm. 5) Furacin: 30 ppm. 6) Furanace: 0.1–1.0 ppm. A combination treatment of flagyl with an antibiotic can also be used.

Popeye (Exophthalmia)

This condition may result from supersaturation or an embolism which results from bringing the fish to the surface from deeper water. Bacteria may invade the site of the original injury. In most cases, little can be done to assist the fish. Sometimes treatment with a wide-spectrum antibiotic such as chloramphenical may be effective. Placing the fish in the dark may facilitate antibiotic treatment.

Toxins

Fishes are highly susceptible to chemicals introduced to the aquarium water. These may come from a wide variety of sources, such as insecticides, paint fumes, heavy metals, or even toxins from other marine organisms. Unexplained deaths for which no external or internal symptoms can be found may be due to a toxin inadvertently introduced into the aquarium.

Domestic drinking water supplies may contain substances that are toxic to fishes and invertebrates. Chlorine, commonly used to sterilize drinking water, is toxic at levels harmless to humans. It can be eliminated by vigorously aerating the water for several hours or a day before use; by filtering the water through activated carbon; or by treating it with a chlorine neutralizer, available from pet stores and water-conditioning companies.

Chloramine, a complex of chlorine and ammonia, is now replacing chlorine in many community water supplies. This substance is much more toxic than chlorine alone and cannot be removed by simple aeration. It can be removed by granular activated carbon filtration, or by the use of commercially available water conditioners. If activated carbon is used, it should be discarded after a single use. If chemical neutralization method is used, it is wise to test the treated water for ammonia as well as chlorine, since ammonia is released in the process. Caution: these treatments can result in low oxygen levels.

Another possible lethal contaminant to your aquarium can be copper ions from the plumbing in your home. This is not likely to be a problem in older homes where the interior of the pipes has become covered with a natural protective coating that prevents dissolution of the copper, but it can certainly be a problem with shiny new pipes. Copper is difficult to remove from solution and the only practical answer if copper contamination is a problem is to seek another source for your aquarium water supply.

Injuries

Newly captured fishes may suffer from a number of injuries that can become the sites of infections. Some aquarists routinely give newly-acquired fish an antibiotic, formalin or copper sulfate bath. Others feel that the fish should be allowed to recover on their own if at all possible, in order to develop a natural immunity. While much may favor the latter course of action, we prefer to quarantine and treat the fish to remove infectious agents.

Some concluding remarks

During the past 20 years at Scripps Aquarium disease problems have been few, due in a major part to a combination of excellent seawater quality and an unstressful environment. Three diseases have accounted for over 90% of all outbreaks: marine white spot disease, gill and external flukes (monogenes). These have been kept under control by early diagnosis and prompt treatment. Copper sulfate is used for marine white spot disease, while formalin and dylox treatments are used for flukes. Marine velvet disease has not yet been encountered, although this has been a problem in some public aquaria and may be found by the hobbyist in imported tropical marine fishes.

Some hints for reducing disease problems

1. Examine the fish carefully and accept only those that are in good condition.
2. Handle fish as briefly and gently as possible to reduce stress.
3. Quarantine new fishes for at least two weeks, preferably four, before adding them to a tank containing other fishes.
4. Provide the best water quality possible.
5. Plan the aquarium habitat to meet the fish's natural needs for cover and space.
6. Plan your species composition in community tanks to minimize aggression. Remove highly aggressive fishes.
7. Provide a varied diet that approximates the fish's natural diet.
8. Once your tank has been set up, minimize disturbance as much as possible.
9. Stock your aquarium at low fish densities, especially initially.
10. Check the aquarium daily for dead or diseased fishes and treat promptly.

Glossary

acid a substance which in water yields hydrogen ions, has a sour taste and turns blue litmus paper red.

adipose fin a small, fatty fin found between the dorsal fin and the tail on some fishes such as trout.

aerobic able to survive only in the presence of oxygen.

albino an animal that lacks dark pigment and appears rather light or transparent.

algae primitive aquatic plants which lack roots and may be unicellular or colonial; includes both plankton and seaweed.

alkaline having the properties of a base; the opposite of acidic.

ammonia a toxic end product of protein metabolism; (NH_3).

anal fin an unpaired fin between the anus and tail on the underside of a fish.

anesthetic a substance that deadens feeling and produces a state similar to sleep.

annual living for one year.

antenna sensor appendage found on the head of crustaceans, insects and other arthropods.

antibiotic a substance that arrests the growth or kills microorganisms.

artemia the generic name for brine shrimp, small crustaceans that live in highly saline water.

arthropod an invertebrate with a segmented body, jointed limbs and a shell-like external skeleton.

bacteria unicellular organisms that lack a nucleus and multiply by division. They may occur singly or in colonies and include both harmful and beneficial forms.

barbel a fleshy, whiskerlike appendage that occurs in the mouth area of some fishes.

base a substance which liberates hydroxyl ions in water, has a bitter taste and turns red litmus paper blue.

benthic occurring on or in the bottom of the sea or other body of water.

brackish having a salinity between that of seawater and that of fresh water.

carnivorous feeds on animals or animal tissues.

caudal fin the tail fin.

caudal peduncle the stalk-like portion of the body in front of the tail fin.

chromatophore a cell containing pigment.

ciliate a protozoan covered with tiny hairs which it uses for locomotion.

cirrus small flap-like extension of the skin which is sensitive to touch.

cloaca the common chamber at the end of the digestive tract into which intestinal, urinary and reproductive materials discharge.

competition a struggle between organisms for common resources.

crepuscular active at dawn or dusk.

crustacea a class of invertebrates which includes crabs, lobsters, shrimps and copepods, etc.

ctenoid scale A fish scale with teeth or ctenes along the posterior margin. It is characteristic of higher bony fishes, such as basses and groupers.

cycloid scale A fish scale characterized by concentric rings which occurs on primitive bony fishes such as salmon.

detritus particulate organic material which occurs on or in the substrate.

diurnal active by day.

dolomite a sedimentary rock composed chiefly of calcium and magnesium carbonate.

dorsal the upper surface or back.

dorsal fin the unpaired fin on the back of fishes and other animals.

echinoderm a member of the phylum Echinodermata which includes the spiny-skinned animals that have tube feet such as starfish and sea urchins.

ecosystem an ecological system that forms a natural unit of living and non-living components.

extoparasite a parasite that lives on the surface of an organism.

endoparasite a parasite that lives within a host or within its tissues.

epidermis the outer layer of skin.

erectile capable of being raised.

ethology the study of animal behavior.

gastropod a member of the class Gastropoda within the phylum Mollusca; includes snails, slugs, etc.

genus a group of closely related species.

gonopodium an anal fin that has been modified to form a copulatory organ in some male fishes.

guanine a pigment which produces white or silvery coloration.

habitat the home or dwelling place of an organism.

hermaphrodite an organism which has both male and female reproductive organs.

homocercal tail tail in which the upper and lower lobes are approximately equal.

hormone a substance secreted by an endocrine gland and which is transported by the bloodstream to other parts of the body where it evokes a reaction.

humus soil composed of decayed plant material.

inert resistant to chemical action.

infection an injurious invasion of the body by disease-producing organisms.

invertebrate an animal without a backbone.

larva an immature form of an organism which is unlike the adult.

lateral line a row of modified scales along the side of the fish which contains sense organs that respond to disturbances in the water.

limestone sedimentary rock composed of calcium carbonate.

metabolism chemical or energy changes which occur within an organism.

metamorphosis a process of transformation from one growth stage to another.

mimicry the superficial resemblance of an organism to another plant or animal.

mollusc a member of the phylum Mollusca, which includes clams, snails, octopuses and sea slugs, etc.

morphology the form of an organism or part of an organism.

mucus slimy substance on the surface of membranes which it serves to moisten, lubricate and protect.

nitrate A salt of nitric acid, for example sodium nitrate $NaNO_3$.

nitrification a chemical process carried out by bacteria that converts salts of ammonia into nitrates and nitrites.

nitrite an intermediate salt in the conversion of ammonia to a nitrate.

nocturnal active at night.

omnivorous feeds on animal and plant material.

operculum bony cover over the gill of fishes or over the opening of a snail shell.

oviparous egg-laying.

ovoviviparous producing eggs developed within the body of the female; the young are nourished by yolk and emerge alive.

ozone a molecule of oxygen containing three atoms. It is a powerful oxidizing agent and is used as a disinfectant.

papilla a small nipple-like projection.

parasite an organism that lives at the expense of another and which is usually incapable of an independent existence.

pathogen a material or organism that causes disease.

pathology the study of diseases.

peat an acidic soil form from partially decomposed plant deposits, usually in swamps or bogs.

pectoral fins the paired fins placed behind the gill openings of fishes.

pelagic living in the open water and not associated with the bottom.

pelvic fins the paired fins attached to the underside of fishes anterior to the anus.

penicillin an antibiotic.

perennial living more than one year.

pH scale the scale from zero to 14 which indicates the acidity or alkalinity of the solution. A neutral solution has a pH of 7 while acidic solutions are less than 7 and alkaline solutions are more than 7.

photosynthesis the formation of sugars by plants from carbon dioxide and water in the presence of light.

physiology the study of mechanisms involving vital functions of organisms.

plankton weakly swimming organisms that live suspended in the water column and are transported primarily by currents. Plankton ranges in size from microscopic to large organisms such as jellyfish.

polyp sessile form of a sea anemone or other coelenterate; cylindrical in form with a mouth surrounded by tentacles.

radula the rasping structure on the "tongue" of a mollusc.

rostrum a beak-like process or structure.

rotifer a tiny freshwater invertebrate with a body that bears a ciliated disk. Rotifers include important food organisms for newly hatched fish; e.g. *Brachionus*.

saline containing salts.

sessile anchored to the bottom.

shoal a group of fishes swimming together; also called a school.

spawning the deposition of eggs by aquatic animals.

species the basic taxonomic unit of plants or animals. Members of a species resemble each other and interbreed but do not normally interbreed with other species.

substrate the bottom material of a body of water, or of an aquarium.

symbiosis the relationship in which two organisms of different species live in close association with each other.

territoriality the tendency of an organism to occupy and defend an area.

toxin an organic poison.

tubercle a small potato-like structure or swelling.

tubifex the genus name for a group of small freshwater segmented worms that live in the mud which belong to the family Tubificidae.

ventral pertaining to the lower surface or underside of an organism.

ventral fins paired fins on the underside of a fish in front of the anus.

virus an ultramicroscopic disease-producing agent, smaller and simpler than a bacterium. Virus cause many diseases in animals, including the common cold and lymphocystis in fishes.

viscera internal organs of animals.

viviparous producing live offspring.

Bibliography

Allen, G. R. *The anemonefishes.* T.F.H. Publications Inc., Neptune City, N.J., 2nd edn, 1972
Damselfishes of the southern seas. T.F.H. Publications Inc., Neptune City, N.J., 1975
Butterfly and angelfishes of the world. Vol. 2, Wiley Interscience, New York, 1979
The anemonefishes of the world. (English edition). Aquarium Systems, Mentor, Ohio, 1980
Amesbury, S. S. and Myers R. F. *Guide to the coastal resources of Guam,* Vol. 1. *The fishes.* University of Guam Press, Guam, 1982
Amlacher, E. *Textbook of fish diseases.* (English edition.) T.F.H. Publications Inc., Neptune, N.J., 1970
Axelrod, H. R. *Mollies in color.* T.F.H. Neptune City, N.J., 1968
Breeding aquarium fishes. Books 1-6. T.F.H. Publications Inc., Neptune City, N.J., 1971
African cichlids of lakes Malawi and Tanganyika. T.F.H. Publications Inc., Neptune City, N.J., 1973
Koi of the world. Japanese colored carp. T.F.H. Publications Inc., Neptune City, N.J., 1973
Böhlke, J. E. and Chaplin, C. C. G. *Fishes of the Bahamas and adjacent tropical waters,* Livingston Pub. Co., Wynnewood, P.A., 1968
Brittan, M. R. *A revision of the Indo-Malayan freshwater fish genus Rasbora.* T.F.H. Publications Inc., Neptune City, N.J.
Brunner, G. *Aquarium plants.* T.F.H. Publications Inc., Neptune City, N.J., 1966
Burgess, W. *Butterflyfishes of the world.* T.F.H. Publications Inc., Neptune City, N.J., 1978
Burgess, W. and Axelrod, H.R. *Pacific marine fishes,* Vols. 2-7. T.F.H., Neptune City, N.J., 1973-76
Fink, S. V. and Fink, W. L. *Interrelationships of the ostariophysan fishes* (Telostei). Zoological Journal of the Linnean Society. 72: 197-353, 1981
Finley, L. *Some* Synodontis *species of the Zaire basin. Freshwater and Marine Aquarium.* 3: (No. 5) 16f., 1980
Frank, S. *The illustrated encyclopedia of aquarium fish.* Octopus Books, London, 1980
Fryer, G and Iles, T. D. *The cichlid fishes of the great lakes of Africa.* T.F.H. Publications Inc., Neptune City, N.J. and Oliver and Boyd, Edinburgh, 1972
Géry, J. *Characoids of the world.* English edition. T.F.H. Publications Inc., Neptune City, N.J., 1977
Goldstein, R. J. *Anabontoids, Gouramis and related fishes.* T.F.H. Publications Inc., Neptune City, N.J., 1971
Goldstein, R. J. *Introduction to the cichlids,* T.F.H. Publications Inc., Neptune City, N.J., 1971
Goldstein, R. J. *Cichlids of the World.* T.F.H. Publications Inc., Neptune City, N.J., 1973
Goulding, J. *The fishes and the forest. Explorations in Amazonian natural history.* U. C. Press, Berkeley, 1980
Grant, E. M. *Guide to fishes.* Primary Industries, Brisbane, Australia, 1965
Greenberg, J. and Greenberg, I. *The coral reef.* Seahawk Press., 6840 S.W. 92nd St. Miami, FL 33156
Greenwood, P. H. *The haplochromine fishes of the East African Lakes.* Cornell University Press, Ithaca, N.Y., 1981
Hervey, G. F. and Hems, J. *The goldfish.* Faber and Faber, London, 1961
Herwig, N. *Handbooks of drugs and chemicals used in the treatment of fish diseases.* Charles E. Thomas, Springfield, IL, 1979
Hubbs, C. L. and Lagler, K. F. *Fishes of the Great Lakes region.* Cranbrook Institute of Science, Bull. No. 26, Bloomfield Hills, MI, 1958
Jackson, P.B.N. and Van Lier, A. J. G. *Mbuna.* T.F.H. Publications Inc., Neptune City, N.J., 1975
Kemp, R. J. *Freshwater fishes of Texas.* Bull. Texas Parks and Wildlife
Kingsford, E. *Treatment of exotic marine fish diseases.* Pet Ref. Series 1. Palmetto Pub. Co., St. Petersburg, FL., 1975
Kirby, R. F., Thompson, K. W., Hubbs, C. *Karyotype similarities between the Mexican and blind tetras.* No. 3: 578-580, 1977
Loiselle, P. V. *Matchmaking for cichliophiles. Freshwater and Marine Aquarium,* V. 4, No. 12, 1981

Loiselle, P. B. *Techniques for breeding polygamous cichlids. General management options.* Freshwater and Marine Aquarium. V. 6, No. 3, 1983a

Loiselle, P. V. *Techniques for breeding polygamous cichlids. Post spawning management options.* Freshwater and Marine Aquarium, V. 6, No. 5., 1983b

McClane, A. J. *McClanes field guide to saltwater fishes of North America.* Holt, Rinehart & Winston, N.Y., 1965

Meinkoth, N. A. *The Audubon Society guide to North American seashore creatures.* Knopf, N.Y., 1981

Mills, D. and Veevers, G. *The golden encyclopedia of freshwater tropical aquarium fishes.* Golden Press, N.Y., 1982

Nelson, J. S. *Fishes of the world.* Wiley, N.Y., 2nd edn, 1984

Post, G. W. *Textbook of fish diseases.* T.F.H. Publications Inc., Neptune City, N.J., 1983

Randall, J. E. *Underwater guide to Hawaiian reef fishes.* Harrowood Books. Newton Sq., PA or Treasures of nature. Kaneohe, 1981

Randall, J. E. *Caribbean reef fishes.* T.F.H., Neptune City, N.J., 1983

Reichenbach-Klinke, H. H. *Fish pathology English edition.* T.F.H. Publications Inc., Neptune City, N.J., 1973

Reichenbach-Klinke, H. and Elkan E. *The principal diseases of lower vertebrates.* Academic Press, N.Y., 1965

Sheel, J. *Rivulins of the old world.* T.F.H. Publications Inc., Neptune City, N.J., 1975

Solz, D. L. and Naiman, R. J. *The natural history of native fishes in the Death Valley system.* Natural History Museum, Los Angeles County, Science Series 30, 1978

Spotte, S. *Seawater aquariums: the captive environments.* Wiley-Interscience, N.Y., 1979

Steen, R. C. *Butterfly and angelfishes of the world.* Vol. 1. Australia. Wiley Interscience, N.Y., 1977

Veevers, G. *A pocket guide to aquarium fishes.* Simon and Schuster, N.Y., 1980

Walker, B. *Sharks and loaches.* T.F.H. Publications Inc., Neptune City, N.J., 1974

Weitzman, S. H. *The osteology* of Brycon meeki, *a generalized characid fish with an osteological definition of the family.* Stanford Ichthyol. Bull. 8(1): 1–77., 1962

Weitzman, S. H., and Cobb, J. S. *A revision of the South American fishes of the genus* Nannostomus *Günther (Family Lebiasinidae).* Smithson. Contrib. 200 No. 186, 1–36, 1975

Yasuda, F. and Hiyama Y. *Pacific Marine Fishes,* Vol. 1, T.F.H. Publications Inc., Neptune City, N.J., 1972

Index of Latin names

(page numbers in bold refer to illustrations)

213